Water Resources Monograph 14

MOUNTAIN RIVERS

Ellen Wohl

 American Geophysical Union
Washington, DC

Library of Congress Cataloging-in-Publication Data
Wohl, Ellen E., 1962-.
     Mountain rivers/Ellen Wohl.
           p.cm.-- (Water resources monograph ; 14)
     Includes bibliographical references (p.)
     ISBN 0-87590-318-5
     1. Rivers. 2. Mountains. I. Title. II. Series.
     GB1203.2.W64 2000
     551.48'3'09143--dc21   00-030617

ISBN 0-87590-318-5
ISSN 0170-9600

Copyright 2000 by the American Geophysical Union
2000 Florida Avenue, N.W.
Washington, DC 20009

Cover photographs by Ellen Wohl.

Printed in the United States of America.

CONTENTS

PREFACE

I wrote this book in response to a need expressed by one of my Ph.D. students, David Merritt, who walked into my office one afternoon for a summary reference on mountain rivers. Search as I might, I could not find such a reference in my files. I did find a stack of individual articles, however, and sent David on his way loaded up with them. As I thought about it, I realized that a summary reference on mountain rivers could be very useful, particularly given the increasing interest in the subject that I have noticed these last few years. Thus I began to write a review of the fluvial geomorphology of mountain rivers and, as such volumes will, this grew into a broader review of physical, biological, and chemical characteristics of mountain rivers, and of human interactions with these rivers.

I have designed this volume to serve as a specialist reference for those already familiar with the basics of river processes and forms. Advanced undergraduates, graduate students, and professional scientists and engineers who possess some general knowledge of river systems will find this volume of use, both for its own sake and to help them build on their knowledge to better understand the unique aspects of mountain rivers. You can read the book straight through, for each section builds upon the sections that precede it, or use the book as a spot reference to provide a synthesis of current knowledge on specific topics.

In the course of writing this volume, I have benefited substantially from discussions with, and critical reviews by, Paul Carling (University of Lancaster,U.K.), Dan Cenderelli (University of Alabama), Alan Covich (Colorado State University), Janet Curran (U.S. Geological Survey), Jim Finley (Shepherd Miller, Inc.), Dave Merritt (Colorado State University), LeRoy Poff (Colorado State University), and AGU reviews by John Costa (U.S. Geological Survey), Avijit Gupta (University of Leeds, U.K.), and Malcolm Newson (University of Newcastle upon Tyne, U.K.). I thank each of these individuals for their efforts. This has been a very enjoyable book to write, and I hope that you gain equal pleasure and understanding from reading it. I would like to dedicate this book to my graduate students, who have been a continuing source of intellectual exchange, inspiration, and surprise.

Ellen Wohl

INTRODUCTION

Rivers are the great shapers of landscape. Rivers transport sediment supplied by hillslope weathering and erosion, in some cases controlling the gradient of the hillslopes (Burbank et al., 1996). As they incise or aggrade to maintain a consistent relationship with their baselevel, rivers create valleys that in turn influence local climate; provide travel corridors for animals and humans; and support aquatic and riparian ecosystems that contain some of the Earth's highest levels of biodiversity.

Rivers have been studied systematically for more than two centuries. Among the questions asked have been: How do rivers interact with other landscape controls, such as lithology and tectonic regime? What governs the spatial distribution of river channels? What factors control the yield of water and sediment from hillslopes to rivers? How does channel geometry reflect the balance between water and sediment yield on the one hand, and substrate resistance on the other hand? This volume summarizes our present understanding of the answers to these questions, in the context of mountain rivers. Although the study of rivers is well-established, the great majority of investigators have worked on the lowland rivers where most people live. Mountain rivers began to receive increasing attention as a subset of rivers only during the last two decades of the twentieth century.

Characteristics of Mountain Rivers

The most obvious definition for a mountain river is that it is a river located within a mountainous region. Because each of the continents includes at least one major mountainous region (Figure 1.1), mountain rivers can be considered widespread. Mountains cover 52% of Asia, 36% of North America, 25% of Europe, 22% of South America, 17% of Australia, and 3% of Africa, as well as substantial areas of islands such as Japan, New Guinea, and New Zealand (Bridges, 1990). A more precise definition of a mountain river, and the one generally used in this volume, is that a mountain river has a gradient greater than or equal to 0.002 m/m (Jarrett, 1992) along the majority of its channel-length. The designation of a majority, rather than the entire, channel-length is important because of the great longitudinal variability in channel gradient that is common in mountainous regions. A channel may have an average gradient of 0.010 for 2 km, for example, then enter a broad, low gradient valley formed above the end moraine of a glacier, meander at a gradient of 0.0015 for 2 km, and then flow through the moraine and continue at a gradient of 0.006 for several kilometers further. Taken as a whole, this is a steep channel that is appropriately desig-

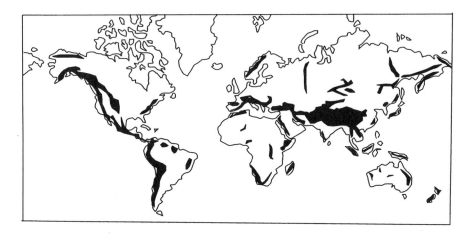

Figure 1.1. Location map of the world's major mountainous regions (shown in black shading).

nated as a mountain river even though it includes a portion of the channel that behaves in a manner similar to low-gradient alluvial channels.

There are many possible ways to categorize the diversity of mountain rivers that are present throughout the world, using such characteristics as hydrologic regime, channel gradient and bedforms, or channel planform. Another approach is to focus on climatic regime. Through its influence on weathering and erosion, climate exerts an important influence on both the discharge of water and sediment to and along the channel, and the channel-boundary characteristics. Many of the standard global climatic classification systems lump together the world's major mountain regions in a single category (e.g. Köppen, 1936; Strahler, 1960). This reflects the ability of extensive highland areas, such as the Tibetan Plateau, to create their own climatic regimes (Price and Barry, 1997). However, individual mountain ranges may share regional climatic characteristics that strongly influence river characteristics.

The climate of a given mountain region will depend on its latitude, altitude, and location with respect to the ocean and the prevailing wind direction (Barry, 1992). As summarized by Price and Barry (1997), average temperature decreases by 1°C per 150 m of altitude or 1.25° latitude. Seasonal temperature ranges average between 25-40°C in mid latitudes, but are lower in coastal ranges and higher in dry continental interiors. The diel (24 hr) temperature range of equatorial mountains may be more than three times the annual range of average daily temperature because of the small annual changes in incoming solar radiation. Cloudiness and precipitation are controlled primarily by cyclonic storms in mid-latitudes, and by meso- and small-scale convective systems in lower latitudes and in continental interiors during the summer. Annual precipitation may be greatest at low elevations in equatorial regions, but tends to increase with altitude on windward slopes in mid-latitude mountains. Local topography may also create annual precipitation totals that increase up to some limiting elevation and then decrease or remain constant. High mountain ranges such as the western Cordillera in North America may create both a precipitation deficit downwind, and distinctive local winds (Price and Barry, 1997).

The distinctively different types of rivers produced by these regional differences in climate serve to illustrate the variety that exists among mountain rivers (Table 1.1). The climatically-based categorization of mountain rivers summarized in this table includes overlaps. For example, the highest elevations (above 2300 m) of the Colorado Front Range are alpine and dominated by winter snowfall, whereas the lower elevations are semiarid. The categorization does recognize broad regional differences, however, as for example between the high weathering rates, slope instability, and perennial flow of the lower to middle elevations of the Japan Alps versus the low weathering rates and ephemeral flow of mountain rivers in the Basin and Range Province of the southwestern United States. Other categorizations of mountain rivers could focus on channel morphology and bedforms (see chapter 4), as these are influenced by tectonic regime, lithology, and structure, acting through valley gradient, boundary resistance, and sediment supply. The point to remember is that although mountain rivers are united in having high bed gradients, diverse climatic and geologic regimes produce a wide variety of channel characteristics.

Other characteristics that differentiate mountain rivers from rivers as a whole include:

- steep average channel gradient;
- high channel-boundary resistance and high boundary roughness from the bedrock and coarse clasts that are more likely to be present along these channels than along low gradient channels;
- highly turbulent flow and stochastic sediment movement resulting from the steep gradient, rough channel boundaries, and limited sediment supply;
- a strongly seasonal discharge regime, whether driven by glacial meltwater, snowmelt or rainfall, with high spatial and temporal discharge variability resulting from the effect of changes in precipitation with elevation and basin orientation;
- channel morphology that has high spatial variability because of the external control of geology (lithology, tectonics, structure, glaciation, sediment supply), but low temporal variability because only infrequent floods or debris flows are able to exceed channel-boundary resistance;
- the potential for extraordinarily high sediment yields over a period of a few years following watershed-scale disturbance (e.g. forest fire, timber harvest); and
- a longitudinal zonation of aquatic and riparian biota that is influenced both by river characteristics and by elevation, which influences the local temperature and precipitation regime.

There are of course exceptions to these general characteristics; mountain rivers in the humid tropics may not have a strongly seasonal flow regime, or arid-region ephemeral channels steeper than 0.002 may have a bed that is predominantly sand. But by and large the characteristics described above serve to define mountain rivers.

Table 1.1.   Climatic classification of mountain rivers.

Climatic regime	Mean annual precipitation	Mean annual temperature	Weathering	Flow regime	Other characteristics	Examples
Warm, arid	< 250 mm	> 10 °C	low rates	ephemeral; occasional flash floods	Channels may be deeply incised canyons in upper reaches, and braided in lower reaches	Basin and Range Province, southwestern U.S.; Middle East (Figure 1.2), western South America, Africa, or Australia
Cold, arid	< 250 mm	< 10 °C	slight rates of physical	ephemeral; dominated by flow during melt season		Parts of Antarctica
Semiarid	250-500 mm	0-30 °C	moderate chemical	ephemeral (rainfall) or perennial (snowmelt)	Sediment transport may be episodic (rainfall) or seasonal (snowmelt)	Colorado Front Range of the USA (Figure 1.3); Pyrenees of Europe
Warm, humid temperate	500-2000 mm	> 10 °C	moderate to strong chemical	perennial; occasional very high discharges caused by dissipating tropical storms	Likely to be influenced by frequently occurring mass movements on adjacent hillslopes	Appalachian Mountains of the eastern USA; mountains of Japan (Figure 1.4)
Cold, humid	500-2000 mm	< 10 °C	moderate chemical weathering with frost action	perennial; rainfall or snowmelt dominated	Likely to have abundant supplies of coarse sediment produced by frost weathering	Western side of the Canadian Rocky Mountains; European Alps; Chilean Andes
Seasonal tropics	1500-3000 mm	> 10 °C	strong chemical	perennial; monsoonal flooding and strongly seasonal discharge	Strongly seasonal sediment transport regimes	Northern Great Dividing Range of Australia (Figure 1.5); Caribbean region
Humid tropics	> 2000	> 10 °C	strong chemical	perennial; lower seasonal discharge variability than other types of mountain rivers		New Guinea; headwaters of the Amazon Basin, South America
Alpine	< 2000	< 10 °C	moderate physical	may be dominated by snow- or glacier-melt, or some combination of the two		Above timberline in most of the world's mountain massifs, such as the High Himalaya (Figure 1.6)

Figure 1.2. Sample mountain channel from a warm arid region. View is looking upstream along Nahal Mishmar, Negev Desert, Israel.

Overview of the Development of Mountain Science

Scholars have been interested in mountain topography and drainages for centuries. Although there was some discussion of these topics in the universities of medieval Europe (Fischer, 1993), the first systematic studies of mountains were initiated by the German explorer-scholar Alexander Von Humboldt (1852), who lived from 1769 to 1859 (Ives et al., 1997). Von Humboldt's studies of the effects of altitude and latitude on vegetation and landforms were conducted during a period when the intellectual community's attitude toward the natural landscape was changing rapidly. James Hutton (1795) and others had proposed that the Earth was much older than suggested by a literal interpretation of the Bible, and that contemporary landscapes were the product of gradual erosion by fluvial processes. Hypotheses of biological evolution had been proposed and would culminate at the end of Von Humboldt's life in Darwin's (1859) *The Origin of Species*. Together, these ideas implied that patterns of landforms and biota reflected continuing adjustment to such factors as climate and geology, and that study of these patterns could potentially reveal the universal controls or laws of geography (Goetzmann, 1986). For example, Von Humboldt's work eventually led to the concepts of altitudinal and latitudinal zonation of plants and animals, which were further developed by C. Hart Merriam late in the 19th century for the western US and by Troll (1954) in Europe. This work

Figure 1.3. Sample mountain channel from a semiarid region. Looking upstream along Loch Vale Creek, Colorado Front Range, Colorado, USA.

has in turn led to continuing attempts to classify mountain regions in terms of biotic patterns.

Von Humboldt's travels and studies exemplify a crucial change in European attitudes toward mountains. The European Romantic movement glorified mountain scenery, encouraging scientists such as Von Humboldt and de Saussure to venture into high-altitude regions that had previously been regarded as threatening wastelands (Price, 1981). Franz Josef Hugi lead a multidisciplinary team of scientists into the Swiss Alps as early as 1830 (Mountain Agenda, 1997).

Much of the early mountain research focused on the distribution and adaptations of terrestrial plants and animals, especially plants in the mountains of Europe.

Figure 1.4. Sample mountain channel from a humid warm temperate region. Looking upstream along Shichiri-gawa, Boso Peninsula, Japan.

Although description of plant species in the Alps and the mountains of central Europe began in the mid 16th century, scientific evaluation of the distribution of vertebrates did not begin until the early 19th century in Europe, and occurred later in other parts of the world (Jeník, 1997). Biological research was hampered for much of the 19th and 20th centuries by the absence of reasonably complete species lists for various groups of life-forms; such lists have become available only in recent decades. As a result of this work, mountains have been recognized as including many centers of endemism, or areas with a high concentration of species that have a highly restricted distribution (Jeník, 1997). Mountain ecosystems have now been recognized as being among the most fragile and endangered ecosystems globally (Jeník, 1997); of the 785 million hectares of environmentally protected lands worldwide, 260 million hectares are in mountains (Ives et al., 1997). The latter part of the 20th century was marked by attempts to integrate understanding of physical and biological processes operating in mountain regions in order to facilitate protection of these regions (Barsch, 1984; Lauer, 1984; Messerli and Ives, 1984, 1997; Ives, 1985; Singh and Kaur, 1985; Ives and Messerli, 1989), and to minimize hazards to humans (Hewitt, 1997).

   Early studies of physical aspects of mountain environments emphasized the role of glaciers and slope processes in shaping the landscape. It was not until geologists ventured into mountain ranges subject to relatively limited glaciation that the role of rivers in shaping mountains received more attention. The government-sponsored

Figure 1.5. Sample mountain channels from seasonal tropical regions. (a) Looking upstream along a channel in the Upper Amazon region of Ecuador.

expeditions to the western United States during the late 19th century, in particular, focused attention on the geomorphic processes of rivers. G.K. Gilbert, for example, examined the relations among flow velocity, sediment transport, channel gradient and basin physiography in reports such *as Geology of the Henry Mountains* (1877). W.M. Davis (1899) drew on this work when developing his idea of a geographic cycle, an idea that dominated geomorphic thought worldwide until World War II, and that characterized mountainous regions as "youthful landscapes." Most of the early 20th century physical studies continued to be largely descriptive.

The two decades following World War II were characterized by a shift in emphasis toward the quantification of geomorphic processes, beginning in the United States

Figure 1.5 (b) Looking upstream along Chayang Khola, Himalaya Mountains, Nepal.

with Horton's 1945 paper on drainage basins (Vitek and Ritter, 1993), and in Japan with Nomitsu's 1943 textbook of potamology, or the science of rivers (Kaizuka and Suzuki, 1993). For mountainous regions, the results of these quantitative studies were summarized in volumes on slopes (Rapp, 1960), and on general physical geography (Slaymaker and McPherson, 1972; Ives and Barry, 1974; Price, 1981; Gerrard, 1990), as well as in numerous summaries of specific regions. The development of remote-sensing data on snow and glaciers, weather radar, and hydrologic models all led to increasing attention to mountain hydrology after World War II (Molnar, 1990; Bandyopadhyay et al., 1997). And the application of radiometric dating of rocks led to increased study of long-term tectonic uplift, river incision, and landscape evolution in mountains (e.g. Young and Twidale, 1993).

Figure 1.6. Sample mountain channel from an alpine region. Looking upstream along a channel in the Swann Range of Montana, USA.

Interest in all aspects of mountain science has been stimulated by Project 6, Study of the Impact of Human Activities on Mountain Environments, of Unesco's Man and the Biosphere Programme, and by a 1974 conference on the Use of Mountain Environments sponsored by the German Agency for International Development (Ives, 1985). The International Mountain Society (IMS) was founded in 1980 and began publishing the journal Mountain Research and Development in 1981. Together, the IMS and the United Nations University started a research and training program on Mountain Ecology and Sustainable Development, which has included a series of regional mountain workshops since 1989. Creation of the International Centre for Integrated Mountain Development, based in Kathmandu, Nepal, has further stimulated interest in mountain environments.

Overview of the Development of Fluvial Geomorphology

The great majority of geomorphic and hydrologic studies of rivers have focused on the lower gradient channels that flow across the broad, low relief regions of the continents where the majority of humanity lives. These channels are formed primarily in finer-grained alluvium (sand to clay) and have been described as "the authors of their own geometries" (Leopold and Langbein, 1962). That is, the morphology of a low-gradient alluvial channel reflects the water and sediment discharges that flow through the channel on a regular, frequent basis. Some of the classic studies on these channels have identified floods that recur every 1-3 years as being the dominant discharge which transports the majority of suspended sediment and controls channel geometry (Wolman and Miller, 1960). Flume experiments and field studies have facilitated the characterization of fluvial processes in low-gradient alluvial channels. Important aspects of this characterization include the logarithmic vertical velocity profile characteristic of flow in these channels (Leopold et al., 1964); the regular progression of bedforms that develops in response to changing flow regime (Simons and Richardson, 1966); the hydraulic geometry relations that govern at-a-site and downstream responses to changes in discharge (Leopold and Maddock, 1953); the changes in suspended and bedload sediment transport as a function of channel geometry and discharge (Einstein, 1950); the conditions under which characteristic channel patterns, such as straight, meandering, and braided, develop (Leopold and Wolman, 1957; Schumm, 1960, 1963a; Schumm and Khan, 1972); and the longitudinal and cross-valley patterns of aquatic and riparian biota (Vannote et al., 1980; Bayley, 1991).

By the end of the twentieth century, physical scientists and engineers had a conceptual understanding of rivers that largely defined the detailed questions that were asked. Kuhn (1962) explained scientific thought as proceeding through periods of normal science, during which observation and hypothesis-testing are governed by a paradigm or generally accepted conceptual model. When sufficient observations accumulate which do not support the paradigm, a scientific revolution occurs during which a new paradigm is developed. Examples of revolutions leading to new paradigms include the theory of natural selection and biological evolution in the late 19th century, and the theory of plate tectonics in the 1960s and 1970s.

The present paradigm for physical aspects of rivers does not have a single, concise formulation, but is defined by at least two principal ideas which most investigators accept. The first of these is a *mechanistic model* in which a drainage basin, or any

Table 1.2. Features of the mechanistic model commonly applied in late 20th century research on fluvial systems.

---

*   the application of systems theory (Chorley, 1962)

*   the idea that form and process reflect some balance between driving and resisting forces, as in Bull's (1979) threshold of critical stream power

*   the various forms of equilibrium as an indicator of the character of the system's reaction to controls (Chorley and Kennedy, 1971; Knighton, 1984)

*   concepts of hydraulic geometry (Leopold and Maddock, 1953) and extremal hypotheses of river behavior (e.g. Langbein and Leopold, 1964, 1966; Yang, 1976)

*   the designation of independent and dependent variables as a function of time and space (Schumm and Lichty, 1965)

*   the ideas of thresholds, lag times, and persistence of a feature versus recurrence interval of the formative event

component of a basin, is viewed as a portion of a system of mutually adapted parts working together. Any given component thus reflects the controls exerted on it by other components, and will respond to changes in those components. There are many different expressions of this mechanistic approach, which is often traced back to the work of G.K. Gilbert in the late 19th century. Features of the mechanistic model commonly applied in late 20th century research are listed in Table 1.2. Ultimately, the mechanistic model encourages investigators to view the physical forms and processes of a river as a response to some combination of physical controls. A strictly deterministic approach implies that it is possible to understand causal relations and the history of cause and effect if the controlling forces can be adequately quantified. This has been tempered by a recognition that our understanding of complex natural systems is unlikely to develop beyond a stochastic or probabilistic level such that system behavior may be analyzed statistically but not predicted precisely. However, the mechanistic model implies that the more precise and quantitative our understanding of process, the better our prediction of controls operating through cause and effect. As a result, much of mid- to late-twentieth century river research focused on detailing and quantifying the processes acting along rivers. This emphasis is reflected in titles such as Leopold et al.'s (1964) volume *Fluvial Processes in Geomorphology* and Ritter et al.'s (1995) textbook, *Process Geomorphology*.

The second primary conceptual aspect of river research, the *basin model*, is in many respects a subset of the mechanistic model in that it applies the principles of the mechanistic model to a variety of temporal and spatial scales. This subset is worth emphasizing, however, because it exerts such an important influence on the questions that are framed to address process, and thus cause and effect. The basin model, as elaborated in Schumm's 1977 volume, *The Fluvial System,* emphasizes that various components of a drainage basin may respond primarily to different controls, and may perform different functions in the operation of the drainage basin as a whole. The basin model is sometimes expressed as upstream (tectonic) and downstream (base-level) controls; as hillslope (sediment production) and channel (sediment transport and storage) processes; or as production (headwaters), transport (middle reaches), and deposition (lower basin) zones. Implicit in the basin model is the recognition that any given fluvial process or form may be responding to controls acting across very large spatial or temporal scales, as when headwaters tectonic regime influences delta morphology, or Pleistocene climatic fluctuations influence Holocene longitudinal profile.

The conceptual framework defined by the mechanistic model and the basin model is implicit throughout this volume on mountain rivers. Research during the 20th century developed this conceptual framework and carried us through the descriptive (qualitative and quantitative) phase of the science to prediction as embodied in models of river behavior. Although there remain a tremendous number of challenging and important questions to be answered, there is little evidence at present that a scientific revolution is necessary with respect to fluvial systems. What is perhaps most necessary are an extension of the mechanistic and basin models to include: (1) how driving and resisting forces have controlled river basins at large temporal and spatial scales—an extension made possible by our increasing understanding of tectonics and climate, and by improved geochronologic techniques; (2) the role of episodic versus sustained events, as for example extreme floods versus annual flood cycles, in river system behavior; (3) the specifics of how relatively unstudied types of river systems (bedrock, mountain, arctic, tropical) compare to better known systems; (4) how physical, chemical, and biological components of river systems interact to create a functioning ecosystem; and (5) how human impacts alter and have altered river ecosystems, and how we can minimize the undesired aspects of those alterations. These issues are particularly important for mountain rivers, which have received little systematic attention relative to lowland rivers.

Beginning in the 1980s, attention began to shift from sand-bedded, low-gradient channels to gravel-bedded, high-gradient channels (Hey et al., 1982; Beschta et al., 1987; Thorne et al., 1987; Billi et al., 1992). The term "gravel-bed" is often used to designate clasts from gravel (≥ 2 mm) up to large boulder size. This shift of attention arose partly from the recognition that these coarser-grained, steeper channels differ in fundamental ways from channels formed at lower gradients in finer alluvium. Many of these differences stem from the coarser, more resistant substrate and its influence on hydraulics, sediment transport, and thus rates and patterns of channel change. Because of these fundamental differences, numerous investigators have repeatedly demonstrated that the predictive equations developed from studies of low-gradient alluvial channels do not apply well to high-gradient gravel-bed channels. Mountain rivers form the high-gradient endpoint of this continuum from lowland alluvial rivers through gravel-bed rivers, and have recently received increasing attention in their own right (e.g. Martinez-Castroviejo, 1988; Lang and Musy, 1990; Molnar, 1990; Sinniger and Monbaron, 1990; Armanini and DiSilvio, 1991; Cotroneo and Rumer, 1994; Ergenzinger and Schmidt, 1994). The majority of these studies have been conducted since the 1970s in the mountains of Europe, North America, and Japan—very few studies published in English describe the mountain rivers of Africa, South America, the Middle East, southeast Asia, Antarctica, or the Himalaya.

At the beginning of the 21st century there are two distinct approaches to studying mountain drainage basins and rivers. The first focuses on the mechanics of processes occurring over relatively short timescales ($< 10^2$ years). This volume on mountain rivers, reflecting the majority of papers published in fluvial geomorphology during the past two decades, continues this focus. A second approach, which has developed rapidly since the late 1980s, focuses on the interaction between crustal and surficial processes at longer timescales ($> 10^2$ years) and larger spatial scales. Merritts and Ellis (1994), in their introduction to a special volume on tectonics and topography, trace the divergence of geomorphology and geology during the later 19th and early 20th centuries. While geologists became more integrated into the quantitative fields of chemistry and physics, geomorphologists followed biological ideas of organic evolution, developing conceptual models that focused on the evolution of landscapes as a function of time and largely independent of geological controls. As geomorphology became increasingly quantitative and linked to hydrology and engineering in the later 20th century, the focus shifted from landscape evolution to the mechanics of local, short-term surficial processes. Partly because of this focus, geomorphologists largely failed to incorporate the conceptual framework of plate tectonics into their approach to landforms. Scientists working in structural geology and neotectonics recognized that inclusion of surface processes in geodynamic models significantly improves understanding of the development of mountain belts, but it was not until the late 1980s that truly cross-disciplinary efforts to understand the links between tectonics and topography brought together investigators in geomorphology, geophysics, structural geology, tectonics, and other branches of geology. This integration has resulted in several regional- to continental-scale numerical models of landform evolution which incorporate the most recent understanding of geodynamics, surficial processes, and climate change. These models have special relevance to the study of mountain rivers, for they provide a conceptual framework within which testable hypotheses can be posed regarding the roles of tectonics and climate in controlling the geometry and processes along mountain rivers. The next chapter briefly reviews some of these models of landscape evolution.

Overview of the Development of Stream Biology

Systematic studies of stream biology began at about the same time that G.K. Gilbert, J.W. Powell and others were initiating systematic study of mountain geomorphology. Following construction of the first microscopes in the 1670s and the development of the Linnaean classification system, the 18th and 19th centuries were largely devoted to discovery and classification of various life forms, including those in rivers (Needham and Lloyd, 1930). With the publication of Darwin's theory of natural selection in 1859, biologists turned their attention to the interpretation of physical traits as adaptations of organisms to their environment. The contemporaneous discovery of plankton as a major aquatic food source also contributed to the development of limnology as a distinct discipline. Although the history of observing and describing stream organisms dates back at least to Izaak Walton (1653), stream biology as a systematic undertaking originated in the 1870s with the work of Louis Agassiz, Joseph Leidy, Alfred Stokes, and others (Needham and Lloyd, 1930).

Stream biology was initially strongly influenced by lake limnology (Minshall, 1988). With an increasing influence from terrestrial ecology, more emphasis was placed on physical environment. For example, Davis' (1899) ideas regarding a geographic cycle stimulated biologists to search for physical controls on the distribution of organisms along rivers (e.g. Adams, 1901; Shelford, 1911). The majority of stream biology studies during the first decades of the 20th century, however, focused on the morphology, life cycles, behavior and trophic (food-web) relations of stream organisms (Minshall et al., 1985), rather than emphasizing physical controls. Numerous natural history surveys were undertaken through the late 1930s, particularly in North American streams, and there were attempts to develop simplifying generalizations for the distribution of organisms (Minshall, 1988). The late 1930s through the 1950s were marked by more inquiry into the role of environmental factors, with an emphasis on autecology, or the ecology of individual species or organisms (Minshall et al., 1985). Since the 1950s the emphasis has shifted toward synecology, or the ecology of whole communities and the interactions among their constituent organisms and species. For example, work by Odum (1957) and Margalef (1960) on whole stream energy budgets led to a more holistic view of stream ecosystems. Minshall (1988) described the major themes of late 20th century stream ecology as being (1) further refinement of earlier topics, with an emphasis on experimental manipulation and the search for explanatory mechanisms (1860s-present), (2) biotic production and energy flow (mid 1950s-early 1980s), and (3) nutrient dynamics (late 1970s-present). The explosion of research in the field is indicated by the publication of nine English-language stream ecology textbooks or multi-authored compilations between 1970 and 1986 (Minshall, 1988).

Development of the watershed approach with its hierarchy of stream order and associated downstream changes in channel width, gradient, substrate, velocity profile and other characteristics was incorporated into stream ecologists' increasingly holistic approach to rivers during the 1980s and 1990s. Key components of this holistic approach are recognition of the critical linkage between a stream and its terrestrial setting (Hynes, 1975), and recognition of the importance of interactions between biotic and abiotic controls within the channel (Minshall et al., 1985). This recognition is reflected in contemporary conceptual models such as nutrient spiraling (Webster and Patten, 1979), the River Continuum Concept (Vannote et al., 1980), the flood-pulse concept (Junk et al., 1989), and the functioning of the hyporheic zone (Stanford and Ward, 1988). A comparison of stream biology textbooks from two different generations clearly reveals these changes. Carpenter's (1928) text *The Life of Inland Waters* has chapter headings similar to Allan's 1995 *Stream Ecology*, but the subtitle of Allan's textbook is telling*; Structure and Function of Running Waters*. The later volume puts much more emphasis on abiotic controls such as stream chemistry, velocity, substrate, temperature, and oxygen; on interactions among organisms and species; and on nutrient dynamics and energy cycling. In other words, late 20th century stream biologists viewed a river as an integrated physical-chemical-biological system that is constantly adjusting to changes among the controlling variables—what Colwell (1998) referred to as biocomplexity. The premise of this view is that adjustments in the river system can be predicted with a higher degree of certainty if we have sufficient quantitative knowledge of the nature of the interactions among specific biotic and abiotic variables.

Mountain rivers have not received the specialized attention from stream ecologists that these rivers have received from geomorphologists and engineers. However, mountain rivers are recognized as having distinctive characteristics in biotic organizational frameworks such as the River Continuum Concept (see chapter 5). The ability to recognize distinctive mountain river ecosystems, and to predict adjustments in these ecosystems, is becomingly increasingly important as human occupation and alteration of mountain regions grows apace. Continuing human development of mountain regions in the form of dam construction, water diversion, agriculture, residence and recreation is multiplying the number and variety of human impacts on, and interactions with, mountain rivers (Davies, 1991). If we are to effectively manage these interactions, we must improve our understanding of the dynamics of mountain rivers.

Purpose and Organization of This Volume

This volume on mountain rivers is intended for the reader who already has a basic understanding of fluvial geomorphology, as developed in texts such as Leopold et al. (1964), Schumm (1977), Morisawa (1985), Easterbrook (1993), Ritter et al. (1995), Bloom (1998), or Knighton (1998). The emphasis of the volume is on channel processes and morphology, but the volume also includes brief reviews of other aspects of mountain rivers. After the discussion of the distribution and characteristics of mountain rivers in this introductory chapter, the text covers drainage-basin-scale processes that control hillslopes, sediment supply, channel initiation and arrangement in a network, and river chemistry, in the second chapter. The hydrologic, hydraulic, and sediment transport processes that control cross-sectional- to reach-scale properties are the subject of the third chapter, and the fourth chapter describes channel morphology at the reach scale. The fifth chapter summarizes knowledge of aquatic and riparian biota along mountain rivers, and specifically how these organisms interact with the physical processes along mountain rivers, and the sixth chapter considers human interactions with these rivers. The diversity of topics is designed to promote the idea that a mountain river is an integrated physical, chemical and biological system that is influenced by controls acting across various scales of time and space. This volume is first of all an integration and synthesis of existing knowledge of mountain rivers. Topics for which our understanding is particularly lacking are highlighted throughout this synthesis, and the concluding discussion emphasizes aspects of mountain rivers on which research is especially necessary. This volume is a progress report; there remains a tremendous amount of work to be accomplished.

2

MOUNTAIN DRAINAGE BASINS

Mountainous regions are produced by four general types of deformation; folding, volcanism, fault block uplift, and vertical uplift (Press and Siever, 1986). Folded mountains result from lateral compression, usually at the convergent boundary between two tectonic plates. Examples include the Appalachian Mountains of the eastern United States, the Alps of southern Europe, the Urals at the boundary between Europe and Asia, and the Transantarctic Mountains. The topography of folded mountains may be controlled by differential weathering of the lithologies exposed by uplift, with more resistant lithologies forming steeper slopes.

Volcanic mountains generally form at a divergent or convergent plate boundary, or at an intraplate hot spot such as the Hawaiian Islands. Examples of volcanic mountain ranges include the highlands of New Guinea, the North Island of New Zealand, the Japan Alps, and the Cascade Range of the northwestern United States. The geologic controls on volcanic islands are a function of the style of eruption and chemical composition of the lava.

Fault block uplift tends to produce mountain ranges with one very steep side parallel to the fault and a gentler side that does not have an active fault, as in the Teton Range of Wyoming, USA. Mountains produced by vertical uplift have faults parallel to both sides of the range, as in the Front Range of Colorado, USA.

Most of the world's major mountain belts include folded, volcanic, and faulted regions, as well as igneous plutons. For example, the Himalaya mountain ranges include the folded and thrust-faulted zone of the Siwalik hills at the southern margin, and thrust-faulted and intruded rocks in the Middle Himalayas and the High Himalayas (Bridges, 1990). The Andes Mountains of western South America include high volcanic peaks, folded belts, igneous intrusions, and extensive faults (Bridges, 1990).

The structure and relief of a mountainous region may influence the development of a drainage network at differing scales. Some of the earliest studies of channel arrangement in relation to topography noted that channels do not always follow existing slopes. Working in the western United States, J.W. Powell (1875, 1876) described both antecedent drainage networks in which pre-existing channels had maintained their spatial arrangement while the underlying landmass was deformed and uplifted, and superimposed channels which had incised downward to a buried structure. In either case, the result could be a river flowing through or across a mountain range, rather than channels draining from the crest of the range downward to the neighboring lowlands (Figure 2.1). Thus, the drainage network was not a consequence of present topography. For cratonic or passive-margin settings, Young (1989) has argued that

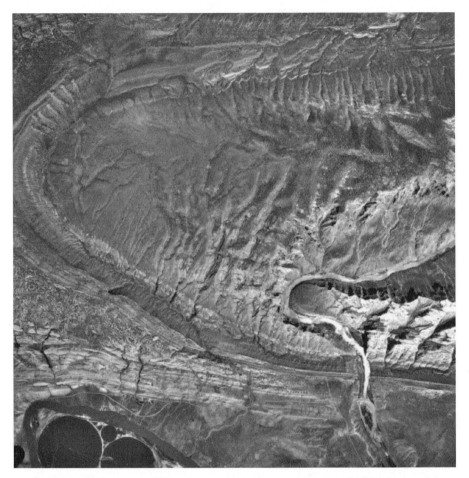

Figure 2.1. Split Mountain, Utah. Aerial photograph showing the Green River flowing through the mountain, rather than around it.

although the alignment and form of individual valleys may reflect surface variations in lithology and structure, deeper crustal features control drainage patterns at the sub-continental scale. These deeper crustal features may only be discernible using remote-sensing technology to detect patterns such as Bouguer gravity anomalies (Young, 1989). Brookfield (1998) describes the importance of tectonic history in creating three regionally distinctive patterns among the major river systems of Asia. Differential compression and right-lateral shear caused anti-clockwise rotation of southern Afghanistan, producing highlands from which rivers with moderate gradients drain into arid depressions that have been separated by arc accretion from coastal rains. Differential shear and clockwise rotation between the compressing Tibetan plateau and Southeast Asia produced large sigmoidal bends in regional rivers. These rivers are widely separated and have low gradients on the Tibetan plateau, and higher gradients as they turn southwards into close and parallel gorges. Southward thrusting and massive frontal erosion of the Himalaya caused progressive truncation of longitudinal rivers on the plateau, with river capture, and glacial and landslide diversions in the south. Rivers of the Himalaya and southern Tibet have steep gradients where they cross the Himalaya, and they occasionally truncate former rivers with low gradients on the Tibetan plateau (Brookfield, 1998).

Arrangement and incision of valley networks may also affect mountain relief and elevation. An early study indicated that rivers remove up to five times more sediment per unit area from mountain basins than from lowland basins (Corbel, 1959). This type of comparison emphasizes the role of mountain rivers as conveyors of sediment from upland regions. The pattern of river incision can affect crustal structure in mountain belts by changing the distribution of stress in the crust (Hoffman and Grotzinger, 1993; Beaumont and Quinlan, 1994). Hack's (1960) concept of dynamic equilibrium in landscape evolution proposed that erosion and uplift reach an equilibrium such that relief becomes independent of time as long as the relative rates of erosion and uplift remain constant. Relief may be altered if the balance between these forces changes, or if the resistance of the exposed rocks changes. This concept is supported by recent work in the Nanga Parbat region of northern Pakistan, where slope angles are largely independent of age, and denudation and uplift rates (Burbank et al., 1996). In this region, mean slope angles are set by rock strength. The association of high river gradients with high uplift rates implies a dynamic equilibrium in which uplift and incision are balanced via adjustments in stream power. Landslides provide a mechanism by which hillslopes can adjust to changes in boundary condition resulting from river incision at their toes. If rapid river incision oversteepens the hillslopes, an increase in landslide activity increases sediment supply to the river (reducing the rate of channel incision) and returns the hillslope gradient to a stable level. Because the landslide threshold is influenced by fractured rock strength, the highest topography develops either where rocks are less fractured or where large rivers are most widely spaced. Mean relief is thus controlled by the spacing of large rivers (Burbank et al., 1996). Arnett (1971) demonstrated a similar influence of river incision on the gradients of, and sediment yield from, adjacent hillslopes in Australia.

Several other recent studies have also addressed the effect of valley incision on mountain topography. Modeling the effect of isostatically compensated valley incision on the elevation of mountain peaks, Montgomery (1994) found that this compensation could account for at most 5-10% of the present elevation of mountain peaks in the central Sierra Nevada of California and the Tibetan Plateau. Such compensation could account for 20-30% of the present elevation of peaks in the Himalaya, however. Work in the highlands of eastern Australia indicates that the headward erosion of river gorges is the most important process denuding these highlands during the last 30 million years (Nott et al., 1996). Stream erosion of new drainage basins in extensional mountain ranges of the southwestern United States exceeds hillslope retreat, leading to elevation of summit plateaus (Harbor, 1997).

Cirque and valley glaciers may strongly control valley morphology and rates of valley incision in mountainous regions glaciated during the Pleistocene and/or the Holocene. In these regions, many rivers are slightly modifying valleys most recently largely shaped by glaciers, although glacial erosion and deposition are extremely variable along a valley (MacGregor et al., 1998). Deeper glacial erosion may occur, for example, where valley width decreases, at a change in valley gradient, or where a tributary glacier enters and reduces the effective width of the main glacier. Because the glacially-shaped longitudinal valley profile can persist for hundreds of thousands of years (Fabel et al., 1998), glacial history sets the framework for the river valley, controlling such characteristics as depth of valley alluvium and bedrock valley gradient. Retreating glaciers, by oversteepening the valley side slopes, can cause mass movements into the valley (Meigs, 1998). And as long as a glacier or icefield is present, it may create large seasonal and shorter period fluctuations in meltwater and sediment discharge to rivers.

Regional rates of uplift may be compared to regional rates of denudation as an index of the efficiency of mountain hillslope and channel processes. As noted by Burbank et al. (1996), mountainous topography results from the imbalance between uplift caused by tectonics and denudation by tectonic (extensional faulting) or surface (glacial, hillslope and fluvial) processes. Rates of both uplift and denudation may have substantial spatial and temporal variability. Leopold et al. (1964) used the 629,520 km^2 basin of the Colorado River in the southwestern U.S. as an example of spatial variability in denudation rate, as estimated from suspended sediment load expressed in centimeters derived from the drainage basin per unit of time. Denudation rate ranged from approximately 0.4 to 17 cm/1000 yr, and showed fairly strong correlation with climate (Leopold et al., 1964). Oguchi (1996b) compared Holocene and contemporary denudation rates for a series of river basins in central Japan and found that contemporary rates were up to three times higher than Holocene rates. Despite this variability, regional rates of the type listed in Table 2.1 may still be useful indicators of relative efficiency of weathering and erosion in various regions. The numerous investigators of this topic all agree that both climate and relief strongly influence denudation rate. Published rates of bedrock channel incision vary from 5 to 10,000 mm/1000 yr, with the highest rates occurring in regions of tectonic uplift (Wohl et al., 1994a; Wohl, 1998). Most of these channel incision rates are long-term (Quaternary) averages for third-order or higher channels, but they indicate that tectonic uplift corresponds with increased transport ability and channel incision in mountainous regions, regardless of climate or lithology.

Schumm (1977) divided the fluvial system into an upstream zone that served as the primary sediment source for a drainage basin, a middle transfer zone, and a downstream zone that is primarily depositional. Mountain rivers occupy the upstream sediment-source zone of a drainage basin, and primarily reflect the controls of climate, geology, and land-use as these influence water and sediment yield to the channel, and channel-boundary resistance. Geology is here taken to include lithology, structure, and tectonic regime. These will, in combination with climate, determine rate and manner of weathering, and thus slope morphology and processes of water and sediment movement.

Table 2.1. Regional rates of uplift and denudation. (After Schumm, 1963b; Ritter, 1967; Saunders and Young, 1983; Press and Siever, 1986, Table 6-1; Summerfield and Hulton, 1994).

Climate	Relief	Reported ranges for uplift (mm/1000 yr)	Typical range for denudation (mm/1000 yr)
Temperate continental	normal	400-4,000 (nw USA) 1,000-2,000 (Japan) 5,000 (Monroe Uplift, USA)	10-500
Rainforest	normal	300-400 (Caribbean) 2,000-25,000 (Costa Rica)	10-1,000
Arid	variable		10 - ?
Semiarid	normal	10,000 (Rio Grande Rift, USA)	100 - 1,000
Polar	steep	2,000-12,000 (n. Pakistan; Burbank et al., 1996)	10 - 1,000
Any climate	badlands		1,000 - 1,000,000
Continental USA; average 3900 km^2 drainage areas	various	7,620	30-915

Slope Processes

Controls on Slope Morphology

Slope morphology is controlled by lithology and climate, which in turn control weathering and erosion and the downslope movement of water. Selby (1982) distinguished among weathering-controlled slopes, transport-limited slopes, and transportational slopes. On *weathering-controlled slopes* the rate at which regolith is produced is less than the potential rate at which it can be removed. The slope profile may reflect relative rock resistance. The profile may also reflect the processes or structural controls that act to undercut or oversteepen the slope with respect to the profile angle at which the slope could theoretically be supported by rock resistance. On *transport-limited slopes* the rate of regolith production is greater than the capacity of transport processes to remove it. On these slopes, regolith accumulates and the slope profile reflects the properties of and processes acting on the regolith. On *transportational slopes* there is an equilibrium between rate of weathering and rate of erosion.

Leopold et al. (1964) noted that all types of slope morphology may be found in a given climate, although others have generalized that slope morphology corresponds to climate (Schumm, 1956; Abrahams and Parsons, 1991; Ritter et al., 1995). Rounded hillslopes with convex upper portions and concave lower portions are more common in humid climatic zones with high weathering rates, thick regolith, and gradual downslope movement of sediment. Angular slopes with cliff faces and talus accumulations are more common in dry regions with low weathering rates, extensive bedrock exposure, and mass movements.

The influence of climate on slope morphology and processes occurs first through the temperature and precipitation regime in which weathering occurs. Dry climates have predominantly physical weathering. Chemical weathering becomes more important as precipitation increases, and as temperature increases (Leopold et al., 1964; Ritter et al., 1995). Polar and desert zones have very thin weathering profiles where the absence of water and plants produce low weathering rates. The rates increase through the temperate latitudes and reach a maximum in the humid tropics (Selby, 1982). The rate of sediment removal from hillslopes does not follow the same pattern with respect to climate. The highest rates of sediment yield consistently come from semiarid and highly seasonal Mediterranean and tropical monsoonal climates (Langbein and Schumm, 1958; Fournier, 1960; Douglas, 1967; Walling and Kleo, 1979). Rates are lower for arid regions because precipitation is not sufficient to mobilize sediment, and for humid regions because abundant vegetation effectively stabilizes hillslope sediment. These trends of weathering and sediment yield are reflected in the suspended sediment and solute loads of rivers. Rivers draining cold humid-temperate regions carry the highest percentage of their total load in solution (e.g. Dietrich and Dunne, 1978), but rivers draining dry or seasonal tropical areas have both the highest suspended sediment concentrations and the greatest total sediment load (Knighton, 1984, Table 3.6).

The influence of geology on slope morphology and processes has been characterized by rating rock-mass strength as a function of intact rock strength; weathering; spacing, orientation, width, and continuity of joints; and outflow of groundwater (Selby, 1980). Higher values of rock-mass strength correlate strongly with steeper slopes (Selby, 1980, 1982), and parallel retreat occurs only when rock-mass strength is uniform into the slope (Moon and Selby, 1983).

Generalized models of hillslope evolution feature (1) *parallel retreat*, in which the slope profile remains constant while the whole landform erodes back; (2) *slope replacement,* in which the steepest angle is progessively replaced by the upward expansion of a gentler slope near the base; and (3) *slope decline,* in which the steep upper slope erodes more rapidly than the basal zone, causing a decrease of the overall slope angle (Strahler, 1950; Schumm, 1966; Young, 1972; Ritter et al., 1995). Howard's (1994) simulation modeling of drainage basin evolution indicated that detachment-limited or weathering-controlled slopes undergo nearly parallel retreat and replacement with alluvial surfaces under fixed base level, whereas transport-limited slopes undergo gradual slope decline.

Downslope Pathways of Water

The processes by which water moves downslope exert an important control on the hydrology of mountain rivers. More than 95% of the water in streamflow has passed over or through a hillside and its soils before reaching the channel network (Kirkby, 1988).

Precipitation falling toward a hillslope may be intercepted by plants and evaporate or evapotranspire back into the atmosphere. Interception losses may be 10-20% beneath grasses and crops, and up to 50% beneath forests (Selby, 1982). Vegetation may also concentrate the movement of precipitation toward the ground surface via stemflow. Precipitation which actually reaches the ground surface may flow downslope at the surface as Hortonian overland flow if the infiltration capacity is low relative to precipitation intensity. Hortonian overland flow is most common in the zones of sparse vegetation cover and thin regolith present in many mountain regions. Working on three New Zealand catchments with low infiltration rates, Pearce and McKerchar (1979) found that moderate storms generated partial Hortonian overland flow, and large storms generated widespread Hortonian overland flow. The overland flow contribution to storm runoff may be greatly reduced by infiltration into the debris-mantled belt that separates the steep upper slope from the channel (Yair and Lavee, 1985)

Precipitation may also move downslope as saturation overland flow, which consists of direct precipitation onto saturated areas, and return flow from the subsurface as saturation occurs. Some water may also remain in the subsurface as throughflow above the water table or groundwater flow below the water table (Knighton, 1984). Infiltration is a function of precipitation intensity and duration, and surface porosity and permeability. Surface porosity and permeability are controlled by slope, vegetation, and regolith grain size, compaction, depth, and areal extent. Reported infiltration capacities range from 2 to 2500 mm/hr (Selby, 1982). Glaciated basins in particular may have large spatial variability of infiltration as a result of spatial differences in glacial and periglacial deposits (Parriaux and Nicoud, 1990). Subsurface flow dominates hillslopes with full vegetative cover and thick regolith (Dunne and Black, 1970a). Water moving downslope via Hortonian overland flow generally has the most rapid rate of movement (50-500 m/hr), whereas groundwater may move as slowly as 1×10^{-8} m/hr (Selby, 1982, Table 5.2). The area of a drainage basin actually contributing water to a channel extends during precipitation and contracts after the precipitation ends, with contributing area reported as ranging from 5 to 80% of the basin (Dunne and Black, 1970b; Selby, 1982).

Saturation overland flow depends on the moisture content of the regolith before, during, and after precipitation. As prolonged precipitation allows deeper and less permeable regolith layers to become saturated, throughflow will be deflected closer and closer to the surface as the level of saturation rises through the regolith (Knighton, 1984). Saturation overland flow is rare outside convergent flow zones (Dietrich et al., 1992), but a study of 17 small catchments in New Zealand found that storm runoff during small events (1-100 day return period) always included saturation overland flow on small proportions of the catchment (Pearce and McKerchar, 1979). A catchment underlain by thick tephra deposits had a sharp initial hydrograph peak derived from saturation overland flow, and a broad secondary peak generated by subsurface flow. For all of the 17 catchments, the bulk of storm runoff in larger events was produced by rapid subsurface flow from 40-90% of the catchment area (Pearce and McKerchar, 1979). Working on small, forested headwater catchments in Finland, Lepistö et al. (1994) found that 50-70% of discharge during the largest stream flow measured came from surface runoff plus some shallow groundwater flow. This contribution dropped off markedly, to approximately 20-25% for lesser rainfall events (the remainder of discharge being shallow to intermediate groundwater flow not connected to the rainfall event) in these catchments with shallow soil depths and relatively high percentages (29-41%) of exposed bedrock.

Infiltration capacity and overland flow may also depend on the nature of soil ice. Working at 2000 m elevation in Nevada, USA, Haupt (1967) found that porous, concrete frost reduced infiltration rates and caused overland flow, whereas needle ice increased infiltration. Rapid fluctuations in the nature of soil ice and freeze-thaw cycles can thus create temporal and spatial variability in the relative importance of overland flow and throughflow, in turn causing variability in mountain-river hydrographs. Slaymaker (1974) found that overland flow on slopes in British Columbia, Canada was concentrated in a 30-40 m band below the snow line, creating a zone that retreated upslope with the snow line during the period of snowmelt. The contributing area of the basin thus changed rapidly in response to weather conditions.

Throughflow may depend on the general porosity and permeability of the unsaturated zone, and on the presence of preferential flow paths in the form of pipes or macropores. These may form just above a zone of lower porosity and permeability, or along a cavity created by a burrowing animal or by the decay of plant roots. Pipe networks may exist at more than one level in the regolith, with each level being activated by precipitation of different magnitude (Gilman and Newson, 1980). Piping is particularly common in arid and semiarid regions, and is frequently found in association with badlands (Graf, 1988).

Flowpaths and transit times for water in a catchment can be studied using artificial tracers such as tritium that are added intentionally to the system, or environmental tracers such as stable isotopes of oxygen and hydrogen, or temperature, that are created by natural processes (Jenkins et al., 1994; Peters, 1994; Kendall et al., 1995). Ideal tracers are those that interact least with their surroundings. Chemical tracers such as chloride, sulphate, silica or bromide may be applied artificially or occur naturally.

Downslope Pathways of Sediment

Sediment may also move downslope in various manners. Precipitation falling on a surface may loosen or detach individual particles (rainsplash), making them more susceptible to entrainment by overland flow (Mosley, 1973; Morris, 1986). Where unvegetated, unfrozen slope surfaces are exposed during the summer months, overland flow may be capable of eroding measurable quantities of sediment and creating selective textural sorting of slope materials (Dingwall, 1972). If the overland flow occurs as sheet flow that submerges individual roughness elements and forms a fairly continuous sheet of water across the hillslope, sediment may be stripped evenly from the slope crest and upper zone during sheet wash. Sheet wash is particularly effective on slopes where cohesion has been reduced by needle ice, trampling, or disturbance to vegetation (Selby, 1982). In semiarid regions with sparse vegetation, sheet wash may account for up to 98% of all sediment moved from a hillslope (Lustig, 1965; Leopold et al., 1966; Emmett, 1978).

As the overland flow progresses downslope and is concentrated by surface irregularities, the increasing water depth increases the shear stress at the base of the flow. Rills and gullies eroded into the hillslope act as conduits for sediment erosion down the slope (Sutherland, 1991). Rills may deliver most of the water and sediment to channels even in arid regions with low infiltration capacities (Yair and Lavee, 1985). Studying long semarid hillslopes subject to Hortonian overland flow, Dunne et al. (1995) found that slopewash becomes competent to transport sediment within a few meters of the drainage divide. However, microtopography generated mostly by biotic processes forces the slopewash to develop a depth distribution that controls its transport capacity, and sediment is released from microtopographic mounds into the slopewash. As a result, the sediment supply is sufficient to prevent rill incision on the upper portion of the hillslope (Dunne et al., 1995).

Although surface erosion dominates on hillslope profile convexities and deposition dominates on profile concavities (e.g., Yamada, 1999b), studies of sediment movement on two disturbed hillslopes in southeastern Australia suggest that sediment movement is extremely variable at a spatial scale of meters. Saynor et al. (1994) found that localized changes in gradient, ground cover, vegetation and microtopography facilitated alternating zones of erosion and deposition, with pulses of sediment moving between the zones over both short (individual events) and medium (40 years) timescales.

Sediment may also be eroded along pipes and macropores (Jones, 1981), or preferential flow paths below the water table (Dunne, 1980). Pipes range from a few centimeters in length and diameter to hundreds of meters long and 2 m in diameter (Selby, 1982). Collapse of the pipe roof, sapping, or concentration of flow downstream from the pipe outlet may enhance surface erosion (Knighton, 1984; Mizuyama et al., 1994).

Subsurface erosion includes both the physical removal of particles and chemical dissolution. More than half the sediment eroded from many catchments is carried in solution (Dietrich and Dunne, 1978; Selby, 1982; Summerfield and Hulton, 1994); the rate is higher in catchments with a greater input of subsurface water (Hohberger and Einsele, 1979) and with carbonate or other soluble lithologies (Waylen, 1979; Selby, 1982).

Mass movement involves downslope transport of aggregates rather than individual particles, and may occur as creep, falls, slides, or flows (Ritter et al., 1995). Each type of movement may be strongly seasonal as a function of moisture availability and freeze-thaw processes (Schumm and Lusby, 1963; Schumm, 1964; Caine, 1976; Yair and de Ploey, 1979; Miyabuchi and Nakamura, 1991; Sawada and Takahashi, 1994). *Creep* is so slow that it can usually only be perceived over long periods of observation. Individual particles and aggregates that are loosened and displaced upward by freezing, wetting, warming, or bioturbation move downslope under the influence of gravity (Kirkby, 1967). Movement is greatest in the upper meter of the regolith, and occurs by deformation at grain boundaries and within clay mineral structures (Selby, 1982). The movement is quasi-viscous, and occurs at a shear stress large enough to produce permanent deformation, but not discrete failure (Carson and Kirkby, 1972). A study of frost creep in northern Japan indicated that movement occurs only when diurnal freeze-thaw occurs in conjunction with nearly saturated soil (Sato et al., 1997). With increasing water or ice content, creep grades into solifluction or gelifluction, respectively; the very slow downslope flow of partially saturated regolith. Creep may be particularly important on steep mountain slopes, where it produces tree curvature, tilting of structures, turf rolls, soil cracks, regolith accumulations upslope of retaining structures, and terracettes (Selby, 1982). Creep may also promote rapid mass movements by decreasing regolith shear strength (Simon et al., 1990).

Falls involve the free fall of rock or soil, usually in response to undercutting of the toe or face of a slope, weathering and enlargement of joints, or seismic vibrations. In densely jointed or fractured rocks, repeated falls may be a dominant source of coarse clasts for a river channel. A *slide* occurs when a mass of unconsolidated material moves without internal deformation along a discrete failure plane (Carson and Kirkby, 1972; Ritter et al., 1995). The slide may occur as a slump that has rotational movement of discrete blocks along a curved failure plane, or it may follow a fairly straight slide plane. This type of failure may be caused by a decrease in the shear strength of the regolith as a result of weathering, increase in water content, seismic vibrations, or freezing and thawing, or by an increase in shear stress because of additions of mass or removal of lateral or underlying support (Varnes, 1958; Brunsden and Jones, 1976; Selby, 1982; Ritter et al., 1995). Slides often change into flows as downslope movement continues. A *flow* occurs when debris is sufficiently liquefied or vibrated that substantial internal deformation accompanies the movement. As with slides, flows may be primarily erosional at high gradients and depositional at low gradients.

Selby (1982) described the feedback between slope morphology and downslope movement of water and sediment. Long straight slopes are dominated by subsurface flow that promotes solution and creep, and are unlikely to slide unless a severe storm or earthquake destabilizes the slope. Hillslope spurs shed water rapidly and are least affected by erosion. Convergence of subsurface and surface flow at slope concavities promotes solution and mass movements because of the high pore-water pressures generated at these locations (Iverson and Reid, 1992). These areas thus have the most erosion. Sediment entrainment by sheet wash or rilling is concentrated at the base of slopes adjacent to channels, in concavities, and in areas of thin and impermeable regolith or disturbed vegetation. The concentration of flow in old mass movement scars increases weathering and promotes further mass movements (Selby, 1982). These feedbacks are incorporated in computer simulations such as TOPOG

(O'Loughlin, 1986) or SHETRAN (Burton and Bathurst, 1998; Burton et al., 1998). These simulations can be used to model shallow landslide initiation by coupling digital terrain data with near-surface throughflow and slope stability models (Dietrich et al., 1993; Montgomery and Dietrich, 1994a).

Slope morphology-process feedbacks are also incorporated in conceptual models such as the process-response model for hillslope-channel sediment transfer in devegetated mountainous terrain developed by White and Wells (1979). They found that sediment yield from burned hillslopes was influenced by: (1) the amount of hillslope devegetation; (2) seasonal variations in weathering and runoff; (3) protective post-fire forest litter; and (4) sediment production from burrowing animals. The multiple sediment pathways of the model were thus spatially and temporally variable. The model also differed significantly from the complex response model for alluvial valleys in that tributary channels adjust independently of trunk channels where a bedrock knickpoint separates tributary and trunk channel.

Benda and Dunne (1997b) describe sediment supply to channels as a process stochastically driven by rainstorms and other perturbations which occur on a landscape with its own spatial variability in topography, colluvium, and state of recovery from previous disturbances. Sediment supply then interacts with transport processes and with the topology of the channel network to create a sedimentation regime that varies systematically with drainage basin area.

In many of the world's mountainous regions, abrupt mass movements recur frequently (almost annually) within a drainage basin, and transport the majority of sediment to or along low-order stream channels (e.g. Blackwelder, 1928; Pierson, 1980; Osterkamp et al., 1986; Swanson et al., 1987; Benda, 1990; Wohl and Pearthree, 1991; Jacobson et al., 1993; Oguchi, 1994). Several studies have demonstrated that as stream order and drainage area increase, sediment yield per unit area or sediment delivery ratio decrease and sediment residence time increases because of increasing storage on hillslopes or valley bottoms (Schumm and Hadley, 1961; Boyce, 1975; Strand, 1975; Schumm, 1977; Dietrich and Dunne, 1978). Long-term average sediment yields for various mountainous regions are given in chapter 3 (Table 3.4). The inverse correlation between stream order and sediment yield reinforces Schumm's (1977) conceptual model of the headwaters of a drainage basin as the primary sediment source for downstream portions of the basin.

Alpine glacier basins form a specialized subset in terms of water and sediment transfer to rivers. The mass balance of the glacier largely controls rate and magnitude of water and sediment transfer. Meltwater leaves the glacier via supraglacial, englacial, and subglacial paths, and may be temporarily stored in proglacial lakes before reaching a river channel (Röthlisberger and Lang, 1987). Sediment may come directly from ice melt or via meltwater transport. Sediment carried via subglacial and proglacial meltwater, and by supraglacial and subglacial ice movement, constitutes the greatest volume in most alpine glacier basins (Fenn, 1987). Rivers in these basins are not generally supply-limited with respect to sediment (Gregory, 1987), in contrast to mountain rivers in many regions.

Channel Initiation and Development

Numerous studies have indicated the difficulty of predicting the conditions under which channel initiation occurs. Multiple potential controls such as gradient, drainage area, infiltration capacity, and permeability/porosity, interact to influence multiple processes (overland flow, subsurface flow, debris flow, etc), and both controls and processes may have high spatial and temporal variability. Within this complex, variable system, channel initiation represents a threshold phenomenon in which surface flow is sufficiently concentrated and persistent to produce a discrete channel. Montgomery and Dietrich (1994b) used a plot of drainage area versus slope to delineate process thresholds for diffusive sediment transport, landslides, overland flow, and other processes. Valley maintenance then reflects spatial transitions in process dominance at timescales of 10^4-10^6 years, and temporal variance in the exceedance of a channel initiation threshold at shorter timescales of 10^2-10^3 years (Montgomery and Dietrich, 1994b).

Drainage networks may be controlled by surface or subsurface properties and processes. Surface-controlled networks develop through rilling, with the greatest surface irregularities concentrating flow in a master rill to which adjacent slopes are cross graded via micropiracy (Horton, 1945). Surface-controlled drainage networks may develop in at least three ways (Dunne, 1980): (1) Rills may develop nearly simultaneously over the landscape and then integrate into a network. (2) On a rising land surface channels may extend downstream during slow warping or intermittent exposure of new land. (3) An increase in slope or the lowering of baselevel may cause headward erosion of channels. (Rills may stabilize and fill through the process of gully gravure, in which coarse, erosion-resistant rock debris concentrates in rills and gradually entraps interstitial finer-grained erosion products (Bryan, 1940; Osterkamp and Toy, 1994).) The rate of headward growth of the master rill and the tributary rills will be partly a function of slope; steeper slopes will produce a more elongated network with less tributary development, other factors being equal (Parker, 1977; Phillips and Schumm, 1987).

Networks may also be controlled by spring sapping, in which subsurface flow returning to the ground surface enhances mechanical and chemical weathering and creates a pore-pressure gradient that exerts a drag on the weathered material (Dunne, 1980). Heterogeneities in hydraulic conductivity and resistance to chemical weathering cause convergence of groundwater flow that leads to piping and sapping failure and a positive feedback with further flow convergence. As the channel erodes headward, this disrupts the flow pattern until water emerging along the valley sides is concentrated along a susceptible zone, initiating a tributary that also erodes headward and branches. The process continues until the increasing number of spring heads decreases the drainage area of each, and limits water supply (Dunne, 1980). Spring sapping may be an important mechanism of drainage development on various lithologies in humid regions, and has also been described for the sedimentary rocks of the semiarid Colorado Plateau (Laity and Malin, 1985).

Drainage networks developed in karst terrains represent an important subset of networks controlled by subsurface processes. Karst features may develop in any mountainous region with carbonate rocks. Fluviokarst terrains contain transitions between surface and subsurface channels and valley networks, whereas in holokarst terrains the surface drainage network has been almost completely disrupted by subsurface piracy (Ford and Williams, 1989). Within fluviokarst terrains, surface streams are commonly diverted underground where incision of a clastic caprock exposes an underlying carbonate unit. The stream may be diverted at the clastic/carbonate contact (White, 1988), or may flow across the carbonate unit for some distance. Subsurface piracy routes may mimic the initial surface drainage pattern, or may divert flow beneath surface drainage divides into adjacent catchments (Ford and Williams, 1989). Within some mature fluviokarst basins, surface streams flow across the clastic-carbonate contact and onto low gradient floodplains within a topographically enclosed karst depression. Upon reaching the opposite wall of the depression, the stream flows directly into a cave. The distance that a stream flows before entering the subsurface has been shown to be a function of contributing basin area (Smart, 1988; Miller, 1996). The cave transmits stream flow beneath depression slopes and eventually discharges the water at a spring. Position of the spring may be controlled by lithology, structure, or base level (White, 1988; Ford and Williams, 1989). In general, such karst streams exhibit the profiles, gradients, and mouth elevations that one would predict for surface streams draining the same basin. Alpine karst is well developed in the Alps and Pyrenees, where glacial meltwater has strongly influenced the type and degree of karst features present (Ford and Williams, 1989).

The development of an integrated drainage network on a hillslope has been studied with experimental apparatus; on surfaces of varying age for which all other variables are held constant (e.g. lava flows or glacial tills); and using computer simulations. Experimental studies and field studies using surfaces of varying age indicate that drainage density tends to initially increase relatively rapidly, then change more slowly, and eventually decrease slightly as relief is reduced (Glock, 1931; Ruhe, 1952; Leopold et al., 1964; Flint, 1973; Parker, 1977).

Field-based studies of network development also indicate that the source area above the channel head decreases with increasing local valley gradient in steep humid landscapes (5-45° slopes) well-mantled with soil (Montgomery and Dietrich, 1988). For the same gradient, drier regions tend to have larger source areas. The smooth, long hills typical of low relief areas result from the large source area necessary to initiate a channel, whereas the discontinuous channels and dissected terrain of steeper areas suggest that channel head locations are controlled by hillslope processes (landsliding) and require much smaller source areas (Montgomery and Dietrich, 1989). Drainage density in steep terrain thus depends at least in part on rate of weathering, regolith storage, and slope stability. Zero-order basins, also known as unchannelized valleys or hollows, may play an important role in regolith storage and slope stability. These features, which have been described for subhumid and humid mountains, store sediment that is periodically mobilized as a debris flow (Hack and Goodlett, 1960; Dietrich and Dunne, 1978; Dietrich and Dorn, 1984; Mills, 1989).

Dietrich and Dunne (1993) have argued that the channel head is a key landscape feature. The distance from the drainage divide to the channel head controls drainage density, and this in turn controls average hillslope length. The channel head is particularly sensitive to changes in external factors such as climate or land use, which affect runoff, surface erodibility and sediment supply. Shifts in the balance controlling channel-head locations may create erosion and deposition cycles which affect the whole drainage basin (Dietrich and Dunne, 1993).

Computer simulations of drainage network development indicate that, in the absence of strong substrate controls such as orthogonal joints, the spatial arrangement of channels can be approximated fairly well with a random-walk model that predicts the most probable state under the constraints postulated (Leopold and Langbein, 1962; Howard, 1971). Most models of river basin evolution also largely ignore substrate heterogeneity (e.g. Willgoose et al., 1991). Rodriguez-Iturbe et al (1992a) have proposed that river networks follow power law distributions in their mass and energy characteristics. These characteristics represent a balance among (1) the principle of minimum energy expenditure in any link of the network, (2) the principle of equal energy expenditure per unit area of channel anywhere in the network, and (3) the principle of minimum total energy expenditure in the network as a whole (Rodriguez-Iturbe et al., 1992b). It is not clear whether such principles apply to mountain river networks or other systems with heterogeneous substrates.

Hovius et al. (1998) describe the development of watersheds during the early phase of mountain growth. As exemplified by observations from different parts of the Finisterre Mountains of Papua New Guinea, watersheds appear to initiate by isolated gorge incision. The watersheds then expand by large-scale landsliding that is controlled by groundwater seepage, and finally entrench by fluvial incision of landslide scars and deposits. Only infrequent, large landslides can modify the drainage pattern once a mountainous system of ridge and valleys is established.

River Chemistry

The chemical contents of precipitation falling over a landmass vary with distance from the ocean, with pollution inputs, and through time. The precipitation then reacts with plants, soils, regolith, and bedrock, so that the chemistry of water entering a river depends more on the hillslope flow paths followed by the water than on the chemistry of the original precipitation. The mixing of at least three sources of water (groundwater, soil water, and overland flow) produces the chemistry of most rivers (McDonnell et al., 1991). Not much natural change occurs in the water chemistry once the water enters a river because of the short residence time of water within the channel (Drever, 1988). Any chemical change that does occur is usually associated with biological processes and trace elements.

Alpine streams draining catchments with thin regoliths and poorly developed soils may be more influenced by precipitation chemistry than are other types of rivers. Studies in mountain drainages indicate that subsurface flow contribution increases as the areal extent and thickness of regolith and soils in the basin increase (Sueker, 1995). An alpine catchment of bedrock and talus may be dominated by surface and shallow subsurface flow (e.g. Finley et al., 1995), whereas a forested mountain catchment with well-developed soils may be dominated by groundwater discharge even during snowmelt (e.g. Shanley et al., 1995). A National Academy of Sciences committee identified understanding the influence of water flow paths on river chemistry as a key issue in the hydrologic sciences (National Research Council, 1991).

The importance of precipitation input will also vary for different elements. A study of sulfur isotopes of sulfate in the Bear Brook watershed in Maine, USA, for example, indicated that sulfur isotopes in this first-order intermittent stream were controlled by the relative contribution of marine versus non-marine sulfate in precipitation; fractionation of stable sulfur isotopes within the watershed had only a minor influence (Stam et al., 1992). However, a study of trends in precipitation and surface water chemistry at 15 small watersheds in the USA found that a relation between precipitation and surface water trends was not evident either for individual inorganic solutes or for solute combinations, despite the small watersheds and generally unreactive bedrock (Aulenbach et al., 1996).

The primary constituents of river chemistry are the dissolved ions HCO_3^-, Ca^{2+}, SO_4^{2-}, H_4SiO_4, Cl^-, Na^+, Mg^{2+}, and K^+; dissolved nutrients N and P; dissolved organic matter; dissolved gases N_2, CO_2 and O_2; and trace metals (Berner and Berner, 1987; Allan, 1995). The sum of the concentrations of the dissolved major ions, known as the total dissolved solids (TDS), is highly temporally and spatially variable in response to precipitation input, discharge, lithology in the drainage basin, and the growth cycles of terrestrial vegetation (Berner and Berner, 1987). An average natural value for rivers is 100 mg/l (20 times the concentration in rain) with, on average, another 10 mg/l contributed by pollution. Ca^{2+} and HCO_3^- from limestone weathering tend to dominate in general (Berner and Berner, 1987). The factors influencing TDS are summarized in Table 2.2.

In the United States, the first comprehensive study of surface water chemical composition was made during the first decade of the 20th century. Approximately 155 sites were sampled initially, but the program was then greatly curtailed until the 1950s (Hem et al., 1990). At present, the U.S. maintains hundreds of stream gaging stations where water quality measurements are made, via programs such as the National Streamflow Quality Accounting Network (NASQAN) and the 59 study sites of the National Water Quality Assessment (NAWQA) program.

Gibbs (1970) classified rivers on the basis of their chemistry as being dominated by (1) precipitation (low TDS, high Na/(Na + Ca) ratio), (2) rock weathering (intermediate TDS, low Na/(Na + Ca) ratio), or (3) evaporation and fractional crystallization of $CaCO_3$ (high TDS, high Na/(Na + Ca) ratio). Subsequent investigators have tended to emphasize the role of geology and erosional regime as the major controls on river chemistry (Garrels and Mackenzie, 1971; Drever, 1982; Berner and Berner, 1987). Stallard and Edmond (1983), for example, describe: (1) rivers drain-

Table 2.2. Environmental factors influencing TDS in rivers (Drever, 1988; Johnson et al., 1994; Moldan and Cerny, 1994; Velbel, 1995).

Rock type

igneous and metamorphic rocks
* waters draining igneous and metamorphic rocks generally have TDS < 500 mg/l, and often < 100 mg/l
* bicarbonate is major anion; Na and Ca major cations
* fine-grained and glassy rocks weather more rapidly and produce higher TDS than coarse-grained rocks
* mafic rocks produce higher TDS with higher Ca^{2+}/Na^+ and Mg^{2+}/Ca^{2+} ratios than felsic rocks
* in dilute waters, contribution of solutes from atmosphere may equal solutes derived from rock weathering; weathering of a volumetrically minor phase (calcite, amphibolite) may be primary source of solutes

carbonates
* Ca, Mg and bicarbonate only significant solutes
* TDS limited by solubility of carbonate minerals in water enriched in CO_2 (g) from soil zone; generally 100-600 mg/l

detrital sedimentary rocks
* waters highly variable in composition and TDS

Relief
* as relief increases, rates of chemical weathering increases because of exposure of fresh rock

Climate
* weathering rates in temperate zone catchments tend to be greater than those of alpine and subalpine catchments due to the temperature dependence of dissolution rate constants and generally higher soil water flow
* as rainfall increases, TDS decreases, but total mass of dissolved solids eroded per unit time increases

Vegetation
* vegetation supplies CO_2 (g) and organic acids to soil, which increases rate of chemical weathering; but, vegetation stabilizes soil and decreases erosion
* uptake or release of common rock-derived elements (K, Ca, Mg) during aggradation or degradation of forest biomass can noticeably affect catchment solute mass balance

Human impact
* atmospheric deposition into the catchment and land-use may affect TDS; acid rain may increase sulfate deposition, for example

ing intensely weathered materials (cation-poor siliceous rocks, deeply weathered soils and saprolites), with TDS less than 20 mg/l, that correspond to Gibbs' precipitation-controlled rivers, (2) rivers draining siliceous terrains of cation-rich igneous and metamorphic rocks and terrestrial shales, with TDS of 20-40 mg/l, that fall between Gibbs' precipitation- and rock-dominated rivers, (3) rivers draining marine sedimentary rocks, with TDS of 40-250 mg/l, that correspond to Gibbs' rock-dominated rivers, and (4) rivers draining evaporites, with TDS greater than 250 mg/l, that correspond to Gibbs' evaporation-crystallization rivers. In general, rivers draining sedimentary rocks tend to have at least two times the TDS of rivers draining igneous and metamorphic rocks (Holland, 1978). Because many of the world's mountain ranges are composed of crystalline rocks, mountain rivers tend to have low concentrations of TDS.

Topographic relief may exert an important influence on river chemistry. Greater relief usually corresponds with greater erosion and faster exposure of fresh bedrock for chemical weathering. Chemical weathering in the soil may be incomplete if the rocks are resistant to weathering, so that spatial variations in lithology can significantly influence river chemistry (Berner and Berner, 1987).

Glaciation may also influence river chemistry. More reactive minerals may contribute to a river's dissolved load in disproportion to their abundance in the local rock, a process known as selective weathering. Selective weathering is more likely to occur in previously glaciated catchments than in non-glaciated catchments, as demonstrated for mountains as diverse as the Pakistan Himalaya (Gazis et al., 1998) and the Colorado Front Range, where Williams and Platts-Mills (1998) found selective weathering of calcite and biotite in talus relative to tundra environments. Chemical denudation rates may also be higher for glaciated areas. A study of cationic denudation for a drainage basin in the Cascade Mountains of Washington, USA found that subglacial waters have a significantly higher yield (800 to 2390 meq/m^2/yr) than extra-glacial waters (580 meq/m^2/yr), although both yields are higher than the world average of 190 meq/m^2/yr (Axtmann and Stallard, 1995).

Studies of Swiss alpine glaciers indicate that the chemistry of glacial meltwater may be highly variable in time and space. Solute concentrations vary inversely in phase with diurnal variations in meltwater discharge, because the average contact time of meltwater with the sediment beneath the glacier varies with discharge (Collins, 1995a). Also, meltwaters initially flow slowly through small channels leading from the bases of moulin shafts. Flow accelerates downstream as water volume increases where confluents join to produce larger conduits. The dissolution of suspended sediments raises solute concentrations considerably more per unit length of channel in the smaller conduits with low velocity flow than in larger conduits with faster flow (Collins, 1995b). Borehole sampling on alpine glaciers indicates that subglacial waters may have distinctly different chemical compositions within a glacier as a result of chemical weathering of bedrock or glacial flour that contains different quantities of reactive trace minerals such as carbonates and sulfides (Lamb et al., 1995). Glaciers in the High Arctic may also have highly variable solute concentrations controlled by meltwater source, rate of melting, and subaerial chemical weathering and flow pathways (Hodgkins et al., 1997, 1998).

Mountain rivers that do not have headwater glaciers also exhibit strong temporal variations in water chemistry in association with seasonal snowmelt. A study of seven streams in high-elevation catchments of the Sierra Nevada in California identified three phases in the chemical composition of streams during snowmelt (Melack and Sickman, 1995): (1) from the onset of snowmelt to peak discharge, solute concentrations decrease; (2) at or near peak discharge, concentrations are at a minimum; and (3) with declining discharge, solute concentrations increase. Although the details vary, this pattern seems to be consistent for alpine catchments around the world. A study of the headwaters of the Urumqi River basin, Tian Shan, China, for example, found that solute concentrations in streamwater are highest at the initiation of snowmelt, decline through the melt season and into the summer, and then increase as the contribution of baseflow increases (Fengjing et al., 1995). In this catchment, as in others, the ionic pulse (the release of solutes from the snowpack and the flushing of weathering products from the soil) and the dissolution of eolian particles are important as meltwater percolates through the snowpack (e.g. Tranter et al., 1986).

In addition to regular seasonal changes in stream chemistry, mountain rivers may be affected by episodic events such as timber harvest (see chapter 6), mass movements, or volcanic eruptions. Immediately following the 1980 eruptions of Mount St. Helens in Washington (USA), for example, some streams northeast of the volcano showed sulfate and chloride increases (Klein and Taylor, 1980). Organic compounds produced when the hot, eruptive debris buried or destroyed forests on the slope of the volcano also influenced water chemistry.

Dissolved Nutrients

The primary nutrients in river water are nitrogen and phosphorus. Nitrogen gas, N_2, must be fixed, or combined with hydrogen, oxygen and carbon, in order to be used by terrestrial organisms. The three major land inputs of fixed nitrogen, in forms such as NO_3^- and NH_4^+, include biological fixation (approximately 60%), precipitation and dry deposition of previously fixed nitrogen (24%), and the application of industrially fixed nitrogen in fertilizers (16%) (Berner and Berner, 1987). River output of nitrogen is about 18% of the total nitrogen loss from the land. Of this, 85% is organic nitrogen, and most of the rest (dissolved inorganic nitrogen and erosion of minerals containing nitrogen) is derived from organic matter decomposition. In general, biological recycling of nitrogen is very efficient; the total river output of organic nitrogen is only 8% of the nitrogen assimilated annually by the terrestrial biosphere (Berner and Berner, 1987). Denitrification in stream sediments is a significant mechanism of within-stream nitrogen loss (Nihlgard et al., 1994). Riparian zone biogeochemical interactions may also influence nitrogen dynamics. In temperate and wet tropical areas nitrate fluxes are rather constant because denitrification and plant uptake remove allochthonous nitrate within a few meters of travel along shallow riparian flowpaths (McClain et al., 1999).

In contrast, relatively little nitrogen processing occurs during transport from upland through riparian zones in arid areas because precipitation moves rapidly across the riparian zone as surface runoff (McClain et al., 1999).

In contrast to nitrogen, most phosphorus that is lost from land moves via river runoff, although phosphorus tends to be efficiently utilized by biological systems. Although the ultimate source of phosphorus is weathering of geologic materials, the main source in many river catchments is precipitation and dry deposition (Graham and Duce, 1979). Because phosphorus is relatively insoluble, it is often a limiting nutrient in biological systems (Berner and Berner, 1987).

Nutrient uptake lengths in headwater streams are particularly short because of autotrophic (algae and moss) and heterotrophic (bacteria and fungi) uptake and release of nutrients (Nihlgard et al., 1994). Because the heavy shade over many forested mountain rivers limits primary production, leaves and small woody material from the surrounding environment are the major sources of energy to many forested headwater streams (Cummings, 1974). Most of this leaf litter input is ingested by aquatic macroinvertebrates, which in turn excrete substantial amounts of potassium, calcium, and dissolved organic carbon to the stream water (Nihlgard et al., 1994).

Interactions between the channel and the surrounding hyporheic (alluvium below the channel), riparian, and floodplain zones may produce spatial and temporal variations in nutrient availability. Studies in the Sonoran desert of the southwestern United States, for example, indicate that the subsurface may be a source of nitrate to the nitrogen-limited stream (Holmes et al., 1994). Nitrification in downwelling regions along desert channels was several times that in upwelling regions (Jones et al., 1995a), illustrating the importance of chemical linkages between the surface stream and the hyporheic zone (Stanley and Boulton, 1995).

Organic Matter and Gases

Organic matter can be present in river water in both particulate and dissolved forms (Berner and Berner, 1987). The dissolved organic matter is usually expressed as dissolved organic carbon (DOC), which is typically between 2 and 15 mg/l, but can reach 60 mg/l in rivers draining wetlands. By comparison, precipitation has DOC values of 0.5-1.5 mg/l, and soil water has up to 260 mg/l (Drever, 1988). The DOC varies with the size of the river, the climate, and vegetation (Thurman, 1985). Mountain rivers in alpine regions tend to have the lowest concentrations (< 1 mg/l) (Berner and Berner, 1987). About half of the DOC present in a river is fulvic acids, the fraction of humic substances soluble at all values of pH (Drever, 1988). The average river ratio of DOC to TDS is low (1:18) (Berner and Berner, 1987).

In small, turbulent, unpolluted streams, such as those characteristic of mountain regions, diffusion maintains O_2 and CO_2 near saturation, although concentrations change seasonally and daily with temperature (Berner and Berner, 1987). A study of dissolved organic carbon during snowmelt in headwater catchments of the Colorado Rocky Mountains indicated that flow paths through, and residence times of water in, the catchments are among the primary controls on DOC variation in headwater streams (Boyer et al., 1995). In the catchments studied, DOC concentrations in the streams increased during the rising limb, peaked before maximum discharge, and then decreased rapidly during the period of snowmelt. Soils are the primary source of DOC to these streams, and the variations in concentration during the snowmelt season reflect both the initial flushing of carbon produced prior to snowmelt, and the changes in flow depth and rapidity of meltwater as the season progressed (Boyer et al., 1995).

Trace Metals and Pollutants

Trace metals generally occur at concentrations less than 1 mg/l in river waters. These can be derived from rock weathering, or from human activities such as mining, burning fuels, smelting ores, or disposing of waste products (Drever, 1988). Often, trace metals are of most concern as a source of river pollution. A trace metal may be a contaminant or a hazard. A contaminant is any element or substance that occurs in the environment at concentrations above background levels, where background refers to the natural concentration of an element in natural materials at a given location (Gough, 1993). A contaminant that occurs at a level potentially harmful to organisms constitutes a hazard. Natural sources of contaminants include mineralized areas and soils enriched in elements such as selenium. A contaminant may enter a river from a point source, which is a single source with a small area (e.g. a mine), or from a non-point source such as agricultural fields or a marine shale or sandstone enriched in uranium (Gough, 1993).

In many of the world's mountains, mine drainage of metal-rich water released during reactions between water and rocks containing sulfide minerals is often associated with acidic water and may be a source of contaminants and hazard. In the United States there are between 100,000 and 500,000 abandoned or inactive mine sites, most of which are in the mountains of the western United States (King, 1995). To date, these mines have created hazards to which the national government has responded by funding more than 50 restoration sites related to non-fuel mining activity (King, 1995). In the Colorado Rocky Mountains, for example, abandoned mines in the Summitville District have seeps throughout the mine workings, and water draining through mine adits and heap-leach sites. This water eventually reaches the Alamosa River, which can have concentrations of aluminum, copper, iron and molybdenum greater than 1 mg/l after rain storms (King, 1995). Attempts to reduce this acid mine drainage include grouting fractures in abandoned mines to prevent the inflow of oxygenated groundwater, and hindering the bacteria that enhance the chemical reactions between water and sulfide minerals (Gough, 1993).

Another potentially substantial source of pollution in many mountain rivers is acid rain. Fossil fuel combustion and the smelting of nonferrous metals produce sulfuric and nitric acid which can be dissolved in precipitation, deposited as particles, or form acid precursor gases such as SO_2 and NO_x that are absorbed directly by plants and other surfaces (Cortecci and Longinelli, 1970; Drever, 1988; Moldan and Cerny, 1994). In areas receiving long-term acid deposition, some rivers may become acidified, such that the carbonate alkalinity is zero or negative, and pH is usually less than 5. The input of acid anions may vary seasonally, with an increase at the time of snowmelt as acid anions, sulfate and nitrate in the snow are flushed into surface waters. The time lag between the input of acid anions from the atmosphere and acidification of the river will depend on soil thickness and cation-exchange capacity in the drainage basin, which will in turn depend on the rate of chemical weathering, and the age and stability of surfaces in the basin (Drever, 1988; Velbel, 1993). A study of mid-Atlantic watersheds in the USA found that lithology is an excellent predictor of the relative buffering capacity of a watershed (O'Brien et al., 1997). Several quantitative models have been developed to relate the chemistry of runoff at a site to the input of acid anions from the atmosphere (egs. Henriksen, 1980; Chen et al., 1984; Cosby et al., 1985; Ball and Trudgill, 1995; Neal et al., 1995; O'Brien et al., 1997). Mountain rivers in eastern North America and northern and central Europe are most affected by acid rain (Drever, 1988). At present, worldwide anthropogenic sulfur emissions into the atmosphere total between 70 and 100 million metric tonnes per year, with approximately 60 million metric tonnes of natural sulfur emissions. In northern Europe, 90% of atmospheric sulfur is of anthropogenic origin (Hultberg et al., 1994). The U.S. Geological Survey has established the 200 sites of the National Atmospheric Deposition Program for monitoring wet atmospheric deposition in the United States. The program is designed to determine whether on-going and future regulatory actions to reduce air pollution are resulting in an improvement in the quality of precipitation chemistry in the United States. However, although acid rain has been reduced in regions such as the northeastern United States, acid streams and lakes have not recovered because the cation-exchange capacity in watershed soils has been stripped (Wathne et al., 1990).

River chemistry is of course very important to aquatic organisms, as discussed by Patrick (1995). Dissolved organic matter is an important energy-nutrient source for many aquatic species. Calcium, magnesium, oxidized sulfur, nitrogen (as nitrates and ammonia), and phosphates, along with small amounts of silicon, manganese, and iron, are also desirable for many species. Aquatic species in rivers vary greatly in their tolerance for trace metals; in some forms these trace metals stimulate growth, in other cases they are toxic. The pH of the water affects the solubility of various elements and thus their availability to aquatic organisms. Numerous studies have shown that the survival of juvenile salmonid fish in headwater streams is influenced by pH, the ionic forms of aluminum, and by calcium concentration, for example (Baker and Schofield, 1982; Brown, 1982; Neal et al., 1997). Colloids such as iron oxyhydroxide minerals may adsorb metals onto their surfaces and thus make the metals less available to organisms.

Case Studies

Studies conducted on the geochemistry of specific catchments illustrate the characteristics of mountain river chemistry.

(1) *Cascade Mountains, Washington, USA*; temperate glacial environment (Drever and Hurcomb, 1986; Drever, 1988). The study region is underlain by migmatites, quartz

diorite, and basalt dykes. Average elevation is 1970 m, and average precipitation is 380 cm/yr. River waters are dilute (15 mg/l TDS), with Ca^{2+} and Mg^{2+} as dominant cations. The rate of chemical weathering in terms of mass removed in solution per unit area per year is approximately twice the average for North America because of the high precipitation in the study area. Calcite constitutes much less than 1% of the bedrock, but is the dominant source of solutes during weathering, with biotite the second most important source.

(2) *Absaroka Mountains, Wyoming, USA* (Miller and Drever, 1977). The study area is underlain by andesitic volcanics. The elevation range is 1760-3700 m, the mean annual temperature is 7° C, and the mean annual precipitation is 40-50 cm. TDS values may reach 120 mg/l during winter, and are generally lower (approximately 75 mg/l) in summer. The chemical denudation rate for the basin, 18 tons/km^2/yr, is lower than the North American average of 33 tons/km^2/yr, mainly because of low precipitation. All ions but potassium, which is controlled by leaching from organic material, decrease during spring snowmelt runoff.

(3) *Snowy Range, Wyoming, USA* (Finley et al., 1995). The study area is underlain by quartzite crosscut by amphibolite dykes. The small (91 ha), high elevation (3280-3500 m) catchment has steep topographic relief. Soils are thin (< 1 m) and immature, and overlie a cover of talus formed during deglaciation. Sparsely forested areas at lower elevations grade to tundra and bare rock higher in the catchment. Snow supplies 80-90% of the mean annual precipitation of 107 cm. Sulfur isotope dynamics indicate that the main hydrologic flow path is the shallow soil zone during snowmelt, and the bedrock aquifer during late summer and fall.

(4) *Loch Vale watershed, Colorado, USA* (Denning et al., 1991; Baron, 1992; Baron et al., 1995; Campbell et al., 1995a,b; Clow and Mast, 1995; Mast et al., 1995). The Loch Vale watershed is 660 ha of land ranging between 3050 and 4026 m in elevation. The watershed is underlain by granite and biotite gneiss. Eighty-three percent of the catchment is bare rock, boulder fields, snow and ice, eleven percent is tundra, five percent is subalpine spruce-fir forest, and one percent is subalpine meadow. Soils are thin and poorly developed. The mean annual precipitation of 100 cm is evenly distributed between winter (Oct-Mar) and summer (Apr-Sep), but stream runoff is snowmelt-dominated. Pre-melt water is rapidly flushed from the catchment during the initial stages of snowmelt. Much of the snowpack runoff flows through shallow subsurface reservoirs before discharging into the stream. During the summer recession period, the soil water is partially recharged by summer rains. The concentrations of most major ions decrease during the snowmelt, and are higher on the rising stage than on a comparable falling stage. In the upper part of the catchment, much of the snowmelt is delivered rapidly to streams by piston-type displacement of shallow groundwater. The shallow groundwater stored in areas such as boulder fields is not large enough to attenuate chemical changes over many weeks time, nor is the hydrologic residence time of sufficient duration for the weathering of primary minerals to control stream chemistry. Because of the ionic pulse effect, meltwater coming out of the snowpack is most concentrated early in the runoff season and becomes more dilute later. The shallow ground-

water is also most concentrated after an autumn and winter of accumulating weathering products, but the groundwater becomes more dilute as it mixes with meltwater. Most of the dissolved load in runoff from the bedrock portions of the catchment is derived from the dissolution of dry deposition that accumulates on the bedrock between storm events.

In the lower part of the catchment, stream water is affected by inputs of soil water with high concentrations of NO_3 and organic acids. During high flows, the short residence times of water in the watershed reduce the importance of these processes. The interannual variability in wet nitrate deposition and stream nitrogen losses are similar to precipitation patterns; years of high precipitation produce greater nitrate inputs and effluxes. The patterns of sulfate efflux, in contrast, bear little relation to input patterns, and instead reflect weathering of sulfur-bearing minerals. Atmospherically derived nitrogen is exported during most of the year, so (a) the ecosystem is saturated with nitrogen, or (b) the terrestrial and aquatic ecosystems are nitrogen-limited, but the hydrologic flow paths and brief residence times limit opportunities for biological uptake of nitrogen.

(5) *Esther Brook, New York, USA* (Miller et al., 1995). This 30 ha catchment in the Adirondack Mountains of New York is at 950 to 1400 m elevation. The mean annual precipitation is 132 cm, 30% of which falls as snow. The basin is covered by a spruce-fir forest. The important sources of ions in runoff shift from snowpack ion load, to the organic soil horizon labile reservoirs, to elemental release from mineral soil and glacial till as the melt season progresses and the flow system deepens.

(6) *Catoctin Mountain, Maryland, USA* (Rice and Bricker, 1995). The study was conducted on two small (550 and 1040 ha, respectively) catchments with second and third growth oak-hickory forest. The climate is humid temperate, with 1110 mm mean annual precipitation, and a mean annual temperature of 12° C. Precipitation is evenly distributed throughout the year, and peak discharge in the winter and spring is from rainfall. The area is underlain by metabasalt and metarhyolite, and the surface varies from exposed bedrock to 10 m thick regolith. Both streams are dilute, with TDS of 70 mg/l. During summer baseflow, streamwater discharge is primarily groundwater from the fractured-bedrock aquifer. The water table is below the regolith-bedrock interface, and the groundwater is rich in cations, alkalinity and dissolved silica as a result of reactions with minerals in relatively unweathered bedrock. Precipitation during summer is largely transpired and very little reaches the groundwater reservoir. Sulfate from atmospheric deposition accumulates in the unsaturated zone. When evapotranspiration is low during the winter, recharge raises the water table into the regolith above the bedrock. This water contributes more sulfate and less alkalinity and silica to streamwaters than does summer discharge, producing regular seasonal cycles in streamwater chemistry.

(7) *Birkenes, Norway* (Christophersen and Wright, 1981). The study area is underlain by biotite granite, and has podzol soils 20-50 cm thick formed on glacial till. The catchment is 0.4 km^2 in area, at elevations of 200 to 300 m, with 89% pine and spruce forest. The precipitation falls as snow and rain, and tends to be acidic. The annual sulfate flux is five to ten times larger than natural, which results in acidification of the stream water (pH 4.5) and increased leaching of base cations from the soil. There is a

seasonal variation in the storage of sulfate in the catchment. A net accumulation occurs in winter because of development of the snowpack, and in summer because of water loss through evapotranspiration. A net release of sulfate occurs during autumn and spring. Sulfate accumulates in the uppermost soil layers because of dry deposition and the evapotranspiration of rain water; this sulfate is then removed from the soil by fast throughflow and pipe flow that contribute to storm flow. Adsorption/desorption of sulfate in the lower mineral soil layers contributes sulfate to the stream during baseflow.

(8) *Khumbu Valley, Nepal* (Reynolds et al., 1995a). The region averages 5000 m in elevation, and is underlain by gneiss, metasedimentary units, and quartzites. Solute concentrations in this region are low compared to global average values. The concentrations are spatially variable, reflecting the complexity of the geology and the presence of moraines with clasts of numerous lithologies. Solutes are dominated by Ca^{2+}, SO_4^{2-}, and HCO_3^-. Aluminosilicate weathering provides the main source of dissolved cations and silica, but carbonates are also important contributors to stream chemistry. Streams draining catchments with forests or agricultural lands have more Ca^{2+}, SO_4^{2-}, K^+, and Mg^+ than high-altitude headwater catchments.

(9) *Rio Icacos watershed, Luquillo Mountains, eastern Puerto Rico* (White et al., 1998). This 326-ha watershed lies at elevations of 600-800 m. Mean annual temperature is 22° C, mean annual precipitation is 4200 mm, and the basin is covered by lower montane wet colorado forest. An ultisol 50-100 cm thick is underlain by a 2-8 m thick layer of oxidized saprolite, with quartz diorite below. The watershed has the fastest documented weathering rate of silicate rocks on the Earth's surface; the regolith propagation rate averages 58 m/Ma. Two distinct weathering environments are present; plagioclase and hornblende react at the saprolite-bedrock interface, whereas biotite and quartz weather in the overlying thick saprolitic regolith. Potassium, magnesium and silica increase linearly with depth in the saprolite porewaters. Stream waters are dominated by calcium, sodium, and silica.

In summary, the chemistry of mountain rivers tends to be characterized by low concentrations of total dissolved solids primarily because of the predominance of crystalline rocks in mountain drainage basins. The chemistry of hillslope inputs to the river is spatially highly variable because of rapid exposure of bedrock and relatively little mediation by chemical weathering in soils. Subtle differences in bedrock lithology may be discernible in the dissolved loads of mountain streams even when the drainage is formed on deeply weathered rocks, as in the case of the Coweeta watershed of North Carolina, USA, where saprolite developed on metasedimentary schists and gneisses averages 6 m in thickness (Velbel, 1992). Mountain river chemistry is also characterized by selective weathering and a contribution of solutes by reactive minerals disproportional to the abundance of the minerals in the local rock. Finally, low concentrations of dissolved organic carbon, and O_2 and CO_2 levels near saturation, are common in mountain rivers. These characteristics may vary as a function of lithology, climate, vegetation cover, relief and flow path for water reaching the river channel. Flow paths, in particular, may vary as a function of regolith accumulation and valley morphology.

Valley Morphology

A common feature of mountain drainage basins is an asymmetry of valley slope profiles on opposite sides of a given valley. This asymmetry occurs in all climatic regions, and is caused by differences in local climate and weathering regime on opposite sides of the valley. The asymmetric profiles thus illustrate the effect of subtle differences in climate on similar lithologies (Leopold et al., 1964). Hack and Goodlett (1960) found that drier slopes in the Appalachian Mountains tend to be gentler and longer, with coarser regolith, higher drainage density, and a predominance of slope wash and channel erosion, whereas wetter slopes are dominated by creep. In contrast, observations in semiarid regions indicate that moister north-facing slopes on which snow accumulates are gentler than drier south-facing slopes (Leopold et al., 1964; Wohl and Pearthree, 1991) (Figure 2.2). Melton (1960) used data from valleys in arid to subhumid temperate climates across the United States to develop the hypotheses that (1) low channel gradients favor the development of valley asymmetry in east- or west-trending valleys, with the north-facing slopes becoming steeper as the rivers are moved against their toes by debris from the south-facing slopes, and (2) steep channel gradients in v-shaped valleys favor more symmetric development of valley sides because erosional debris is carried downstream rather than accumulating as asymmetrical valley fill that shifts the channel laterally.

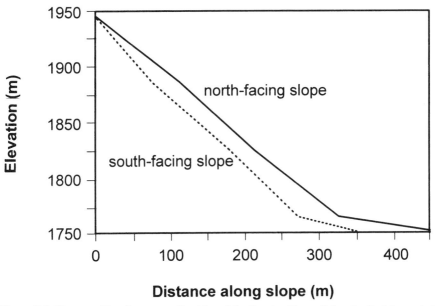

Figure 2.2. Slope profiles from opposite sides of the Poudre River, Colorado. In this semiarid environment, the gentler, north-facing slope is covered with thick coniferous forest, whereas the steeper south-facing slope has grasses and sparse shrub cover. This relation is not consistent along the river; in some locations the north-facing slope is steeper because of structural controls, for example.

Büdel (1982) attributed consistent valley geometries to each of the ten major morphoclimatic zones that he designated. Similarities in valley cross-profile, longitudinal profile, drainage pattern, and rate of incision among valleys in each zone reflect the similar relief-forming mechanisms operating in that zone. Büdel distinguished between valleys in the periglacial region, with their smooth longitudinal profiles, broad, gravel-floored valleys, and rapid rates of incision, for example, and the stepped, narrow, bare bedrock valleys of tropical regions. Other investigators have concluded that tectonic regime or lithology and structure (e.g. Harden, 1990) exert the dominant control on reach-scale valley cross-sectional and longitudinal morphology. If one among these various controlling factors dominates valley morphology, that dominance probably varies among individual drainage basins.

Basin Morphometry

Basin Morphometry and Hydrology

Drainage basin morphometry has been characterized with linear, areal, and relief indices (Strahler, 1964; Ritter et al., 1995; Yamada, 1999a). These measures have been used to compare development of distinct drainage basins, and to provide insight into hydrograph characteristics (e.g. Strahler, 1964; Saxena and Prakash, 1982; Patton, 1988a). For example, hypsometric curves of mass distribution within a drainage basin may be used to infer the history and processes of basin development. Figure 2.3 illustrates hypsometric curves for three small (4-7 km^2), steep (530-820 m relief) drainage basins. The catchment in the Colorado Front Range begins on a broad, low relief upland and then descends steeply through a narrow canyon into the Poudre River. The catchment in the Great Smoky Mountains of North Carolina is well dissected, with no alluvial fans, no floodplains, and minimal deposition in the valleys. The catchment in Virginia's Blue Ridge Mountains has alluvial fans at the base of the ridges, and extensive valley infill; hence, more of the mass in this catchment is at lower elevations. The shapes of these hypsometric curves indicate the degree to which mass has been erosionally transferred from higher to lower elevations within each drainage basin. Another example of using drainage basin morphometry to interpret basin development comes from Oguchi (1997b). He found a constant value of drainage density for 8 mountain river basins (drainage area 12 to 78 km^2) formed on various lithologies and varying relief in central Japan. The uniform frequency or spacing of ridges and hollows in these rugged humid mountains suggests that erosion has continued without effecting a change in the spatial distribution of ridges and hollows, because valleys have undergone straight downcutting while maintaining the drainage density of antecedent drainage systems. Comparison of basin morphometric indices for mountain and lowland rivers around the world indicates the expected differences in valley side slopes, relief, and relief ratios, but no significant difference in drainage density (Table 2.3).

Drainage basin morphometry strongly influences the movement of water from hillslopes to channels and along the channel network. Various investigators have focused on the hydrophysical influence of specific drainage basin characteristics as a means of devel-

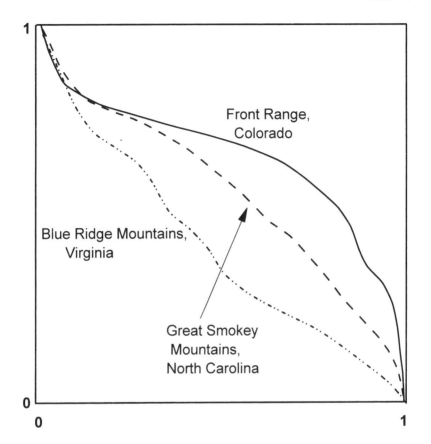

Proportion of Basin Area

Figure 2.3. Hypsometric curves for three small drainage basins in mountainous regions of the Colorado Front Range (USA), the Blue Ridge Mountains of Virginia (USA), and the Great Smokey Mountains of North Carolina (USA). Figure courtesy of Gregory S. Springer.

oping predictive models for hydrographs (Horton, 1932, 1945; Morisawa, 1962; Patton and Baker, 1976). These studies were the precursors to more sophisticated models of runoff that incorporated geomorphic characteristics and the concepts of flood storage and flood routing to create geomorphic unit hydrographs (Patton, 1988a; Rodriguez-Iturbe, 1993). Geomorphic unit hydrograph models have been successfully applied to small (< 60 km²) mountain drainage basins in the former Czechoslovakia (Pristachová, 1990).

Geomorphic characteristics that exert some control on the basin hydrograph include the following: (1) *Drainage area* is important as it controls the volume of runoff collected in a channel network. Discharge increases at a lesser rate than drainage area,

$$Q_x = aA^b \qquad \text{(Patton, 1988a)} \qquad (1)$$

where Q is discharge, x is recurrence interval, A is drainage area, and $b = 0.5\text{-}0.9$.

Table 2.3. Measures of drainage basin morphometry for selected mountain and lowland rivers. A relief ratio of ≥ 0.02 is used to distinguish mountain rivers from lowland rivers

River	Drainage Area (km²)	Relief (m)	Climate	Lithology	Valley side slope max:mean	Drainage density (m/m)	Relief ratio (mm)	Strahler basin order	Reference
Mountains									
Thulo Khola, Nepal	13.7	1135		granite, phyllite, schist, marble			0.15	6	Caine & Mool, 1981
Melinau River, Borneo	260	2201		sandstone, shale, limestone	0.6: 0.5	1.8	6.8	5	Rose, 1984
Dry Creek, Texas	4.7	155		limestone		8.9	0.04	4	Patton & Baker, 1976
Rick Creek, Utah	6.1	1307		metamorphic rocks		7.0	0.27	4	Patton & Baker, 1976
Holmes Creek, Utah	6.5	1246		metamorphic rocks		9.2	0.27	4	Patton & Baker, 1976
Fern Canyon Cr., s. California	5.7	881		igneous and metamorphic		18.5	0.22	5	Patton & Baker, 1976
Bronco Creek, Arizona	49	954	arid			5.4	0.08		Costa, 1987
Rattlesnake Cr., Arizona	6.5	1171	arid	metamorphic rocks	0.47: 0.39	1.5	0.23	3	
Cañada del Oro Arizona	92	1678	arid	metamorphic rocks	0.34:0.27	0.6	0.11	4	Ghose et al., 1957
nw India	167		arid	granite		1.3	0.12	4	"
nw India	15		arid	sandy alluvium		0.8	0.08	3	
Lost Creek Washington	1	365	humid temperate		0.30:0.24	2.4	0.15	2	
S.F. Foundation Cr., Washington	5.7	730	humid temperate		0.24:0.17	0.7	0.13	2	
Newport Creek, Washington	3.5	839	humid temperate		0.46:0.26	1.5	0.18	2	
Charlie Creek, Qld., Australia	96	490	seasonal tropical		0.16:0.10	1.4	0.07	4	
Pebble Creek, Qld., Australia	6	440	seasonal tropical		0.44:0.32	0.7	0.11	2	
N. Branch Creek, Qld., Australia	33	920	seasonal tropical		0.32:0.24	1.6	0.11	3	

River	Drainage Area (km²)	Relief (m)	Climate	Lithology	Valley side slope max:mean	Drainage density (m/m)	Relief ratio (mm)	Strahler basin order	Reference
Nigeria[2]	2.7	131		sandstone	0.20 (avg)	2.9	0.06	3	Ebisemiju, 1987
S. Boulder Creek, Colorado	282	1942	cold temperate	granite	0.45:0.21	1.14	0.05	3	
E. St. Louis Cr., Colorado	8	1095	subalpine	granite	0.34:0.28	0.9	0.15	2	
Allegheny River, Pennsylvania	88		humid temperate	sedimentary		3.3	0.015	5	Morisawa, 1962
Susuki River, Japan	78	1284	humid temperate	igneous & sedimen.		9.9	0.10	6	Oguchi, 1998 (pers. comm.)
Chi River, Japan	38	1820	humid temperate	granite		10.7	0.22	6	"
Ashima River, Japan	12	1465	humid temperate	granite		14.0	0.26	5	"
	1-260					0.6-18.5	0.015-6.8	2-6	
Lowlands									
Amazon	5.98 x 10⁶	5486	humid tropical				0.002		Summerfield & Hutton, 1994
St. Lawrence	1.05 x 10⁶	1066	cold temperate				0.0006		"
Dnieper	540,000	304	humid temperate				0.0004		"
Murray	1,140,000	1524	semiarid				0.001		"
Mukewater Cr., Texas	10.4	41		limestone		5.7	0.007	4	Patton and Baker, 1976
Hinkle Creek, Indiana	47	33	humid temperate	glacial sediments		6.6	0.004	6	Patton and Baker, 1976
Buck Creek, Indiana	88	14	humid temperate	glacial sediments		5.7	0.0008	6	Patton and Baker, 1976
Daddys Creek, Pennsylvania	243	222	humid temperate	sedimentary rocks		2.9	0.005	6	Patton and Baker, 1976
Mailtrail Creek, Texas	195	192	semiarid			5.5	0.01		Costa, 1987
Beech Creek, Ohio	49		humid temperate			2.8	0.007	5	Morisawa, 1982
Mamu Lowland, Nigeria[1]	7.5	53		clay shale	0.01 (avg)	2.0	0.017	3	Ebisemiju, 1987
	8-6x106					2.6-6	0.0004-0.01	3-6	

1. Average of 32 drainage basins; 2. Average of 36 drainage basins

(2) *Drainage density* reflects the effectiveness of surface runoff and erosion, and influences concentration time of flow in a channel network. Drainage density reaches the highest values in semiarid and tropical environments, and in basins with non-resistant lithologies (Gregory and Gardiner, 1975). However, drainage density is not sensitive to changes in the hydrologic response of a basin that occur during an individual storm (Day, 1978). (3) *Stream order and basin magnitude.* Strahler stream order correlates directly with discharge within a basin, presumably because of the correlation between drainage area and order for basins in similar climatic and geologic regions (Leopold and Miller, 1956; Blyth and Rodda, 1973; Patton and Baker, 1976). (4) *Drainage basin relief* is important in that higher relief is associated with steeper hillslopes, higher stream gradients, shorter times of runoff concentration, and larger flood peaks (Patton, 1988a). (5) *Drainage basin shape* also influences time of concentration and magnitude of peak discharge, with equant-shaped basins tending to produce larger, shorter peak discharges than linear basins (Strahler, 1964).

Some of the difficulty in developing a model of a hydrograph that adequately simulates a range of drainage basins stems from our incomplete understanding of, first, how the actual contributing drainage net changes with rainfall intensity and duration and, second, the distribution of lag time as a function of stream order within a basin (Patton, 1988a).

Drainage networks in a mountainous basin may be substantially modified if a severe or widespread storm produces extensive mass movements and associated erosion and deposition, or if seismic or volcanic activity alter basin relief. Channel networks may also respond to changes in water and sediment yield associated with land-use activities such as timber harvest or agriculture. Over longer timescales, drainage morphometry may respond to glaciation or climatic change.

Hydraulic Geometry

Hydraulic geometry, as developed by Leopold and Maddock (1953), assumes that discharge is the dominant independent variable of channel and flow geometry, and that dependent variables such as channel width, flow depth, slope, or velocity are related to discharge in the form of simple power functions. These basic assumptions may not hold for mountain river channels that are shaped by debris flows or glaciation. In addition, the recurrence interval of the water discharge that shapes channel geometry may vary greatly among basins (see discussion, chapter 3). Some studies have indicated, however, that mountain channels may correspond to the lowland alluvial channels from which hydraulic geometry was originally developed. Using peak discharge information for 43 gaging stations during an average monsoon season in two drainage basins in the Middle Hills of Nepal, Caine and Mool (1981) found that the hydraulic geometry relations were generally similar to those reported from other regions of the world. The two Nepalese catchments were slightly longer than normal and had a quicker hydrologic response, both of which presumably reflect the steep terrain. Fenn and Gurnell (1987) found that the usual linear power functions described the relation between discharge and the dependent variables for a proglacial braided channel in Switzerland. In contrast, Ponton (1972) found that two tributaries of the Lillooet River of British Columbia, Canada did not follow the expected downstream hydraulic geometry trends because of gradient changes related to glaciation. Phillips and Harlin (1984) described a mountain river in Colorado (USA) that did not follow predictable downstream changes in hydraulic geometry because of substantial changes in alluvial substrate.

An approach related to hydraulic geometry is to consider downstream trends in flow energy expenditure. Knighton (1999) proposed a model of downstream variation in stream power. Based on the assumption that the longitudinal profile of the river has an exponential form, the model predicted that total stream power peaks at an intermediate distance between the drainage divide and the mouth, the position of which depends on the ratio of downstream rate of change of discharge and downstream rate of change in slope. Unit stream power, which is more sensitive to rate of change in slope, is predicted to peak closer to the headwaters, about half-way between the source and the location of the total stream power maximum, although this will depend on how channel width varies downstream. Tests of the model in lowland alluvial channels indicate that site-specific variations in discharge and slope create discrepancies between the observed and predicted locations of the maxima. These discrepancies might be more pronounced in high-relief drainage basins because of substantial downstream variability in slope.

As might be expected, the degree to which a mountain river approximates alluvial hydraulic geometry relations and energy expenditure models will reflect the relative importance of substrate and sediment supply in controlling channel geometry. Because mountain rivers often do not follow the trends of channel and valley gradient predicted by hydraulic geometry, it is appropriate to consider in more detail the controls on gradient.

Longitudinal Profiles and Channel Incision

Longitudinal profiles of rivers have been studied for more than a century (e.g. Powell, 1875, 1876; Gilbert, 1877; Davis, 1902; Mackin, 1948; Hack, 1957; Pazzaglia et al., 1998; Weissel and Seidl, 1998). Because overall stream gradient decreases downstream, longitudinal profiles of large drainage basins generally have a concave upward shape, which Hack (1957) expressed as

$$s = k \, L^n \tag{2}$$

where s = slope, L = distance, and the exponent n is an index of profile concavity. Mountain rivers may have concave profiles, but they are also very likely to have straight or convex profiles with knickpoints (Figure 2.4). These characteristics reflect the relative inability of smaller, headwater channels to incise rapidly enough to keep pace with tectonic uplift, baselevel fall, glacial effects, or climate change, partly

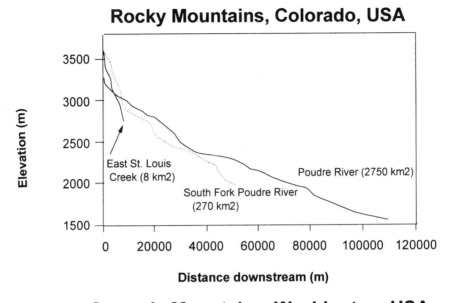

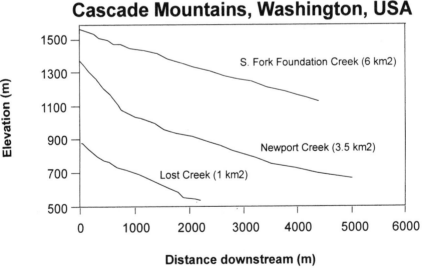

Figure 2.4. Sample longitudinal profiles from mountain rivers in various regions of the world. Drainage area for each basin is included in the graph text.

because of greater bedrock exposure than downstream channel reaches (Merritts and Vincent, 1989; Howard et al., 1994). Disequilibrium in the form of deviation from a semi-log straight line longitudinal profile may persist for millions of years along headwater bedrock channels (Goldrick and Bishop, 1995).

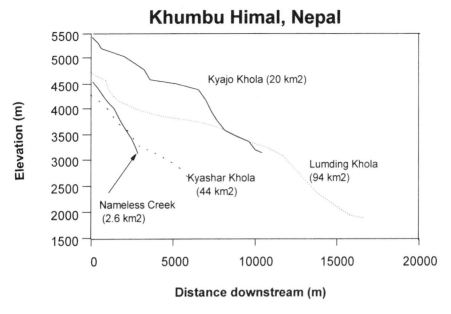

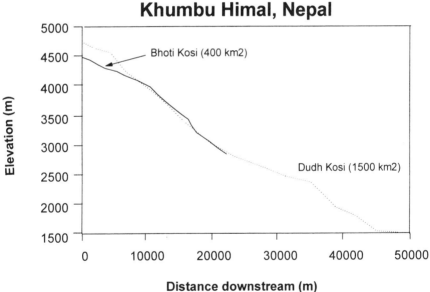

Figure 2.4 (continued).

One of the key components of explaining mountain-river longitudinal profiles is understanding the processes by which channels incise (Hancock et al., 1998; Wohl, 1998). Bedrock channels are particularly important in this respect because the rate of

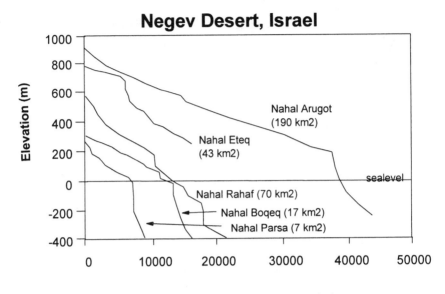

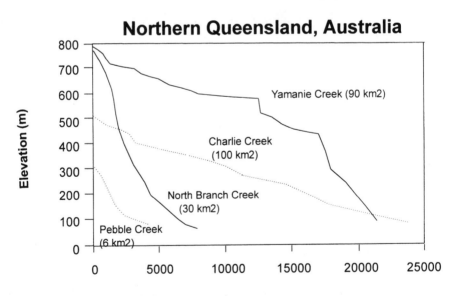

Figure 2.4 (continued).

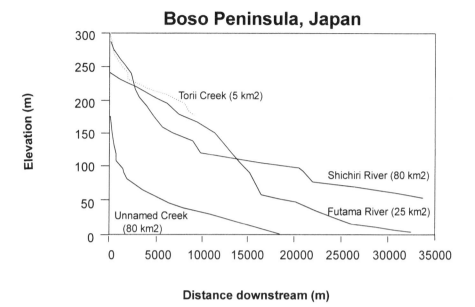

Figure 2.4 (continued).

bedrock incision may limit the rate at which baselevel change in transmitted along a drainage basin (Tinkler and Wohl, 1998). Natural discontinuities or thresholds occur along a channel between substrates of bedrock, coarse-grained alluvium, and fine-grained alluvium (Yatsu, 1955; Schumm, 1956; Howard, 1980). The gradient of alluvial channels is determined by hydraulic regime, whereas the gradient of bedrock channels may be an independent variable in that weathering must precede erosion (Howard, 1980, 1998).

Alluvial channel segments will develop if the local or ultimate baselevel remains constant or lowers very slowly, or where the gradient of the underlying bedrock is lower than that required for transport of sediment supplied from upstream (Howard, 1980). Local baselevels may be resistant lithologies or large woody debris jams (Montgomery et al., 1996a). Channels are expected to have fine-grained alluvium where sediment concentrations are high but grain size range is narrow. Coarse-grained alluvial channels are favored by low sediment loads and relatively large proportions of coarse sediment (Howard, 1987).

Fine-grained alluvial channels may be referred to as "live-bed" or "regime" channels because sediment transport occurs at all but the lowest flows. Coarse-grained alluvial channels are sometimes called "threshold" or "stable" channels because sediment moves only near bankfull discharge (Howard, 1980), or during extreme floods or debris flows. Mountain rivers tend to have substrates of coarse-grained alluvium or bedrock, so that channel incision occurs only episodically. The conditions under which sediment transport and channel incision occur along a channel in coarse-grained alluvium may be predicted in terms of the hydraulic conditions necessary to mobilize most of the sediment (see chapter 3). These channels often have gradients near the threshold of motion (Howard et al., 1994).

Two key unresolved questions about the long-term evolution of mixed bedrock-alluvial channels are (1) how and when the bedrock is eroded, and (2) whether channel gradient is determined by the necessity to transport the alluvium, or to erode the bed (Howard, 1998). Interpreting field data from the Indus River in Pakistan, Hancock et al. (1998) suggest that block quarrying is the most efficient bedrock erosive process when joints and bedding planes are sufficiently close, whereas abrasion is most effective in regions of separated flow. Sklar and Dietrich (1998) developed a mechanistic hypothesis for the effects of sediment supply on incision rates which predicts that incision rates are highest at intermediate levels of sediment supply and transport capacity, and that channel slope-drainage area relationships of bedrock rivers predominantly reflect sediment supply and grain size rather than bedrock erosion.

The erosion of bedrock channels has been expressed as a rate law of the form

$$E = k A^\phi S^\sigma \qquad \text{(Howard, 1980)} \qquad (3)$$

where E = average erosion rate, which increases in proportion to drainage area A and gradient S; ϕ and σ are constants, and k includes the inherent bed erodibility and the magnitude and frequency characteristics of the flow. If erosion rates were directly proportional to bed shear stress, ϕ would equal 0.38 and σ would equal 0.81 (Howard, 1980). Because substrate erodibility can vary so greatly along bedrock streams, these streams have no simple downstream hydraulic geometry, and gradient is a semi-independent variable (Howard, 1980).

Seidl and Dietrich (1992) applied the erosion rate law to mountain channels in the western U.S. and found that a single rate law could not approximate incision across an entire channel network because of differences in mechanism of erosion across the network. Steep tributaries incised primarily through scour by periodic debris flows, whereas other channels eroded by knickpoint propagation or by vertical wear via abrasion and dissolution (Seidl and Dietrich, 1992). Application of the erosion rate law to mountainous streams in regions of moderate tectonic activity and semiarid climate indicated that the law did not accurately predict vertical fluvial incision rates because downstream trends in drainage area-discharge varied significantly, and because stream power is apportioned among processes such as lateral incision and bedload transport, as well as vertical bedrock incision (Mitchell and Pazzaglia, 1999). However, bedrock channel incision along some channel reaches does appear to be linearly related to stream power (Young and McDougall, 1993; Rosenbloom and Anderson, 1994; Seidl et al., 1994).

Stock and Montgomery (1999) used mapped paleoprofiles and modern river profiles for simulating the lowering of ancient river profiles under scenarios of varying ϕ, σ and k. They found that along rivers with relatively stable baselevels, incision occurs concurrently along the entire profile, and there is a strong area dependence on incision rate. For rivers subject to abrupt baselevel change, long-term lowering rate is a function of the frequency and magnitude of knickpoint erosion, and there is a small area dependence on incision rate. For rivers with stable baselevels, k may vary over 5 orders of magnitude as a function of lithology (Stock and Montgomery, 1999).

Comprehensive modeling of the profile evolution of bedrock channels will require the develpment of rate laws for dissolution; abrasion (Foley, 1980a,b); knickpoint evolution; and boulder production, breakdown, and removal (Howard et al., 1994; Seidl et al., 1994, 1997; Hancock et al., 1998). The ability to model profile evolution as a function of these processes will also facilitate our understanding of changes in rates and types of hillslope and channel processes that have occurred during the past two million years (Pazzaglia et al., 1998).

Quaternary Changes

The climatic changes of the past two million years have dramatically affected the rivers of most of the world's mountainous regions. Many mountain river basins were completely covered by ice during periods of glacial advance, and received greatly varying water and sediment yields during periods of glacial retreat and interglacial episodes. Even regions not directly covered by ice had changes in temperature and precipitation regime that in turn altered weathering, vegetation, and slope processes. The magnitude of river response to these changes varied as a function of the magnitude of climatic change, and as a function of the "original" climate. Brunsden and Thornes (1979) defined the sensitivity of a landscape to change as "the likelihood that a given change in the controls of a system will produce a sensible, recognizable and persistent response." Changes in controlling factors must overcome five basic sources of resistance to change in order to produce a landscape response. These are strength resistance, morphological resistance, structural resistance, filter resistance, and system-state resistance (Brunsden, 1993). *Strength resistance* depends on rock properties such as strength and erodibility, which produce a limited range of geometrical outcomes such as joint spacing, orientation, and continuity. *Morphological resistance* depends on the slope, relief, and elevation of a landscape, which vary across space and over time. *Structural resistance* depends on the closeness of sensitive elements to the processes initiating change (e.g., closeness to baselevel), and the ability of the landscape to transmit the impulse of change. *Filter resistance* is governed by the way in which kinetic energy is transmitted through or absorbed by the landscape. *System-state resistance* is largely a function of history and trend of the system at the time of disturbance. Because of the great variety in these sources of resistance among the world's mountainous regions, mountain-river responses to Quaternary climate changes have also varied greatly.

Geomorphic response to climate change may take the form of a change in drainage density. Oguchi (1997a,c) describes increased channelization of hillslope hollows in Japan by landslides and gullying during a period of wetter climate at the Pleistocene-Holocene transition. Sediment yields also increased during this period of rapid incision. Schumm (1997) summarizes studies indicating that lithologies which weather to produce a soil with a high permeability produce drainage networks that are less closely linked to climate than those formed on readily eroded materials with low permeability. Shale basins, for example, more readily reflect current climate conditions than granite basins. Drainage density response to climate change may ultimately depend on corresponding changes in the threshold of channelization in terms of minimum upslope source area necessary to support a channel (Montgomery and Dietrich, 1992).

Bull (1991) focused on how interactions between hillslopes and channels during episodes of climatic change resulted in aggradation, degradation, or stability along mountain channels. Changing baselevel may also cause aggradation or degradation independent of climatic change (Figure 2.5), although fluctuating sealevel during the Quaternary is inextricably tied to climate change. The post-glacial isostatic rebound of regions covered by ice sheets also altered baselevel and caused channel incision (Krzyszkowski and Stachura, 1998).

Bull (1991) conceptualized geomorphic response in terms of a threshold of critical stream power. The threshold of critical power is defined as the ratio of power available (stream power) to power needed (resisting power) for entrainment and transport of bedload (Bull, 1979). When the threshold is exceeded, degradation occurs. When conditions fluctuate close to the threshold, the channel follows Mackin's (1948) definition of a graded river as "one in which, over a period of years, slope is delicately adjusted to provide, with available discharge and with prevailing channel characteristics, just the velocity required for the transportation of the load supplied from the

Hillslope Subsystem

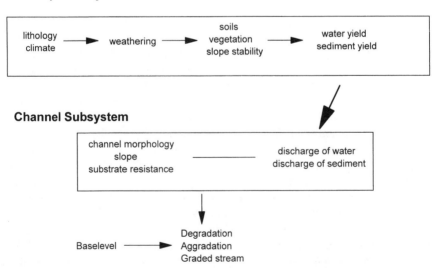

Figure 2.5. Schematic diagram of relations between hillslope and channel subsystem as these influence channel stability.

drainage basin. The graded stream is a system in equilibrium ..." Aggradation occurs when the threshold of critical power is not exceeded.

Episodes of aggradation or degradation leave a record in the form of changes in channel and floodplain sediment storage, strath (bedrock) or fill (alluvial) terraces along a channel, and changes in fan morphology at the base of the mountains. These depositional features may exhibit fairly straightforward relations to climate change, where a period of wetter climate results in greater sediment yield and aggradation, for example. Or the channel may exhibit what Schumm termed complex response (Schumm, 1973; Schumm and Parker, 1973; Schumm et al., 1987). An example of complex response is a fall in baselevel that initiates headward incision. After the incision has progressed upstream, the lower portion of the channel may aggrade because of the increased sediment supply from the incising reach upstream. Once incision ends in the upstream reach, the decrease in sediment supply may initiate a new phase of incision in the lower reach, so that a single fall in baselevel is associated with two sets of fill terraces. Other studies have also demonstrated that physically continuous terrace treads may not be time-equivalent surfaces (Germanoski and Harvey, 1993; Merritts et al., 1994). The lag times associated with adjustments to changing baselevel or sediment supply may be hundreds of thousands of years for rivers incising into bedrock (Merritts and Vincent, 1989).

Bull (1991) compared geomorphic responses to climate change of a semiarid to subhumid mountain range in southern California, a humid mountain range in central New Zealand, and a hyperarid mountain range in southern Israel. In each case the ratio of water discharge and sediment discharge was critical in determining whether or not the threshold of critical power was exceeded, but a single climatic change could produce different results in channel behavior depending on whether the change was from an arid to semiarid climate, for example (increase in sediment yield), or from a semiarid to a subhumid climate (decrease in sediment yield). In the Charwell River basin of central New Zealand, channel response varied along the basin as a function of elevational controls on climate (Figure 2.6). Thus, although mountain rivers in each of the three regions that Bull studied underwent Quaternary episodes of aggradation and degradation, these episodes were not synchronous between regions or even within single large drainage basins that spanned a range of elevations. During full-glacial and subsequent transitional climates, hillslopes in hot deserts accumulated colluvium that was stripped during the Holocene to aggrade valley floors. Hillslopes in the humid mesic mountain ranges, in contrast, had maximum sediment yields during full-glacial climates, resulting in channel aggradation. The humid mountain ranges also had more frequent episodes of aggradation, suggesting a more rapid rate of hillslope and channel adjustment to climate change. In arid regions where sources of bedload are limited, sufficient accumulation of hillslope regolith must precede channel aggradation (Bull, 1991).

Studies of mountain-river terrace chronologies and slope incision generally support Bull's work. Schick (1974) noted that specific aspects of climate change, such as the frequency of large floods, may be particularly important in controlling terrace formation along arid-region mountain rivers, a conclusion also reached by Bull and Knuepfer (1987) in the Charwell basin of New Zealand. Patton and Boison (1986) found Holocene chan-

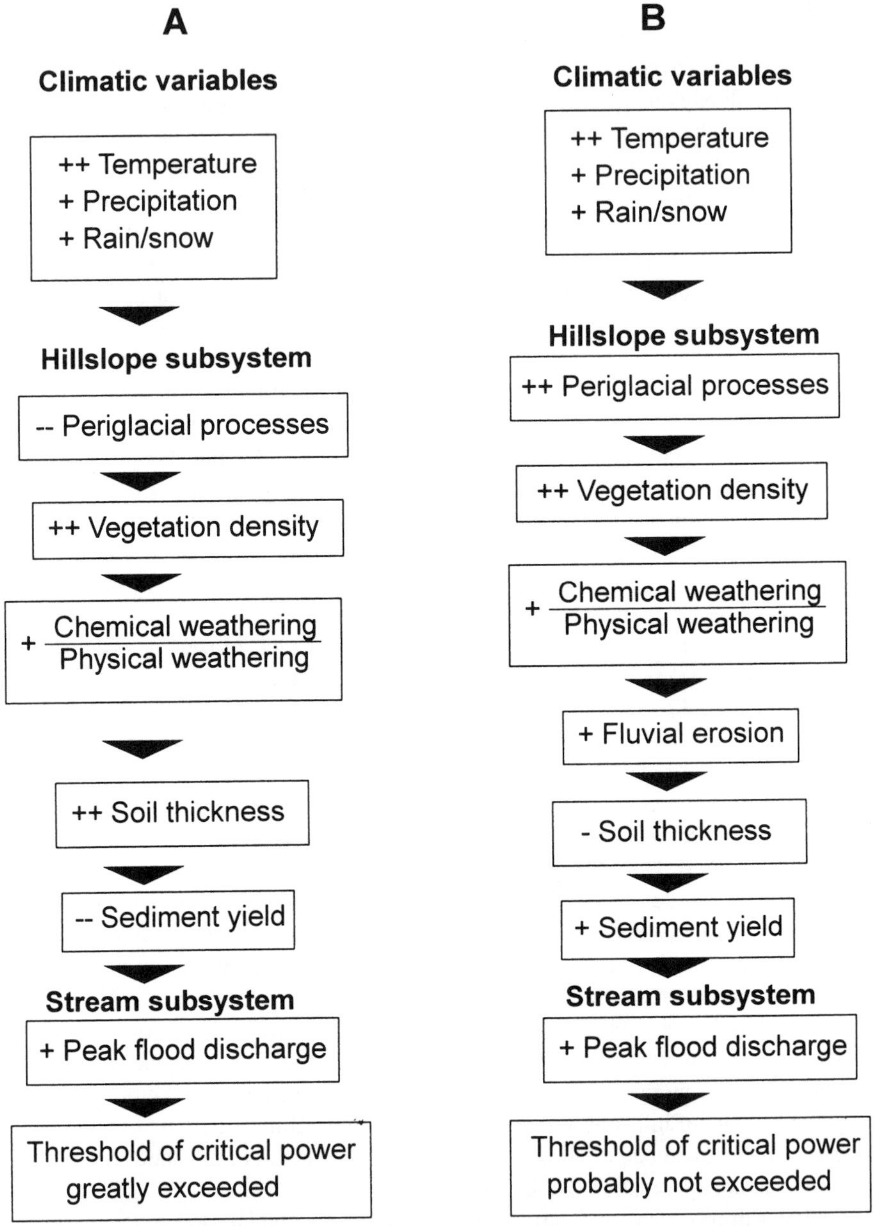

A

Climatic variables

| ++ Temperature |
| + Precipitation |
| + Rain/snow |

▼

Hillslope subsystem

-- Periglacial processes

▼

++ Vegetation density

▼

+ $\dfrac{\text{Chemical weathering}}{\text{Physical weathering}}$

▼

++ Soil thickness

▼

-- Sediment yield

▼

Stream subsystem

+ Peak flood discharge

▼

Threshold of critical power greatly exceeded

B

Climatic variables

| ++ Temperature |
| + Precipitation |
| + Rain/snow |

▼

Hillslope subsystem

++ Periglacial processes

▼

++ Vegetation density

▼

+ $\dfrac{\text{Chemical weathering}}{\text{Physical weathering}}$

▼

+ Fluvial erosion

▼

- Soil thickness

▼

+ Sediment yield

▼

Stream subsystem

+ Peak flood discharge

▼

Threshold of critical power probably not exceeded

Figure 2.6. Process-response model for hillslopes of the Charwell River basin of New Zealand for a change from semiarid pergelic to humid mesic conditions. Symbols for moderate change are (+) and (-) and for major change are (++) and (--). (a) Watershed from the basin mouth to the present treeline, 450 m to 1200 m. Self-enhancing feedback mechanism is shown by the dotted line with arrow. (b) Watershed from the present treeline to highest part of the basin, 1200 to 1600 m. (After Bull, 1991, Figure 5.15.)

nel aggradation in semiarid regions. Aggradation occurred during glacial intervals in the subhumid Rocky Mountains of Wyoming, USA (Moss and Bonini, 1961; Moss, 1974); during the Pleistocene-Holocene transition in the humid Coast Range of western Oregon, USA (Personius et al., 1993); during the late Glacial in the humid mountains of central Japan (Oguchi, 1996a); and during the interglacial in the extremely humid Melinau drainage basin of Borneo (Rose, 1984).

Terraces

Among the principal features created by changes in water and sediment yield throughout the Quaternary are river terraces. Terraces represent channel and floodplain surfaces no longer subject to active fluvial modification. Terraces may be created by crossing the threshold of critical power as a result of change in climate, land use, baselevel, or tectonic regime. As expressed by Gilbert (1877), Mackin (1948), and Leopold and Bull (1979), a graded stream is one in which the slope is adjusted to prevailing water and sediment discharges, such that the channel is neither aggrading nor degrading, and slope remains constant through time. A change in baselevel or water or sediment discharge would cause a response in the form of aggradation or degradation, and a change in gradient. This leads to questions of how, and how far, changes in controlling factors are transmitted along a channel (Merritts et al., 1994).

Working in the active orogenic belt of northern California, Merritts and Vincent (1989) demonstrated that a river incising into bedrock in response to an effective baselevel fall can maintain uniform incision and a steady longitudinal profile along its length if the river is able to transmit all of the baselevel fall from its mouth upstream along its length. For a given rate of uplift, smaller rivers will be steeper than larger rivers in order to maintain the stream power required for incision. If stream power along a channel reach falls below what is required for incision to match uplift rate, then the gradient will increase along that reach relative to the next downstream reach, and a terrace may be formed (Merritts and Vincent, 1989). Computer formation of terrace simulation has indicated that although the inputs of climate and tectonics may change continuously, the output of the simulation is discontinuous in the formation of terrace steps (Boll et al., 1988).

Because changes in the causal factors of terrace formation may occur simultaneously, one of the most straightforward means of classifying terraces is to focus on terrace composition rather than genesis. Strath terraces have low-relief bedrock treads mantled with a thin veneer of alluvium. The existence of strath terraces implies a period of vertical stability during which a relatively planar bedrock valley bottom could be formed by lateral stream erosion. As uplift rate and rate of river incision increase, strath terraces are less likely to be formed (Merritts et al., 1994). Fill terraces are alluvial sequences too thick to be mobilized throughout their entire depth by the river. Each type of terrace may record a prior longitudinal profile of the river, although terraces may be tectonically deformed after formation.

Terraces are readily formed along many mountain rivers, in part because the relatively low sediment storage along hillslopes and valley bottoms facilitates aggradation of a new, high surface whenever sediment supply increases, and incision into bedrock whenever sediment supply decreases. Terrace formation is also enhanced by the relatively high rates of uplift and associated channel incision in many mountainous regions; by the substantial fluctuations in water and sediment discharge associated with advances and retreats of upstream glaciers; and by the occurrence of landslides that cause upstream aggradation and subsequent degradation when the landslide toe is eroded (Ryder and Church, 1986). Terraces formed by these various mechanisms are often preserved only as discontinuous fragments because of subsequent slope instability and river incision along narrow mountain valleys. Discontinuous terrace remnants along ephemeral channels in arid regions may also result from periodic incision during major floods (Schick, 1974; Schick and Magid, 1978), and from alternating episodes of aggradation-degradation that appear to be inherent in the operation of these channels (Womack and Schumm, 1977).

The longitudinal continuity of terraces depends on processes of both formation and preservation. Studies of terraces along rivers in coastal mountain ranges, for example, have noted distinct longitudinal differences (Rose, 1984). Working in the Coast Ranges of northern California, Merritts et al. (1994) found that the lower reaches of rivers are dominated by the effects of oscillating sea level. Aggradation and formation of fill terraces extend tens of kilometers upstream during sea level highstands, with a depositional gradient about half that of the original channel. The middle and upper reaches of rivers are dominated by the effects of long-term uplift. Strath terraces with gradients steeper than the modern channel bed form along middle reaches that are upstream from the aggradation associated with sea level rise, but far enough downstream from the drainage divide that stream power exceeds what is necessary to transport the prevailing sediment load (Merritts et al., 1994).

Rates of fluvial incision, timing of effective baselevel rise or fall, and timing of climatically-induced changes in water and sediment yield have been determined from terrace chronologies. Ages of terraces have been estimated using ^{14}C dating (Personius et al., 1993; Merritts et al., 1994), weathering rinds (Colman and Pierce, 1981; Birkeland, 1982; Knuepfer, 1988; Adams et al., 1992), soils (Knuepfer, 1988), lichenometry, and cosmogenic isotopes. Over longer time periods during which substantial changes may have occurred in lateral channel location, drainage network pattern may be reconstructed from relict fluvial gravels (Larsen et al., 1975; Scott, 1975; Bartholomew and Mills, 1991).

Summary

Hillslope processes controlling water and sediment yield are linked to channel processes in all drainage basins. In mountain drainage basins this link is particularly strong because of the proximity of hillslopes and channels. Many mountain rivers have relatively narrow valleys with limited floodplains. Hillslopes serve as a primary and direct source of water and sediment, and changes in hillslope morphology or processes are not buffered by valley-bottom storage. The relatively shallow regoliths and short lateral paths of subsurface flow in mountain catchments commonly produce streams with low concentrations of dissolved solids and spatially and temporally variable input chemistry. Mountain drainage basins may respond more readily than lowland basins to fluctuations in climate or geology. In high-relief mountain regions, climate changes translate into elevational shifts in vegetation and weathering regime, and the commonly thin regolith and low slope stability ensure that these shifts will alter water and sediment yield. Changes in tectonic regime or exposed lithology are also more likely to alter water and sediment yield in mountain drainage basins than in lowland basins because of the absence of filtering mechanisms associated with thick, stable regolith. Although the world's mountain regions are diverse in climate and geology, drainage basins formed in these regions share a strong structural influence on drainage development; relatively high rates of bedrock channel incision; a role as the primary sediment source for lowland drainage basins; straight or convex longitudinal profiles characterized by knickpoints; and evidence of substantial changes in channel pattern and process associated with Quaternary glacial and climatic changes.

3

CHANNEL PROCESSES

Hydrology

Mountainous regions provide the major water source for many parts of the world. The mountains provide temporary water storage in the form of snow; natural and artificial storage reservoirs; and potential energy for hydroelectric power (Bandyopadhyay et al., 1997). In arid and semiarid regions, runoff from mountains may be the principal source of water for the surrounding lowlands (Liniger, 1992). In the western United States, for example, eighty percent of the water used for agriculture, industry, and domestic purposes originates from mountain winter-spring snowpacks (Price and Barry, 1997).

The hydrologic regime of a mountain river is predominantly controlled by climate as expressed directly through precipitation and indirectly through the influence of weathering, soils, and vegetation on runoff and infiltration. The hydrologic regimes of mountain rivers can be subdivided at the first level into those dominated by glacier melt, by snowmelt runoff, or by rainfall runoff (Table 3.1; Figure 3.1). Rainfall runoff regimes may be further subdivided based on the type of atmospheric circulation pattern producing the rainfall, and the associated differences in rainfall intensity, duration, spatial extent, and frequency of occurrence. Although the specifics of precipitation distribution within a mountainous region commonly differ from the precipitation distribution of adjacent lowlands, the mountainous region is influenced by regional atmospheric circulation patterns.

Glacier- and Snowmelt

The relative importances of glacier melt, snowmelt, and rainfall commonly vary by elevation within a mountain region. Glacier and snowmelt are more important at higher elevations, and the seasonal melt contribution is delayed later into the summer with increasing elevation. As the basin area covered by ice increases, the ratio of summer to annual runoff increases, the occurrence of maximum monthly runoff is delayed, and interannual runoff variation is reduced (Chen and Ohmura, 1990; Collins and Taylor, 1990). Because of differences in the percentage of catchment area covered by permanent snow and ice, drainage area-discharge relations may not be linear in mountain regions. For example, the Upper Hunza River drains 5,000 km^2 on low mountains north of the main Karakoram chain that do not have major glaciers. The discharge of the Upper Hunza River is doubled by the confluence of a short river draining the 300 km^2 Batura glacier (Gerrard, 1990).

Table 3.1. Hydrologic regimes of mountain rivers (after Hirschboeck, 1988, and others).

Regime type	Duration of high flow	Spatial extent	Frequency of occurrence	Approximate ratio of high flow to base flow or to average discharge	Example locality
Snowmelt	days to weeks	$10-10^2$ km^2	annual	250	Upper Hunza River, Pakistan
Rainfall					
convective	hours	$1-10^2$ km^2	seasonal	4,500-50,000	Plum Creek and Bijou Creeks, Colorado, USA
frontal	days	10^4 km^2	seasonal	44-142	Missouri River, USA (Ritter, 1988)
cyclonic	days to weeks	10^5-10^7 km^2	seasonal	330	Puerto Rico (Scatena and Larsen, 1991)
monsoonal	months	10^5-10^7 km^2	annual	11-138	Ganga River (Gupta, 1995)
rain-on-snow	days	$10-10^2$ km^2	seasonal	4-10 X mean annual flood	Tenaya Creek, Sierra Nevada, California, USA (Kattelmann, 1990)
Glacier melt	days to weeks	$10-10^2$ km^2	seasonal	10-20	Bas Glacier d'Arolla, Switzerland (Warburton, 1994)

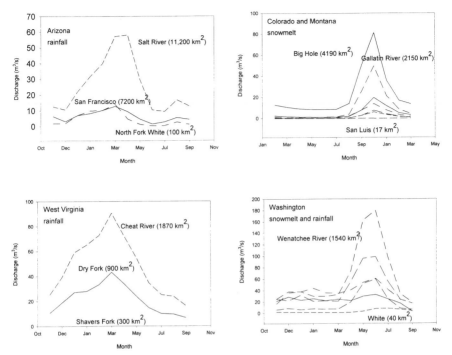

Figure 3.1. Sample hydrographs for mountain rivers of varying drainage area and from varying climatic regimes.

Rivers controlled by glacier melt or snowmelt have a strongly diurnal discharge pattern during the melt season. For example, Slaymaker (1974) recorded daily fluctuations from 4 to 6 m³/s and, later in the season, 7 to 10 m³/s on Miller Creek in British Columbia. Hodgkins (1997) reported similar fluctuations in proglacial discharge from a glacier in the Norwegian High Arctic. The timing of the daily peak is a function of distance downstream from the melt source.

Glacier outflow hydrographs consist of a base flow component supplied by groundwater discharge, runoff from storage zones within the ice, runoff from the firn water aquifer, and regular drainage from lakes (Gerrard, 1990). A diurnally peaked component of flow is fed by supra- and subglacial meltwater, and by meltwater from the snow-free part of the glacier. Discharge from the glacier varies systematically during the melt season as a system of channels develops on and within the glacier (Fenn, 1987; Nienow et al., 1998). An initial peak flow may result from melt of seasonal snow cover on the glacial tongue and on non-glacial surfaces, followed by a second peak of melt from the glacial ice (Aizen et al., 1995). Interannual discharge variations result from fluctuations in glacier mass balance, particularly as a function of summer weather (Gerrard, 1990). Models of seasonal snow distribution (Elder, 1995) and runoff processes (Ersi et al., 1995) on glaciers may be used to predict glacier- and snow-melt hydrograph characteristics.

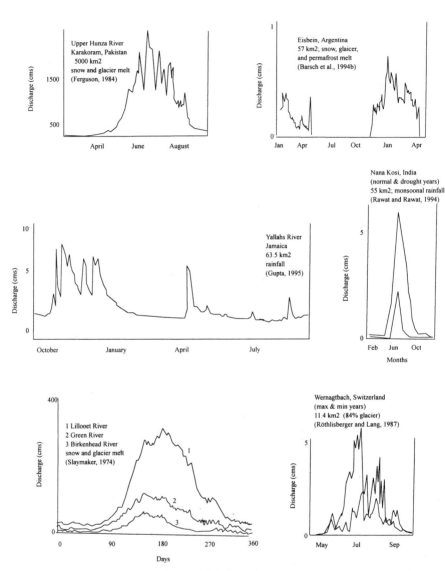

Figure 3.1 (continued)

Spatial Hydrologic Patterns

Hayden (1988) has designated seventeen types of flood climate regions, and each of these regions includes at least one mountain chain. At the first level, regions are divided into barotropic (gradients of pressure and temperature intersect) and baroclinic (temperature and pressure gradients are weak and nearly parallel). Barotropic conditions occur predominantly in low-latitude tropical regions where convection

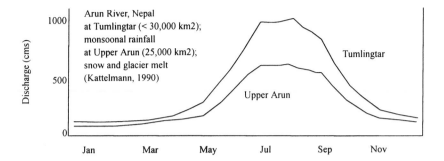

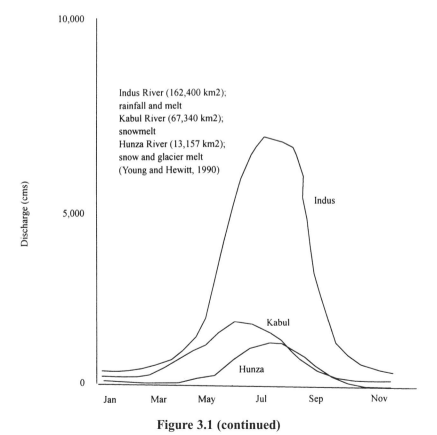

Figure 3.1 (continued)

through a deep layer of the atmosphere can generate high rainfall rates. Baroclinic conditions typify the higher latitudes, which tend to have more modest rainfall rates (Hayden, 1988). These different hydrologic regimes, in combination with substrate resistance and sediment supply as influenced by geology, produce a diverse array of sediment transport regimes and channel morphologies.

The hydrology of mountain rivers at more local scales is strongly influenced by orographic and elevation effects. Many of the world's mountain ranges have a pronounced rain shadow. As air masses are forced to rise in passing over the mountains, the drop in air temperature causes water vapor in the air masses to condense and fall as precipitation. The windward side of a mountain range is thus commonly much wetter than the leeward side. This effect is most pronounced where the mountain range is close to a large body of water. The Cascade Range of Washington, USA, for example, parallels the coastline with the Pacific Ocean. The western side of the range has mean annual precipitation values of 2500-3500 mm, whereas the leeward eastern side has values of 400-1000 mm (Barry and Chorley, 1987). This effect may be reduced for mountain ranges that are far inland or that lie near a body of water with low sea surface temperatures. The Andes Mountains parallel the western coast of South America, but the western side of the mountains from central Peru south to Chile are a desert because the cold Humboldt Current minimizes evaporation from the Pacific Ocean immediately off the west coast.

Orographic effects may cause different types of hydrology on the windward and leeward sides of a mountain range, as well as differences in total precipitation. Mountain ranges in northwestern-most Montana (USA) in the northern Rocky Mountain chain, for example, have snowmelt-dominated hydrology with occasional mid-winter rain-on-snow floods (Madsen, 1995). The next mountainous area to the east does not have rain-on-snow floods because Pacific maritime fronts moving eastward no longer contain sufficient moisture to produce winter rains (MacDonald and Hoffman, 1995). Studies elsewhere in the Rocky Mountains have demonstrated that, although snow depth may be similar on windward and leeward sides of a mountain range, water equivalent decreases inland (Rhea and Grant, 1974). Accurate estimation of snow input to a catchment and of the snow water equivalent are difficult tasks (Sommerfeld et al., 1990). In general, the effect of topography on spatial patterns of precipitation is strongly dependent on basic airflow characteristics and on synoptic or regional scale features such as hurricanes. Both of these may vary significantly among storms (Givone and Meignien, 1990).

The high relief of mountain environments also promotes more localized elevational effects on precipitation. Precipitation volume and type are highly dependent on elevation, and thus tend to be extremely spatially variable in mountains (Figure 3.2). Data from 25 rain gages in the foothills of South Africa indicated that differences in precipitation between ridges and valleys regularly exceeded 200% during an individual storm (de Villiers, 1990). Price and Barry (1997) suggest that the mosaic of climate on individual slopes is composed of numerous topoclimates (100 m area) and site-specific microclimates (1-10 m scale) associated with patches of vegetation and irregular topography.

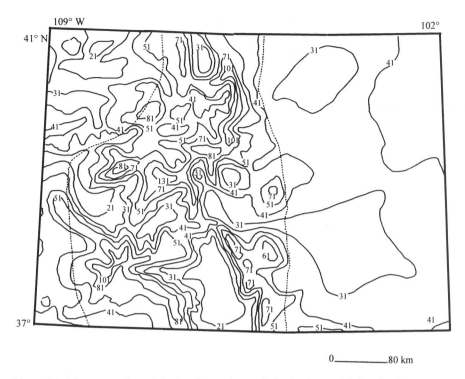

Figure 3.2. Mean annual precipitation (in centimeters) for the State of Colorado. The approximate eastern and western boundaries of the mountains in Colorado are shown by dashed lines. The contour intervals for precipitation are not consistent, because the original data were in inches (after Berry, 1974). This map illustrates the spatial variability of precipitation in the high relief mountainous region of the central part of Colorado, in comparison to the low relief plains to the east and the plateaus and canyons in the western part of the state.

This variability in mountain precipitation may have important implications for flood intensity and for estimates of flood recurrence interval, as illustrated by the Colorado Front Range. The Front Range lies in a semiarid region of the interior western USA. Precipitation increases with elevation from 380 to 1200 mm (Figure 3.2), and the proportion of solid to liquid precipitation increases with elevation (Ives, 1980). The rivers above approximately 2300 m are dominated by seasonal snowmelt floods, which have a broad, less peaked flood hydrograph and unit discharges of approximately 1 m³/s/km². Rivers below 2300 m are subject to snowmelt and to rainfall-generated floods which may reach unit discharges of 40 m³/s/km² (Jarrett, 1989). Flood frequency curves generated from separate and combined rainfall and snowmelt datasets also have very different recurrence intervals for a given discharge (Figure 3.3) (Jarrett, 1990a). Jarrett (1993) has extended the elevation limit for flash flooding along the Rocky Mountains from Montana south to New Mexico, with the latitude-

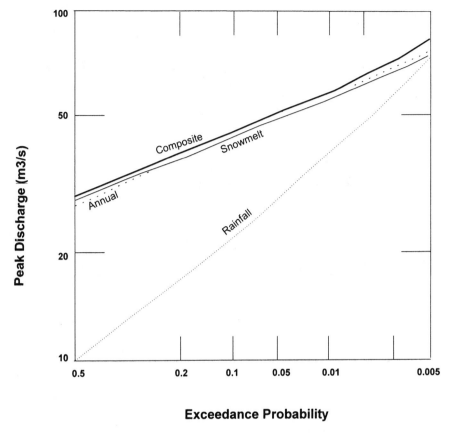

Figure 3.3. Example of differences in frequency curves for floods caused by different hydro-climatic regimes at the same gaging station. This example is from Jarrett (1990a, Figure 1a), for Clear Creek, Colorado (drainage area 381 km², gage elevation 2463 m).

dependent elevation limit being a function of distance from the primary moisture source in the Gulf of Mexico. Parrett and Holnbeck (1994), however, question the relation between unit discharge and elevation in Montana because of the sparsity of high-elevation data.

As another example of elevational effects on hydrology, the Himalayan massif has rivers dominated by monsoonal flood peaks at the lower elevations. Rivers in the lower parts of the southern slope obtain up to 60-80% of discharge from monsoon rains. Glacier and snowmelt increasingly control seasonal high flow at higher elevations, contributing 50-70% of total discharge in the Pamirs and Tien Shan regions (Gerrard, 1990; Wohl and Cenderelli, 1998).

Hirschboeck (1987, 1988) has demonstrated that precipitation may also exhibit long-period variability such that periods up to several decades in length are characterized by more zonal or more meridional circulation patterns. Periods of more meridional circulation tend to produce more severe flooding. Other investigators have also detected fluctuations in flooding at timescales of decades (Webb and Betancourt, 1990), and of centuries to millenia (Ely et al., 1993, 1996; Wohl et al., 1994b; Benito et al., 1996).

Discharge Estimation and Flow State

One of the challenges to fully understanding the temporal and spatial variability of mountain-river hydrology is the sparsity of direct, systematic discharge records. According to Bandyopadhyay et al. (1997), the percent of mountainous area in each of the world's major terrestrial regions ranges from 39% (Asia) to 16% (Africa), but the percent of water level observations in mountains is generally less than 13% (except for Asia, with 34%). Although the World Meteorological Organization recommends the highest densities of instrument networks in mountains, these are in practice low density networks. For smaller channels, weirs may be established for discharge gaging (Hudson et al., 1990; Moschen, 1990), but these will obviously not provide long-term records for some time to come. As a result of this lack of direct data, discharge information is commonly based on indirect methods. The assumptions that are often made regarding flow state when indirectly estimating discharge have led to much discussion of the appropriateness of these methods for mountain rivers.

Most indirect methods of peak discharge estimation, such as slope-area computations based on the Manning equation (Dalrymple and Benson, 1967), step-backwater methods (O'Connor and Webb, 1988), or a simplified slope-area method that does not require an estimate of Manning's n (Sauer et al., 1985), all assume steady, uniform flow. Floods along steep rivers, however, may be unsteady, rapidly varying, and debris-charged (Glancy and Williams, 1994). Indirect discharge estimates may therefore be in error because of scour and fill, rapid changes in flow, substantial sediment transport, and flow transitions between subcritical and supercritical (Jarrett, 1987; Sieben, 1997). Bathurst (1990), for example, estimated that the accuracy of the slope-area method when applied to mountain rivers may typically be as poor as 30%.

Small, ephemeral desert channels may have especially unpredictable and brief flows. After five years of research in the mountainous 0.6 km² Nahal Yael drainage of southern Israel, Schick (1970) reported that typical runoff events are produced by a period of effective rainfall lasting 15 minutes, with a median flow rise lasting 2.5-5 minutes, and peak discharges of 4-8 minutes. Such flows may nevertheless yield up to 152 tons/km² of sediment. For these types of channels, Glancy and Williams (1994) suggest the use of flow-triggered video cameras to assess water-surface profiles; recording streamflow gages; direct velocity measurements to verify roughness coefficients; and scour chains to record depth of scour and fill. These types of data may be used to assess how well the flow approximates steady, uniform conditions.

Another method of indirect discharge estimation was proposed by Tinkler (1997b). He found that the Kennedy (1963) equation for the mean velocity of a critical wave train

$$v = 1.2495 \sqrt{\lambda} \qquad (1)$$

where λ = wavelength of the standing waves, may be used to estimate the mean velocity in rigid-boundary channels with little sediment transport at wavelengths of 0.5-7 m. This provides an accurate, economical, and fairly simple means to measure mean velocity during high discharges, and is not hampered by the requirement of steady flow. It does, however, require direct observation or photography of standing waves during peak flow.

Much of the debate regarding the appropriateness of applying traditional indirect discharge estimations to mountain rivers arises from the observation of hydraulic jumps along these rivers. Hydraulic jumps form at the rapid change in depth associated with a transition from a supercritical to a subcritical flow regime (Elevatorski, 1959; Dingman, 1991). Hydraulic jumps create intense turbulence and large kinetic energy losses, with the amount of loss depending on the change in depth across the jump (Roberson and Crowe, 1993). Hydraulic jumps in mountain rivers occur (1) over substantial obstacles on the bed, (2) at converging or irregular banks or at a strong eddy that acts as an effective bank, (3) at a contraction or expansion of flow, or (4) below vertical drops (Kieffer, 1985; Zgheib, 1990; Carling, 1995; Tinkler, 1997b). Flow velocities decrease substantially across hydraulic jumps and bedload can be deposited downstream, stabilizing the position of the jump (Whittaker and Jaeggi, 1982; Kieffer, 1985). Because hydraulic jumps indicate at least locally occurring supercritical flow, their presence along mountain rivers has been taken to indicate that supercritical flow may be more prevalent along these rivers than along low-gradient channels. If supercritical flow dominates these channels during floods, then most indirect discharge estimation methods would provide a very inadequate approximation of actual discharge.

The consensus regarding flow state along mountain rivers seems to be that supercritical flow across an entire cross-section does not persist for lengths of more than approximately 8 m along most channels because of extreme energy dissipation in the form of hydraulic jumps, turbulence, and obstructions (Trieste and Jarrett, 1987; Trieste, 1994). Jarrett and Costa (1986), for example, noted the occurrence of predominantly subcritical flow for a dambreak flood in a channel reach with an average slope of 0.10. Tinkler (1997a), however, discusses the persistence of central zones of critical or supercritical flow for lengths greater than 8 m within a range of channel types. Grant (1997) hypothesizes that channel hydraulics and bed configuration interact to produce the Froude numbers close to 1 that are observed along many steep, competent streams. Total energy loss must increase as slope and depth increase if flow is to remain critical. The increased roughness required for flow to remain critical comes principally from increased shearing and vorticity between central critical/supercritical flow and adjacent subcritical lower-velocity water (Tinkler, 1997a), and from bedload transport where possible. Tinkler (1997a) suggests the following boundary to define the lower limit of slope for channels in which central flow is critical or supercritical:

$$S = g\ n^2\ h^{-0.33} \qquad\qquad (2)$$

where S is channel gradient, g is gravity, n is Manning's roughness coefficient, and h is flow depth. Careful application of equations such as this one should help to define probable flow conditions and to constrain errors associated with indirect discharge estimation, but our understanding of mountain-river hydraulics remains insufficient for confident reconstruction of discharge in many cases.

Paleoflood Indicators

As noted previously, systematic hydrologic records are inadequate for a detailed understanding of flood hydrology in many mountainous regions because of the combined sparsity of precipitation and gaging stations and the spatial and temporal variability in precipitation and flow (e.g. Klemes, 1990; Kostka and Holko, 1994). Even at sites with systematic precipitation and streamflow records, these data commonly span less than a hundred years, making it difficult to accurately estimate the magnitude and frequency of extreme floods using conventional flood-frequency analysis. The design of dams and other structures, land-use management, and the siting of critical installations require an evaluation of flood risk. Consequently, flood-frequency curves developed from short-term systematic records may be extrapolated to longer timespans; systematic records from lower elevation areas near the mountains may be used to approximate mountain-river hydrology via storm transposition; or PMP/PMF scenarios based on worst-case rainfall-runoff predictions may be used (Jarrett and Costa, 1988; Schulze et al., 1994). Sieben (1997) characterizes these and other approaches as statistical models or deterministic models. A statistical model is based on statistical analyses of empirical data; represented trends are assumed to be consistent and continuous, and are extrapolated to extreme events. For a deterministic model, one formulates a mechanistic concept suitable for deterministic simulation of the processes of interest, and then imposes on the model boundary conditions that correspond to an extreme event scenario. Numerous studies have indicated that these techniques tend to overestimate maximum floods at higher elevations (Baker et al., 1987; Jarrett and Costa, 1988; Pruess et al., 1998; Carling, 1994a; Carling and Grodek, 1994). This overestimation may have serious economic consequences for land-use zoning and the design of flood-control or hydraulic structures.

Historical, botanical, and geologic records of past flow have been used successfully in mountainous regions to extend short-term or nonexistent systematic discharge records (Jarrett, 1990b; Enzel et al., 1993). Historical records that may be used to estimate the magnitude and frequency of past flow include diaries and journals, damage or insurance reports, and marks of peak flow stage that people create on buildings or along channel boundaries (Hooke and Redmond, 1989; Fanok and Wohl, 1997). These types of records are limited by the length of human occupation of a region and are generally qualitative. They are also filtered through human perceptions in the sense that the lower discharge level defining a "flood" may become smaller as population density along a channel increases. An example of historical records of past flow comes from Buddhist monasteries in Nepal, where monks preserve the memory of floods that occurred prior to systematic discharge records (Bjonness, 1986).

Botanical records take the form of either damage to riparian trees caused by high or low flows, or the structuring of riparian vegetation by age and type in response to stability and inundation of riparian habitat (Sigafoos, 1964; Everitt, 1968;Yanosky, 1982a; Hupp, 1988; Hupp and Osterkamp, 1996). Flood damage to riparian trees includes impact scars and adventitious or split-base sprouts caused by flood-borne debris, and adventitious roots associated with overbank sedimentation (Figure 3.4). Tree rings may be used to establish a chronology for each of these morphological responses to flow conditions (Yanosky, 1982b; Phipps, 1985). Variations in tree ring width and symmetry may also be used to infer past episodes of high and low flow (Yanosky, 1983, 1984; Jones et al., 1984; Meko, 1990; Earle, 1993). Stands of individual riparian species of differing ages may be used to infer frequency of inundation and lateral stability of a channel (Sigafoos, 1961; Everitt, 1968; Helley and LaMarche, 1973; Gottesfeld and Gottesfeld, 1990; Hupp, 1990; Hupp and Simon, 1991; Scott et al., 1996, 1997). Botanical records may provide chronologically precise information for a wide range of discharges, but these records are limited by the presence and age of woody riparian vegetation (Wohl and Enzel, 1995).

Geologic records of past flow may be used for regime-based reconstructions, competence estimates, paleohydraulic estimates, or stage estimates. Most of these techniques for estimating past discharge may be related to flood occurrence using chronologic methods involving tree-ring analysis, radiocarbon dating of organic materials associated with the flood deposits, soils analysis, or other relative methods (Costa, 1978). Regime-based reconstructions rely on alluvial channel geometry as preserved in relict channels. This approach is poorly suited to the confined valleys and partially bedrock-controlled rivers present in most mountainous regions.

Competence estimates involve using either the average clast size, bedforms, and bedding structure to estimate past flow (Baker, 1974; Church, 1978; Maizels, 1983, 1989; Nott and Price, 1994), or using the largest clasts likely to have been transported by fluvial processes to estimate the shear stress, unit stream power, or velocity of the associated flow (Birkeland, 1968; Inbar and Schick, 1979; Bradley and Mears, 1980). The underlying assumption is that the channel is transport-limited (rather than supply-limited) with respect to competence. Care must be taken to avoid debris-flow deposits or rockfall into the channel that may have been rounded in place. Competence estimates of past flow are generally imprecise in comparison to other indirect methods of estimating discharge and hydraulics (Costa, 1983; Williams, 1983; Komar, 1987a,b; Wohl, 1992a), and are limited to information about the single largest flow down the channel, generally with minimal information as to when such a flow might have occurred. The same stochastic and site-specific controls that make it difficult to predict sediment entrainment and deposition along a contemporary channel make it difficult to retrodict the conditions of past flow represented by coarse-clast deposits. As has been noted by O'Connor (1993), most equations devel-

Figure 3.4. Two impact scars on a cottonwood tree growing beside an ephemeral channel in southern Utah, USA.

oped from contemporary process observations focus on entrainment, whereas paleo-hydrology is of necessity focused on sites of deposition. An exception is the work of Bordas and Silvestrini (1992), who proposed thresholds for coarse sand deposition, as a function of unit stream power, for isolated grain, bulk, and mass transport. Komar and Carling (1991) and Wilcock (1992b) question how representative one or a few of the largest particles are of the transported sediments and of flood hydraulics. They note that flow competence relationships differ from one stream to another, depending on the pattern of grain sorting, which is a function of the bed-material grain size distribution. Nevertheless, competence estimates may be the best option available along some mountain channels.

Paleohydraulic estimates rely on depositional or erosional indicators of flow hydraulics. Carling (1995) described lateral gravel berms deposited adjacent to hydraulic jumps in bedrock channels, and noted that the angle subtended by the berm crestline with respect to a regular bankline could be used to estimate Froude number of the flow. Carling and Grodek (1994) and Nott and Price (1994) used the bars at the downstream end of plunge pools to estimate discharge and hydraulics through the pool. Zen and Prestegaard (1994) found that the geometry of flow separation zones and thus the location of lateral potholes are scaled by flow Reynolds number. These potholes could thus be used to reconstruct paleoflow depths and velocities if parts of the channel bed adjacent to the flow obstruction are preserved.

Stage estimates use erosional or depositional records of maximum stage, in combination with channel geometry, to infer past discharges. Erosional records take the form of scour lines (Figure 3.5) (Wohl, 1995), lichen limits (Gregory, 1976), or the truncation of landforms such as alluvial fans which impinge on the channel (Shroba et al., 1979). Depositional evidence of peak stage includes silt lines (O'Connor et al., 1986), organic debris (Carling and Grodek, 1994), boulder bars (Elfström, 1987; Jarrett et al., 1996; Cenderelli and Cluer, 1998), and fine-grained slackwater sediments (Figure 3.6)(Baker, 1987; O'Connor et al., 1994). Some of these features are more accurate as a stage indicator than are others. Fine-grained organic debris or silt lines formed by the adhesion of fine sediment and organic materials along the valley

Figure 3.5. Scour line in hillslope colluvium and vegetation. Created during a flood in 1983, Redfield Creek, Arizona, USA. White lower portion is exposed bedrock; hat for scale.

Figure 3.6. Slackwater deposit perched in a channel-margin alcove formed in sandstone valley wall about 3 m above the channel bed, Muddy Creek, Utah, USA.

walls may be highly accurate but ephemeral features unless they are protected from subsequent erosion, as at the back of an alcove formed in a bedrock valley wall. Boulder bars and slackwater sediments, on the other hand, are likely to provide a minimum estimate of peak stage, although the degree of underestimation produced by using these indicators may vary, depending on the geometry of the depositional site and the sediment concentration of the flow (Baker and Kochel, 1988).

The use of paleostage indicators (PSI) relies on the assumption that channel geometry has not changed substantially since the time of the flood that created the PSI, and that scour and fill were minimal during the flood. Paleostage indicators are thus most commonly used along stable boundary channels formed in bedrock or very coarse alluvium. Channels with a fairly deep, narrow cross-sectional geometry that maximizes stage change as a function of discharge make it easier to differentiate PSI from individual floods. Erosional landforms or boulder bars may facilitate estimation of only the largest flood to have occurred along a channel, but slackwater sediments may record numerous floods. Slackwater sediments settle from suspension at sites of flow separation such as channel expansions, tributary channel mouths, or channel-margin alcoves and caves (Baker, 1983, 1987; Springer and Kite, 1997). At these sites, each depositional unit records a flood, and a chronology of depositional units may be established with radiocarbon, thermoluminescence, or ^{137}Cs dating (Ely et al., 1992).

Historical, botanical, and geologic records of past floods may be used to refine the estimated probable maximum flood for a basin because these records indicate the largest discharge to have occurred within a period that may be several hundred years or, in some cases, ten thousand years long (Webb and Rathburn, 1988). These records may also be used to improve flood-frequency estimates for more frequent flows if the non-systematic data can be appropriately integrated with the systematic data. Systematic data represent the population of all floods above a fixed discharge threshold that have occurred during a known timespan. For non-systematic data, the discharge threshold may have varied through time as a function of changes in depositional geometry at a site. As a result, different statistical distributions must be applied to each type of data (Benson, 1950; Stedinger and Cohn, 1986; Stedinger and Baker, 1987; Salas et al., 1994).

The increasing use of paleoflood indicators in regions such as the Rocky Mountains (Jarrett, 1989, 1990b; Grimm, 1993; Pruess et al., 1998) is helping to define the magnitude and frequency of flood occurrence, and the hydraulic conditions during floods. Field and lab studies of flow hydraulics along mountain rivers are complementary in that they permit the refinement of methods of indirect discharge estimation, and the use of paleoflood data to define the extreme conditions present along a given channel. The non-uniform character of slope, width, sediment size and composition, and discharge and sediment transport along mountain rivers can create various types of wave phenomena, such as propagation of hydrographs or aggradation fronts, that can develop into discontinuous profiles (Sieben, 1997). These discontinuities in flow and sediment movement make it very difficult to model flood hydraulics and morphology along mountain rivers.

Hydraulics

Despite a rather extensive technical literature, the hydraulics of mountain channels remain poorly understood relative to low gradient alluvial channels. What has become clear is that the standard hydraulic equations developed for low gradient sand-bed channels do not apply well to mountain channels along which steep gradients and large grain and form roughness promote non-logarithmic velocity profiles, localized critical and supercritical flow, and strongly three-dimensional flow. The complex hydraulics of mountain rivers are perhaps best described as stochastic, but it may become possible to quantify mean hydraulic conditions once the effects of slope, grain and form roughness on velocity distribution are quantified as a function of flow stage. Much of the research done on mountain-river hydraulics has therefore been devoted to developing equations that (1) adequately predict resistance coefficient as a function of gradient, relative submergence, flow depth, particle size distribution, or other channel characteristics, (2) quantify the contribution of the components of grain and/or form roughness to total flow resistance, or (3) characterize cross-stream velocity and vertical velocity distribution and the associated forces of lift or shear stress exerted on the channel boundaries.

Resistance Coefficient

Although energy must be conserved within a system, viscous forces can transform kinetic energy of river flow into heat energy that represents a loss to the river system (Roberson and Crowe, 1993). Energy equations for rivers thus quantify the transfer of energy between potential and kinetic energy, and thermal energy losses resulting from resistance to flow (Julien, 1995). A commonly used version is that of the Bernoulli equation modified with a head loss function:

$$\alpha \, v_1^2/2g \; + \; p_1/\gamma \; + \; z_1 \; = \; \alpha \, v_2^2/2g \; + \; p_2/\gamma \; + \; z_2 \; + \; h_L \qquad (3)$$

where α is the energy coefficient, a velocity head correction factor that varies from 1.03 to 1.36 for fairly straight, prismatic channels. This coefficient is generally higher for small channels, where it may exceed 2. The largest known value for laboratory measurements is 7.4 (Chow, 1959). For the other variables, v is mean velocity (m/s), g is gravity (m/s^2), p is the system pressure (N/m^2), γ is the specific weight of the fluid (N/m^3), z is the elevation of the fluid element (m), h_L is the head loss resulting from resistance (m), and the subscripts denote values at upstream and downstream locations. The first term ($\alpha v^2/2g$) represents kinetic energy, and the second (p/γ) and third (z) terms represent potential energy.

The head loss over a given length of channel (the energy slope) represents the loss of kinetic energy caused by resistance along the channel, including skin friction and form resistance. Form resistance is further subdivided into grain, form, bank, obstruction, and sediment-transport components of resistance (Roberson and Crowe, 1993). Because flow velocities vary from a maximum near the free-surface of the flow to zero at the wall, shear forces are created and produce viscous energy dissipation, known as skin-friction (Tritton, 1988). Form drag occurs because localized flow separation can create a high pressure upstream from objects and low pressure in the object's wake. The resulting pressure-gradient force opposes flow and creates viscous energy losses downstream from the object (Tritton, 1988; Roberson and Crowe, 1993). All of these forms of energy dissipation are subsumed into a single resistance coefficient such as Manning's n, but accurate estimation of such coefficients has proved difficult in mountain rivers.

The three most commonly used resistance coefficients (n, f, c) relate to velocity as follows:

Manning
$$v = \frac{R^{0.667} \, S^{0.5}}{n} \qquad (4)$$

Darcy-Weisbach
$$v = \frac{8g \, RS}{f}^{0.5} \qquad (5)$$

Chezy
$$v = c \, (RS)^{0.5} \qquad (6)$$

Inaccurate estimation of a flow resistance coefficient may produce inaccurate indirect discharge measurements. A discharge value computed by the slope-area method, for example, is inversely proportional to Manning's n value, so that selection of an n value is very important (Eddins and Zembrzuski, 1994). Several methods have been proposed for estimating n values, including visual comparison to various rivers for which n-values have been empirically determined (Barnes, 1967). Another method involves a subdivision of n into a base value and additive values (Cowan, 1956; Arcement and Schneider, 1989):

$$n = (n_b + n_1 + n_2 + n_3 + n_4)\, m \qquad (7)$$

Equation 7 applies to reach n values. Roughness coefficients are determined for each subsection of each cross section in a reach, and then composited. For equation 7,

n_b = base value for a straight, smooth, uniform channel, in natural materials (0.028-
 0.70 for gravel to boulder bed)
n_1 = a correction factor for bank surface irregularities (0.0-0.02)
n_2 = a value for variations in shape and size of the channel cross section (0.0-0.015)
n_3 = a value for obstructions (0.0-0.05)
n_4 = a value for vegetation and flow conditions (0.002-0.1), and
m = a correction factor for meandering of the channel (1.0-1.30).

The various components of equation 7 may be visually estimated using the descriptions in Arcement and Schneider (1989).

Limerinos (1970) relates n to hydraulic radius and particle size based on data from primarily lower gradient (0.00068-0.024) channels with small gravel to medium-sized boulders (d_{84} of 75-2 cm; R/d_{84} of 47.2 to 0.9) for bed material at discharges of 5.62-427 m^3/s:

$$n = \frac{(0.1129)\, R^{0.167}}{1.16 + 2.0 \log (R/d_{84})} \qquad (8)$$

where d_{84} is particle intermediate diameter (in m) that equals or exceeds 84% of the particles, and R is hydraulic radius (m).

Bray (1979) used a dataset of gravel-bed rivers with gradients of 0.00022-0.015 (Q of 5.5 to 8140 m^3/s, R/d_{84} of 85 to 11) and modified equation 8 to:

$$n = \frac{0.113\, R^{0.167}}{1.09 + 2.2 \log (R/d_{84})} \qquad (9)$$

Griffiths (1981) used a gravel-bed river dataset from New Zealand (Q of 0.05 to 1540 m^3/s, S of 0.000085 to 0.011, d_{50} of 0.013 to 0.301 m; R/d_{50} of 3 to 53):

$$1/\sqrt{f} = 0.76 + 1.98 \log (R/d_{50}) \qquad (10)$$

where f is Darcy-Weisbach friction factor (see equation 5). This may be re-stated as

$$n = \frac{(0.1129\ R^{0.167})}{[0.76 + 1.98 \log (R/d_{50})]} \tag{11}$$

Hey (1979) developed an equation for gravel-bed rivers using data from rivers in the United Kingdom (Q of 0.995 to 189.82 m³/s, S of 0.0090 to 0.031, d_{84} of 0.046 to 0.250 m; R/d_{84} of 0.97 to 17.24):

$$1/\sqrt{f} = 2.03 \log (aR/3.5d_{84}) \tag{12}$$

where a varies between 11.1 and 13.46 as a function of channel cross sectional shape. This may be re-formulated as

$$n = \frac{(0.1129\ R^{0.167})}{[2.03 \log (aR/3.5d_{84})]} \tag{13}$$

Noting that the Darcy-Weisbach friction factor tends to underestimate the rate of change of resistance at a site (as discharge varies) at higher gradients, Bathurst (1985) developed an empirical equation for the friction factor in gravel-bed rivers (Q of 0.14 to 195 m³/s, S of 0.004 to 0.04, d_{84} of 0.113 to 0.740 m, $R/d_{84} < 10$):

$$(8/f) = 5.62 \log (R/d_{84}) + 4 \tag{14}$$

which can be re-formulated as

$$n = (0.3193R^{0.167})/ [5.62 \log (R/d_{84}) + 4] \tag{15}$$

None of these methods of estimating a flow resistance coefficient is designed specifically for steep channels. Field data indicate that n values are much greater on high gradient cobble- and boulder-bed streams than on low-gradient streams having similar relative roughness values (R/d_{50}) (Jarrett, 1987). As gradient increases, energy losses increase as a result of wake turbulence and the formation of localized hydraulic jumps downstream from boulders (Jarrett, 1992). Using empirical data from numerous channels with slopes greater than 0.002 (d_{84} of 0.1-0.8 m, S of 0.052 to 0.002, Q to 0.34 of 127 m³/s, R of 0.15 to 2.2 m), Jarrett (1984, 1985, 1987) developed an equation that uses energy gradient and hydraulic radius to predict an n value:

$$n = 0.32\ S^{0.38}R^{-0.16} \tag{16}$$

where S is energy gradient and R is hydraulic radius (m). Jarrett (1994) noted that n values computed in this manner were on average 53% larger than field-estimated n values, and that discharges computed using equation 16 varied accordingly from indirect peak discharge measurements using field-selected n values.

Working on experimental channels with gradients up to 20% and high sediment transport rates, Smart and Jaeggi (1983) developed the empirical equation:

$$(8/f)^{0.5} = 5.75 \left[1 - \exp(-0.05 (R/d_{90}) (1/S^{0.5})) \right]^{0.5} \log(8.2 (R/d_{90})) \qquad (17)$$

which may be re-formulated as:

$$n = \frac{(0.3193 \, R^{0.167})}{5.75 \left[1 - \exp(-0.05 (R/d_{90}) (1/S^{0.5})) \right]^{0.5} \log(8.2 (R/d_{90}))} \qquad (18)$$

Wahl (1994) tested several of these equations for n using a composite data set. He found that all of the equations significantly underestimate n for relatively low discharges (< 0.2 median annual flood discharge). Moderate to large discharges (> 0.2 median annual flood discharge) were approximated fairly well by the equations. Extrapolation of any of the equations to discharges greater than about 1.5 times the median annual flood discharge is not yet warranted because of the lack of data for large discharges (Wahl, 1994), especially as roughness coefficient is commonly inversely related to hydraulic radius and discharge (Coon, 1994).

Working specifically on a small mountain stream (hydraulic radius less than 0.25 m, S of 0.02 to 0.16, R/d_{84} of 0.5 to 2.8), Marcus et al. (1992) evaluated the Limerinos, Jarrett, Bathurst, and Cowan methods of estimating n, as well as four other techniques. They found that observed roughness values were significantly under-predicted, often by an order of magnitude, by all the techniques except Jarrett's, which over-estimated roughness by an average of 32%. Under-estimation resulted from inadequately addressing the effects on flow resistance of large sediment sizes, low ratios of flow depth to hydraulic radius, steep slopes, and severe turbulence, as well as the tendency for observers to use lower visual estimates of n because of experience in lower gradient channels. Marcus et al. (1992) conclude that discharge should be measured directly whenever possible, particularly during low flows when R/d_{84} values are low.

In summary, there is not at present a well-tested, consistently accurate equation for calculating the resistance coefficients of mountain rivers. Steep gradients, poorly-sorted beds, coarse particles with median diameters that may approach the flow depths, and localized flow transitions all complicate the estimation of total resistance.

Grain and Form Resistance

Under conditions of steady, quasi-uniform, two-dimensional, fully developed turbulent flow over a deformable channel bed, flow resistance is caused by (1) viscous and pressure drag on grains of the bed surface (grain roughness), (2) pressure drag on bed undulations (form roughness), and (3) pressure and viscous drag on sediment in transport above the bed surface (Griffiths, 1987). Grain resistance represents the channel-bed roughness that induces energy losses resulting from skin friction and form drag from individual bed particles. As depth increases, the individual particles influence a lower proportion of the flow and the effect of grain resistance is diminished. However, the coarse, poorly sorted clasts and relatively shallow flow of mountain rivers tend to make grain resistance more important in these channels than in most low-gradient rivers, even during high flows.

Working in a steep, small channel (flow depth 0.2-0.5 m, width 2.9 m, gradient 0.034), Thorne (1997) found that a stable bed element that is small relative to the flow depth (≤ 1 m in streamwise dimension) does not represent a significant obstacle to flow. Streamwise acceleration over the feature and a minor component of steering occur. In contrast, large particles or clusters ≥ 2 m in the streamwise dimension substantially obstruct flow. The steering of flow around the obstacle is more significant than acceleration over it, and the creation of an extensive backwater zone significantly influences the local evolution of the channel bed.

Prestegaard (1983b) suggested the existence of downstream variations in the variables that influence water-surface slope and resistance, with individual grains most important in the headwaters, bedforms dominating the middle reaches, and channel bends increasingly important at lower gradients. Similarly, Bathurst (1993) noted changes in flow resistance throughout a channel network, with transient bedforms dominating flow resistance in sand-bed channels, bed material and pool-riffle sequences creating most of the resistance in gravel-bed rivers, boulder form drag dominating boulder-bed channels, and ponding dominating step-pool channels.

Much attention has been devoted to developing a single index of grain roughness that may be incorporated into calculations of the flow resistance coefficient. This index most commonly takes the form of roughness height. In the absence of strong secondary current, total flow resistance can be expressed by the Darcy-Weisbach friction factor, f:

$$f = [2.03 \log ((12.2 \ R)/k_s)]^{-2} \qquad (19)$$

where k_s is roughness height.

Several investigators have fit field or flume data to equation 19 to calculate k_s, and then expressed k_s as equal to $C \ d_x$ where C is a constant and d_x is the grain diameter for which x% is finer. These values range from $k_s = 1.25 \ d_{35}$ to $k_s = 3.5 \ d_{90}$ (Millar and Quick, 1994), but those from high gradient channels commonly use a large d_x value. Hey (1979, 1988) used $3.5d_{84}$, for example; Parker and Peterson (1980) used $2d_{90}$. The use of $k_s = 3d_{84}$ originated with experiments using quasi-homogeneous sand roughness and assuming a logarithmic velocity distribution (Nikora et al., 1998). Wiberg and Smith (1991) demonstrated theoretically that the log formula for hydraulic resistance with $k_s = 3d_{84}$ is valid even for flows with large relative roughness, despite velocity profile deviations from the log law in these flows. Wiberg and Smith (1991) also demonstrated that k_s depends significantly on the concentration of bed roughness elements, suggesting that k_s is a function of several characteristic scales, rather than just d_{84} (Gomez, 1993).

Clifford et al. (1992) suggest that C, the multiplier of characteristic grain size, is attributable to the effect of small-scale form resistance, and that there are two discrete scales of bed roughness, associated with grain and microtopographic roughness elements. Grain resistance is quantified using a modified form of Keulegan's relation:

$$C_G^{-0.5} = 1/k \, [\, \ln \, (d/d_{90}) + A]$$ (Parker and Peterson, 1980)   (20)

where k is von Karman's constant (0.40 for clear water), and

$$A = \ln \, (11/m), \text{ where } m = k_s/d_{90}.$$

Prestegaard (1983a) used this equation to determine the component of total resistance attributable to grain resistance at bankfull stage along 12 gravel-bed channel reaches (Q of 0.8 to 33.0 m³/s, S of 0.0012 to 0.036, d_{84} of 0.315 to 0.053 m). She then assumed that the remaining resistance was associated with bars. Bar resistance thus accounted for 50-75% of the total resistance in these gravel-bed channels. Parker and Peterson (1980) found that the percentage of total resistance caused by bars increased as stage declined. In a study of 62 sites in the United Kingdom (S of 0.0012 to 0.0215), Hey (1988) found that bar resistance ranged from 7% to 86% of the total resistance during high flows. Using the flume data from Meyer-Peter and Muller (1948) and Smart and Jaeggi (1983), Griffiths (1987) found that dimensionless form shear stress exceeds dimensionless particle shear stress for values of approximately three times critical Shields stress in subcritical flow, and five times in supercritical flow. For given Shields stress and increasing relative roughness, relative form shear stress increases in subcritical flow because of bedform influences but decreases in supercritical flow because of transport rate effects (Griffiths, 1987).

The factor R/k_s (see equation 19), often expressed as R/d_{84}, is relative submergence. Several investigators have suggested subdividing flow into large-scale roughness ($0 < R/d_{84} < 1$), intermediate-scale roughness ($1 < R/d_{84} < 4$), and small-scale roughness ($R/d_{84} > 4$) (Bathurst, 1985; Ugarte and Madrid, 1994). Empirical formulas for n have then been calculated for each roughness criteria. For example, Ugarte and Madrid (1994) propose:

$$n = 0.183 + \ln \, [(\, 1.3014 \, S^{0.0785} \, (R/d_{84})^{0.0211})/ \, F^{0.2054}] \, (d_{84}^{1/6}/g^{0.5})$$ (21)

where F is Froude number and d_{84} and R are as in equation 8, for $1 < R/d_{84} < 12.5$ and S of 0.2% to 4%. To some extent, this incorporates the changes in resistance as a function of flow depth that were discussed earlier. Much more of this type of research is necessary before we can accurately estimate n for varying channel configurations and flow conditions.

Studies of grain and form resistance have largely been conducted on pool-riffle gravel-bed rivers. Because riffles serve as hydraulic controls of flow along such channels, the flow resistance depends on variations in flow geometry between pools and riffles, and reflects local accelerations and decelerations. Form resistance associated with step-pool sequences is undoubtedly also significant, but remains largely unquantified.

An additional complication in some mountain rivers is the presence of large woody debris (LWD). Individual pieces of LWD may create grain resistance. Debris jams, or LWD incorporated into bed steps, may produce form roughness. Very few investigators have attempted to quantify these effects. Shields and Gippel (1995) developed an equation for the drag coefficient of LWD in low-gradient, sand-bed channels, but this equation does not adequately describe the roughness produced by LWD in steep channels with non-uniform bed gradients (Curran, 1999).

Velocity and Turbulence

Flow velocity and the associated shear stress and lift forces are strongly related to flow resistance because velocity distribution is also affected by bed material size distribution, relative submergence, and channel gradient, and ultimately reflects the balance between energy available and energy expended on overcoming resistance. The ratio of lift and shear force depends upon surface roughness, for example; the rougher the surface, the greater the shear stress compared to dynamic lift (Dittrich et al., 1996). Empirical mean velocity equations for mountain rivers recognize these inter-relations between velocity and flow resistance, as for example Rickenmann (1994a):

$$v = 0.37 \ g^{0.33}Q^{0.34}S^{0.20}/ \ d_{90}^{0.35}, \qquad \text{for } S > 0.6\% \qquad (22)$$

$$v = 0.96 \ g^{0.36}Q^{0.29}S^{0.35}/ \ d_{90}^{0.23}, \qquad \text{for } S < 1.0\%. \qquad (23)$$

The empirical data from which mean velocity is estimated may be obtained using at least two methods, point measurements and dilution tracers. Point measurements utilize various types of current meters, including mechanical impellor (cup and vane), electromagnetic and ultrasonic current meters, and laser velocimeters. As reviewed by Clifford and French (1993b), mechanical impellor current meters are low cost, durable field instruments, but have a poor frequency response (< 1 Hz), provide only one-dimensional information, and require maintenance and re-calibration. Electromagnetic current meters are robust, of intermediate cost, have a good frequency response (5-20 Hz), tolerate particle and other contamination in the flow, and provide one-dimensional or two-dimensional measurements, but frequency response is affected by head design. Ultrasonic current meters are expensive, fragile, and sensitive to particle and air bubble contamination, but provide three-dimensional measurement with an excellent frequency response (up to 30 Hz). Laser velocimeters have the highest cost and are sensitive to suspended sediment, but produce very high frequency response and three-dimensional measurement without perturbing the flow (Clifford and French, 1993b). A primary difficulty with using any type of point measurement to estimate mean velocity along mountain rivers is that numerous measurements are necessary to estimate a mean value which accounts for the high levels of vertical, lateral, temporal, and downstream variability in velocity characteristic of mountain rivers.

Although point measurements are most appropriate for characterizing the spatial and temporal variability of velocity along mountain channels, dilution tracers may more accurately characterize the mean velocity of a channel reach. Dilution tracer techniques involve introducing a fluorescent dye (Gees, 1990; Graf, 1995) or a chemical such as NaCl (Day, 1977) into the flow. The tracer may be introduced steadily over a finite time period, or introduced instantaneously (slug injection). The tracers must be miscible and not alter the density or velocity of the fluid flow. Some minimum channel length (the mixing length) is required before the cross-sectional distribution of the tracer concentration is nearly uniform for constant flow injection, or the amount of dilution is constant for slug injection. In turbulent flow, complete mixing may occur within fifteen times the mean channel width (Elder et al., 1990). Beyond this mixing length, the properties of the tracer reflect flow velocity rather than injection procedure. For a slug injection of NaCl, for example, tracer concentration is measured with a conductivity meter, and times of peak concentration at two points separated by a known distance are used to calculate mean flow velocity. In a comparison of salt tracers and current meters, Benischke and Harum (1990) concluded that both methods may yield adequate results within a 2% average deviation, but salt tracers are most appropriate for channels with turbulent flow and irregular geometry.

Spatial and temporal distributions of velocity and other hydraulic variables may also be examined using flow models. One-dimensional step-backwater models such as HEC-RAS (Hydrologic Engineering Center, 1997) are the models most widely applied to resistant-boundary channels (O'Connor and Webb, 1988), but these models do not adequately approximate the highly turbulent flow along high-gradient channels. Two-dimensional models such as RMA2 (Donnell et al., 1997) or HIVEL2D (Berger and Stockstill, 1995) require considerably more expertise to use, and require more spatially detailed channel geometry data to produce adequate approximations of flow conditions (Miller and Cluer, 1998). Three-dimensional models have a limited predictive ability because of problems of specifying topographic complexity, but they do provide more reliable estimates of bed shear stress and the three-dimensional flow field that is important for mixing processes (Lane et al., 1999; Nicholas and Sambrook Smith, 1999).

Flow along channels with low gradients and fine bed material is commonly approximated by a semilogarithmic velocity profile in which velocity varies with the logarithm of distance from the bed (Leopold et al., 1964). Even fairly well-sorted beds may have a well-developed roughness sublayer near the bed, where the velocity profile becomes more uniform than the log-law profile, under conditions of low relative submergence (Nakagawa et al., 1991; Tsujimoto, 1991). Flow along mountain rivers includes a substantial proportion of flow between the larger boulders, or below the surface that defines the general bed-water boundary. This low velocity flow gives way fairly abruptly to high velocity flow above the boulders. This two-part

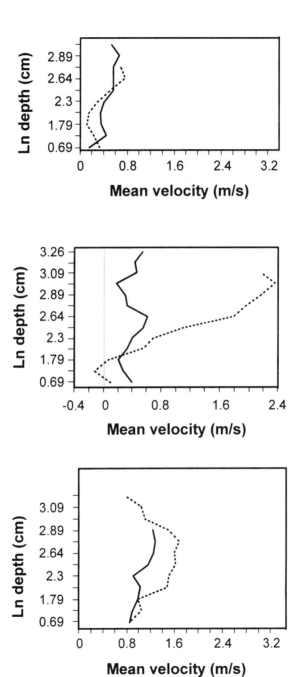

Figure 3.7. Examples of non-logarithmic velocity profiles from a small mountain channel in Colorado (East St. Louis Creek, drainage area 8 km², elevation 3000 m).

velocity profile has been described as s-shaped (Jarrett, 1991; Marchand et al., 1984; Bathurst, 1988), although the profile varies widely as a function of grain roughness and bed roughness (Figure 3.7) (Robert et al., 1993; Bergeron, 1994; Wohl and Ikeda, 1998). Byrd (1997), for example, found that 40% of the local profiles of streamwise velocity measured in a steep (0.034 m/m), bouldery channel in Colorado approach a linear form, whereas 10% are nearly logarithmic, and the remaining 50% have various forms. Use of the semilog velocity profile results in a significant overestimation of flow resistance along mountain rivers at high flows (Bathurst, 1994), with the degree of overestimation depending on k_s and R/k_s.

In addition to variation in mean velocity as a function of height above the bed, Smart (1994) found that turbulent fluctuations decreased at greater distances from the bed, both in terms of amplitude and relative to the mean velocity at the depth being considered. When the bed material was in motion, turbulence increased relative to the mean velocity, especially in the lower third of the profile (Smart, 1994). Turbulence in the roughness sublayer is commonly measured using laser doppler anemometry (Hammann and Dittrich, 1994).

Turbulence in high gradient, coarse-grained channels may differ in significant ways from turbulence in other channels. Long velocity records from the gravel-bed North Fork Toutle River, Washington, sampled at 2 Hz, indicate low-frequency fluctuations over a range of coherent wave periods. If these represent discrete fluid structures, the structures would be 2-3 times longer than predicted by empirical relations for mean boil periods in lowland streams, and those predicted by published relations for eddy lengths.

Furbish (1993) has mathematically described longitudinal flow structures in coarse-grained mountain channels using depth-averaged equations of momentum and continuity that are linearized and solved in the wavenumber domain. He found that the velocity field and water-surface topography can exhibit a systematic structure over a distance of tens of channel widths and longer, although the structure is partially obscured by noise caused by local variations in channel width and bed roughness. The structure takes the form of a filament of high streamwise velocity which exhibits a near-oscillatory structure as it threads back and forth across the channel. Subsequent work indicated that bed topography significantly affects the water surface, whereas velocity structure is affected equally by width variations (Cudney, 1995).

All scales of turbulence exert important influences on momentum transfer (Tennekes and Lumley, 1994) and sediment transport (Clifford, 1993a; Carling and Tinkler, 1998). Turbulence generation and amplification require (1) Reynolds numbers high enough to induce instability, (2) shear flow with the introduction of vorticity, and (3) a perturbation to the flow (Mollo-Christensen, 1971; Tennekes and Lumley, 1994). A vortex is a periodic, whirlpool-like turbulence feature (Lugt, 1983) that is associated with flow separation. Flow separation occurs when flow along a physical boundary develops an adverse pressure gradient (decelerating flow in the upper part of the profile), becomes unstable and detaches from the wall, and forms reverse flow adjacent to the physical boundary (Schlichting, 1968; Tritton, 1988). Because fluid inertia can be important, flow separation is more common at high Reynolds numbers (Tritton, 1988).

The separated boundary layer functions as a zone of high shear between the downstream and recirculating flow (Tennekes and Lumley, 1994). This zone of high shear produces vorticity.

Flow separation may occur at channel bends (Leeder and Bridges, 1975), channel expansions (Middleton and Southard, 1984; Carling, 1989b), pools (Kieffer, 1985; Thompson et al., 1996, 1998), bedforms, and large grains. Kirkbride (1993) used flume experiments over poorly sorted fluvial gravels (d_{84} = 22.1 mm, S = 0.002, h = 15 cm) to observe the influence of bed roughness on turbulence. He noted a near-bed zone dominated by obstacle-derived vortices (see also Nakagawa et al., 1991), and an outer zone of mean unidirectional flow. Interaction between the zones resulted in the intermittent shedding of vortices from the lee of obstacle clasts into the outer zone. If vortices form at the zone of flow separation, vortex shedding may create a series of paired eddies with opposite senses of rotation, known as a von Karman vortex street (Tritton, 1988). As the vortices disintegrate downstream or detach from the bed they create areas of strong upwelling known as boils. Matthes (1947) suggested the term kolk for the combined vortex-boil system. He noted that this represented the most powerful concentration of energy in natural rivers and strongly influenced bed scour and sediment transport. Other researchers have suggested that kolks are related to the bursting phenomenon, which includes four main momentum transfer mechanisms (Nelson et al., 1995): (1) *Sweeps* - high velocity pulses originating in the main flow that move toward the bed. Sweep-like motions may dominate shear stress production in the near-bed region (Roy et al., 1996), or in the outer flow region (Ferguson et al., 1996) of gravel-bed rivers. (2) *Bursts* - slow-moving parcels of water originating in the boundary layer that move toward the main flow. (3) *Outward interactions* - high velocity pulses from the boundary layer toward the main flow. (4) *Inward interactions* - low velocity pulses from the main flow toward the bed. The bursting phenomenon represents the exchange of eddy inertia and momentum between the boundary layer and the free-stream zone (Thompson, 1997).

Sweep impacts may be grouped, and may create patches of entrainment on a mobile bed (Best, 1992). Visualization experiments also suggest that larger clasts on a bed are entrained by downstream rushes, whereas the smaller clasts are more likely to be entrained by chaotic transient vertical flows associated with the obstacle-derived vortices (Kirkbride, 1993). Motion pictures taken through the clear water of Duck Creek in Wyoming, USA indicated that the collective motion of bed gravels (d_{50} = 4 mm) was characterized by frequent, brief, localized, random sweep-transport events that in the aggregate transported approximately 70% of the total load moved (Drake et al., 1988).

Field data from gravel-bed rivers with pools and riffles indicate systematic differences in turbulence characteristics in association with changing bedforms (Clifford and French, 1993a; Clifford, 1996). Under the high relative roughness of riffles, turbulence is dominated by vortex shedding processes. Under the low relative roughness of pools, the outer zone flow structure is dominated by inner-outer zone roll-up structures more akin to burst-sweep features: The distortion of streamwise subparallel vortices and the localized collapse of the sublayer organization cause bursts (Robinson, 1990). The ejection of low momentum fluid into the outer flow results in a compensating inrush of outer flow fluid towards the bed, which probably generates the next generation of vortices and distorts the sublayer to initiate further bursting (Grass, 1971; Kirkbride, 1993). High speed sweeps occur as wall-directed inrushes of higher than average downstream velocity fluid (Best, 1993). Once the sweeps contact the channel boundary they spread laterally and lose momentum downstream (Grass, 1971).

Robert's (1998) measurements of velocity profiles in pools and riffles illustrate the results of these differences in turbulence-generating mechanisms. At low flows, riffles are characterized by higher near-bed velocity gradients than pools, and have a greater resistance and bed shear stress. The differences in near-bed velocity gradients decrease as discharge increases, although velocities higher in the water column remain significantly different between pools and riffles.

Analogous differences have been found along step-pool channels (Wohl and Thompson, 2000). Locations immediately upstream from bed-steps and at step lips are dominated by bed-generated turbulence. Locations immediately downstream from bed-steps are dominated by wake turbulence from mid-profile shear layers associated with roller eddies where the flow from the step plunges into the pool below. Adverse pressure gradients (decelerating flow in the upper profile) up- and downstream from steps may be enhancing turbulence generation, whereas favorable pressure gradients (accelerating flow in the upper profile) at steps suppress turbulence (Wohl and Thompson, 2000).

Downstream passage of mobile bedforms such as gravel bedload sheets may also have coincident velocity fluctuations (Dinehart, 1999). Understanding of flow and turbulence characteristics is increasingly being applied to understanding the mechanics of bedload entrainment and transport along mountain rivers. The conditions under which sediment movement occurs are commonly defined in terms of bed shear stress.

Bed Shear Stress

Attempts to measure or calculate bed shear stress values in mountain rivers are complicated by the channel-bed roughness and the associated turbulence and velocity fluctuations. Because of these conditions, the Shields' entrainment function commonly used for lower gradient channels with uniformly sized grains does not adequately predict initiation of motion (Reid et al., 1985; Graf, 1991). Dietrich and Whiting (1989) review nine equations available for estimating local bed shear stress from field data. Many of these equations use terms such as the fluctuating component of downstream or vertical fluid velocity, which may be difficult to define accurately in field studies.

The only method for directly measuring shear stress may be expressed as

$$\tau_b = \rho \, \overline{u' w'} \tag{24}$$

where τ_b = boundary shear stress,

u', w' = fluctuating component of downstream and vertical fluid velocity, and

ρ = density of fluid.

Turbulence measurements have proven difficult to obtain in natural rivers with mobile beds (McLean and Smith, 1979), leading to the use of relations derived from theoretical models. The two most commonly employed relations are:

$$\tau_b = \rho\,g\,h\,S \qquad (25)$$

where h = depth of flow, and S = downstream water-surface slope, and

$$\tau_b = \frac{\rho\,(uk)^2}{(\ln\,(z/z_0))^2} \qquad (26)$$

where k = von Karman constant, u = velocity, z = near vertical coordinate, perpendicular to bed, and z_0 = roughness parameter including effect of saltating grains.

In general, z_0 is hypothesized to be (1) proportional to the saltation height of the moving grains, or (2) controlled by a representative coarser fraction of the moving or static bed surface. Equation 25 is only approximately correct over short channel reaches because of convective accelerations (Dietrich and Whiting, 1989). When using equation 26, it is difficult to make reliable velocity profile measurements over mobile beds and beds with large grain sizes. It becomes necessary to make profile measurements very close to the bed to avoid the form drag of bedforms (Dietrich and Whiting, 1989).

Wilcock (1996) noted that bed shear velocity u_* can be estimated within 3% using the depth-averaged velocity in the vertically averaged logarithmic velocity profile, if the channel has a relatively simple flow geometry that approximates a log profile. Estimates of u_* made from a single near-bed velocity measurement are less precise by a factor of 3 (for Wilcock's sites; d_{90} of 85 to 120 mm, Q of 23 to 80.5 m³/s, h of 0.75 to 2.6 m) because of the larger uncertainty associated with a single measurement (Wilcock, 1996). Estimates of u_* from the slope of the near-bed velocity profile are the least precise, but may be made without independent knowledge of bed roughness.

Part of the difficulty in obtaining useful estimates of bed shear stress arises from the relatively high temporal and spatial variability of this factor along mountain rivers. The turbulence described previously can lead to substantial variability in velocity and shear stress at a point during constant discharge. Heterogeneities of the channel-bed caused by grains and bedforms may create substantial velocity and shear stress variations across a cross section or downstream during a constant discharge. Measuring shear stress across alternate bars on a gravel-bed channel (h = 0.4 m, S =

0.0010, d_{84} = 16.1 mm), Whiting and Dietrich (1991) found that large cross-sectional area changes resulting from variation in depth forced large stream-wise accelerations and cross-stream flow off the central bar. These topographically driven downstream and cross-stream accelerations produce a pattern of boundary shear stress that decreases out of the upstream bend, increases over the bar top, and then decreases in deeper flow (Whiting and Dietrich, 1991). The convective accelerations across the channel become progressively less important as stage increases (Whiting, 1997).

The primary reason for estimating bed shear stress is that of calculating the bedload sediment entrainment and transport, and the associated erosion, deposition, and channel change. Because rates of sediment entrainment and transport can increase in a rapid and nonlinear manner with increasing bed shear stress, the accuracy of estimation of bed shear stress becomes critical, particularly at conditions near the entrainment threshold (Wilcock, 1996). Spatial and temporal variability in bed shear stress are sufficient that the sum of local transport rates across a cross section may be substantially different from the total load calculated using the section-averaged shear stress (Carson and Griffiths, 1987; Wilcock et al., 1994; Wilcock, 1996). Because of these complications, estimates of bed shear stress used for estimates of sediment movement commonly focus on temporally and spatially averaged conditions or probability distributions (Powell, 1998).

Sediment Processes

Bed Sediment Characterization

Critical shear stress for sediment movement will be a function of local hydraulics, as well as grain size, shape, sorting, and packing (Barta et al., 1994; Bartnik and Michalik, 1994; Moore and Diplas, 1994). Ergenzinger and de Jong (1994), for example, found that shear forces dominate clast entrainment only when a clast protrudes into the flow; lift force dominates when the clast is level with neighboring particles. One of the first challenges to accurately predicting bedload transport is therefore that of characterizing the bed surface sediments which both affect local hydraulics and may provide the source material for bedload transport.

The grain-size distribution of channel-bed sediments may be characterized via bulk (volumetric) sampling or clast measurements in situ. In either case, the spatial variability in grain-size distribution (e.g. between pools and riffles, or pools and steps) along the channel must be addressed. Wolcott and Church (1991) proposed that a representative sample could be obtained by combining subsamples of equal volumes. Bulk sampling may be extremely difficult along mountain rivers with sediment coarser than gravel. In a study of a braided gravel-bed river (d_{50} = 16 mm), Mosley and Tindale (1985) concluded that accurate determination of mean grain size required a sample of approximately 100 kg, although samples in which the weight of the largest clast is less than 5% of the total weight have unbiased estimates of mean grain size. Ferguson and Paola (1997) found that bias is likely in small samples of river bedload, and that good precision requires very large samples of poorly sorted gravel deposits. As the b-axis of the largest clast at a site approaches 64 mm, required sample sizes become impractical (> 400 kg) for field sieving by hand (Church et al., 1987). Consequently, some type of in situ clast measurement is more commonly used, although such methods do not consistently sample clasts smaller than 15 mm (Fripp and Diplas, 1993). These measurements may employ a grid (Wolman, 1954); a random walk (Leopold, 1970); a visual comparator (Billi, 1994); areal sampling with clay or with wax (Diplas and Fripp, 1992); Fourier analysis of particle outlines on digitized photographs (Diepenbroek and de Jong, 1994); a systematic unaligned method in which the study area is divided into a number of arbitrary cells within each of which a sampling position is chosen (Wolcott and Church, 1991); or an area count of all clasts exposed at the surface within a given unit area (Kellerhals and Bray, 1971; Wohl et al., 1996).

Diplas and Sutherland (1988) noted that each grain on a surface projects, on average, an area proportional to the square of its sieve diameter, facilitating the comparison of bulk and surface samples. If the results of surface sampling are adequately described by the binomial distribution (Fripp and Diplas, 1993), then surface samples require only about a third of the material that a bulk sample requires to meet the low accuracy levels described by DeVries (1971) (Crowder and Diplas, 1994). This still requires 200-400 clasts for surface samples (Fripp and Diplas, 1993). Fripp and Diplas (1993) proposed a method to determine the required sample size based on the percentile value (size fraction) of interest and the level of accuracy required in the study.

Different methods of surface sampling may not produce equivalent results, however. Wolcott and Church (1991) found that approximately 500 random sites were equivalent to 100 systematic unaligned or grid sites. Wohl et al. (1996) found that random walk and grid methods produced statistically indistinguishable values of d_{50} and d_{84} when performed by a single operator, although multiple operators could generate statistically different population measures. Differences between operators occur because of differences in clast selection, and become statistically significant as sample size increases past 100 clasts (Hey and Thorne, 1983). The standard deviation about replicated means increases linearly with sediment size, with larger standard deviations for samples collected by different individuals than for sampling by one person (Marcus et al., 1995).

Wolman (1954) advocated a surface sample size of 100 clasts, and this remains the most commonly used sample size. Each clast is commonly characterized by the diameter of the b-axis. Clast measurements may be used to determine (i) frequency by weight, where particle volume is computed and a constant specific weight is assumed, so that the frequency of each size interval may be expressed, or (ii) frequency by number, where the frequency of each size interval is expressed as the percentage by number of the total number of particles in the original sample. Leopold (1970), Kellerhals and Bray (1971), and Diplas and Fripp (1992) proposed methods for converting frequency by number to frequency by weight data, although the Kellerhals and Bray method may bias the finer particles (Ettema, 1984).

Buffington and Montgomery (1999a) proposed a two-tier system of ternary diagrams for classifying textural patches (grain-size facies) in gravel-bed channels. The

Figure 3.8. (a) Surface of lateral bar along Poudre River, Colorado, USA. Photo scale at center of photograph is approximately 15 cm long. (b) Subsurface of same bar, with surface layer of clasts removed. Photo scale at center rear of photograph.

procedure identifies the relative abundance of major size classes (boulder, cobble, gravel, sand, silt) and subcategories of the dominant size (very coarse, coarse, medium, etc). The procedure may be used to create facies maps which provide stratification for sampling both physical and biological conditions.

Nikora et al. (1998) propose using a random field approach for characterizing the roughness of gravel-bed channels. They demonstrate that the bed elevation distribution is close to Gaussian, and apply the second-order structure function $D(\Delta x, \Delta y)$ of bed elevation $z(x, y)$ to describing gravel-bed roughness:

$$D(\Delta x, \Delta y) = 1/\,(N\text{-}n)(M\text{-}m) \cdot \sum_{i=1}^{N\text{-}n} \sum_{j=1}^{M\text{-}m} \{Z\,(x_i + n\delta x, y_j + m\delta y) - Z\,(x_i, y_j)\}^{\,2} \qquad (27)$$

Figure 3.8 (b)

where $\Delta x = n\delta x$, $\Delta y = m\delta y$, δx and δy are the sampling intervals and N and M are the total numbers of measuring points of bed elevations in directions x and y, respectively. This model describes the gravel-bed roughness only at the level of individual particles; hydraulically important particle clusters are ignored, restricting the model's use in flow resistance and bedload investigations. However, the model may be able to improve the ability to predict bulk flow velocity by providing an estimate of roughness height k_s (here, $k_s = f(\sigma_z, \Delta x, \Delta y)$, where σ_z is degree of particle sorting in the z direction).

Particle clusters have been observed in gravel-bed channels with low bed-material transport rates (Church et al., 1998), and have been produced experimentally during a two-dimensional kinematic simulation of a gravel streambed (Tribe and Church, 1999). These structures develop simultaneously with the armor layer by particles moving from less stable positions into more stable configurations against each other, and substantially reduce sediment transport. The timescale of particle cluster development suggests that the bed structure of gravel-bed channels may reflect the history of dominant flows rather than more recent flows (Church et al., 1998).

The surface of the channel bed may also be described in terms of selective size distribution by depth. Carling and Reader (1982) distinguish among three types of coarse surface layers: (1) pavement - a coarse surface layer that is rarely disrupted (Figure 3.8); (2) armor - a coarse lag layer developed at waning flows that is regularly disrupted; and (3) a censored layer that forms as matrix material is removed from around the surface framework particles as stage increases. Many investigators have noted that the bed of a channel may have a coarse-grained surface that is characteristically one grain diameter thick and is both coarser and better sorted than the underlying material (Moss, 1963, 1972; Gessler, 1965). Bray and Church (1980) proposed the term "armor" for such a surface when particle motion was a relatively frequent occurrence over a period of years. It has also been noted that bedload is characterized by grain-size distributions which are finer than, and may be completely distinct from, the grain-size distributions of the bed material (DiSilvio and Brunelli, 1991). Theoretical models of armoring processes vary from one-step models that predict equilibrium compositions and scouring depths, to multiple-step models that describe different stages of coarsening processes (Sutherland, 1987). No consensus has yet been reached as to how the coarse surface layer forms, however, at least in part because the mechanism of formation undoubtedly differs among channels (Table 3.2). For example, Carling and Reader (1982) described a scenario for upland streams in the United Kingdom in which fine sediments are winnowed from the interstices of the coarse surface layer by intermediate flows, forming what Sutherland (1987) described as a static armor layer. (In contrast, a mobile armor layer is a coarse surface layer that is maintained in the presence of an upstream sediment supply and during flows capable of moving all grain sizes (Powell, 1998).) The fine sediments winnowed from a stable armor layer may be temporarily stored in the separation flow downstream from large bed elements. Alternatively, the fine sediments may be transported as an under-capacity bedload over a stable cobble-bed. The resulting open-work surface gravel has the same grain-size distribution as the subsurface layer and is not really an armor layer.

Table 3.2. Explanations for the presence of a coarse-grained surface layer in the channel bed.

Processes	Reference
Fine sediments winnowed from interstices of coarse surface layer by intermediate flows	Carling and Reader, 1982
Coarse surface layer is constructed and maintained when all sizes of bed material are moving	Parker and Klingeman, 1982 Andrews and Erman, 1986 Suzuki and Kato, 1991
Coarse surface layer develops where reduced flow velocity causes deposition of large clasts, and where particle clustering or traction clogging occur	Dunkerley, 1990 Moss, 1963, 1972
Coarse surface layer present where bedload supply from upstream is less than ability of flow to transport that load	Dietrich et al., 1989 Buffington and Montgomery, 1999c

Parker and Klingeman (1982) noted that bedload and subpavement size distributions are similar, and interpreted this to indicate that the coarse half of a subpavement moves through a reach at nearly the same rate as the fine half. Because coarser grains are intrinsically less mobile than fine grains, some mechanism must act to nearly equalize mobility. They hypothesize that the pavement seen in gravel bed streams at low flow is in place during typical flows capable of moving all available grain sizes. This pavement provides the equalizing mechanism by exposing proportionally more coarse grains to the flow. Pavement is thus a mobile bed phenomenon. Andrews and Erman (1986) and Suzuki and Kato (1991) reached a similar conclusion. Andrews and Erman found that a significant quantity of sediment representing a majority of the particle sizes present at the channel surface was transported during a period of sustained, large discharge. The relatively coarser surface layer that is present during smaller discharges was also in place and unchanged. Only a few clasts, though representing nearly all available sizes, were entrained at any instant by even the peak flows. Thus, differential entrainment is not a significant process, and the coarse bed surface is constructed and maintained when all sizes of bed material are moving.

Dietrich et al. (1989) noted the tendency for coarse surface layers to be well developed when local bedload supply from upstream is less than the ability of the flow to transport that load, as occurs downstream from dams. Dunkerley (1990) described a slightly different situation, with coarse grains carried in traction to the sites which they armored, and deposited over preexisting bodies of sediment. Armor layers could thus develop in zones where reduced flow velocities caused deposition of large clasts, and where particle clustering or traction clogging occurred.

Some of the variability in mechanisms of forming and maintaining the coarse surface layer may reflect position within the drainage basin, as this influences channel gradient, grain-size distribution, and channel morphology. Combining data from 13 gravel-bed drainage basins (drainage area 1.5 to 28,000 km²) from around the world, Lisle (1995) found that in channels with high ratios of bed-material d_{50} to bedload d_{50}, significant volumes of fine bedload are transported during discharges less than bankfull while the coarser bed material substrate remains stable. Moving downstream, the bed as a whole is accessed for bedload by deeper annual scour, and the difference between transport of finer and coarser portions of the grain-size distribution decreases (Lisle, 1995). The coarse surface layer may also be spatially variable at the reach scale as a result of variations in shear stress and sediment transport associated with alternate bar topography (Lisle and Madej, 1992); as a result of hydraulic roughness caused by large woody debris (Buffington and Montgomery, 1999b); or as a result of variations in sediment supply rate (Buffington and Montgomery, 1999c).

Most coarse-grained rivers show a downstream decrease in average grain size at scales of tens to hundreds of kilometers, although this downstream trend may be interrupted by coarse sediment from hillslope or tributary inputs (Wohl and Pearthree, 1991; Grimm et al., 1995), or from knickzone erosion (Deroanne and Petit, 1999). Rice (1998) has developed a procedure for identifying significant lateral sediment sources using drainage basin area, network magnitude, and the basin area-slope product to define individual channel links within which downstream fining occurs. Downstream decrease in grain size has been attributed primarily to selective sorting (entrainment, transport, and deposition) (Brierley and Hickin, 1985; Paola et al., 1992; Werritty, 1992; Ferguson and Wathen, 1998), to abrasion in place (Schumm and Stevens, 1973) or during transport, or to some combination of these processes (Mikos, 1994). Experimental simulations suggest that the relative importance of selective sorting is partly a function of clast resistance, with abrasion roughly equal to selective sorting in producing downstream fining for less resistant lithologies (Parker, 1991). Powell's (1998) review of sediment sorting in coarse-grained alluvial rivers notes that multiple scales of bed material sorting exist, with relationships between pattern and process likely to vary as a function of scale. At present, we have only a limited understanding of the many feedback linkages which govern these patterns and processes.

Sediment Entrainment

Although the amount of sediment moving as bedload may be less than a quarter of that moving in suspension along many rivers (Williams and Rosgen, 1989), studies of high-gradient rivers indicate that bedload composes a much higher proportion of the total sediment load along these channels than along low-gradient channels (Hayward and Sutherland, 1974; Nanson, 1974; Mosley, 1978; Bradley and Mears, 1980; Harvey, 1980; Schick and Lekach, 1993). Bedload is also generally much more important than suspended load in forming and changing the channel of a mountain river (Pitlick and Thorne, 1987; Leopold, 1992). As a result, much more attention has been devoted to bedload processes along mountain rivers than to suspended sediment processes.

Emphasis in the 1980s on gravel-bed rivers led to increased attention on bedload entrainment and transport from poorly-sorted channel beds. Earlier attempts to quantify conditions of entrainment balanced drag and body forces acting on a grain by specifying critical shear stress, packing, pivoting angle, and grain diameter. This approach ignores lift force, and describes instantaneous conditions which may deviate substantially from the measured mean shear stress (Richards, 1990). Consequently, this deterministic approach has been largely replaced by physically based stochastic models that treat the two distinct phenomena of velocity fluctuations and variations in grain size and pivoting angle (Richards, 1990).

Pivoting angle represents the particle's resistance to movement. This is dependent on the ratio of grain diameter d to the underlying grain size, as this affects relative protrusion of the grain into the flow; on particle shape; and on packing (imbrication) (Komar and Li, 1986; Li and Komar, 1986). Although Shields' critical shear stress predictions work well for uniformly sized sediment, critical shear stress is lower than predicted when d is larger than the length scale of the bed roughness, k_s ($d/k_s > 1$), and higher when $d/k_s < 1$ (Wiberg and Smith, 1987). A pivoting angle expression may be developed for entrainment of a single grain, such as:

$$\zeta = \cos^{-1} [(d/k_s + z)/ (d/k_s + 1)] \qquad \text{(Wiberg and Smith, 1987)} \qquad (28)$$

where z = grain protrusion, and ζ = pivoting angle. However, there have been few attempts to estimate representative pivoting angles and exposure parameters for entire regions of a mixed grain size bed so that general transport rates can be predicted (Richards, 1990). As a result, many assumptions are made when applying an equation such as Wiberg and Smith's to an actual field setting (Chase, 1994).

An exception to the lack of field studies of pivoting is that of Johnston et al. (1998). They used a digital load cell to directly measure the force required to pivot or slide a particle out of its resting place for 8000 particles in five rivers. These measurements indicated that relative grain size (d_i/k_s) is the only statistically significant variable for predicting median ζ within a site. Johnston et al. (1998) also concluded that particle resistance to motion should be measured in the field. Location-general empirical relations that attempt to predict pivoting angle at a given site without direct in situ measurements will have uncertainty on the order of $\pm$ 10 degrees.

Experimental flume studies of initial motion in mixed grain size beds variously focus on vibration in situ, single grain movement (e.g. Andrews and Smith, 1992), or general motion of the bed (Richards, 1990). These studies indicate that the grain shear stress effective in entrainment and transport is systematically less than the total shear stress estimated from the law of the wall or the depth-slope product because of form drag effects from pebble clusters and other bedforms (Petit, 1989). Other flume studies suggest that discharge or stream power may be more effective predictors of entrainment and transport for steep, poorly sorted beds (Bagnold, 1977; Bathurst, 1987b; Bathurst et al., 1987; Ashmore, 1988; Ferguson, 1994).

Field studies of entrainment are difficult to compare because of a variety of measurement techniques and sampling procedures (Komar, 1987b). Initial entrainment may be defined by the largest grain size caught in a Helley-Smith sampler, or by extrapolating size-fractional transport rates to a low value at which shear stress is identified and related to grain size characteristics (Parker et al., 1982). Shear stress may be estimated using various time- and space-averaging procedures, as explained earlier.

Field studies of entrainment by Parker et al. (1982) and by Andrews (1983) led to the concept of *equal mobility*. According to equal mobility, the exposure of large grains compensates sufficiently for their greater submerged weight so that all grain sizes are entrained at approximately the same shear stress. Critical shear stress is thus independent of a grain's size, but dependent on the substrate median size d_{s50}. This relation is expressed by using a hiding factor d_i/d_{s50}:

$$\theta_{ci} = 0.0834 \, (d_i/d_{s50})^{-0.872} \qquad \text{(Andrews, 1983)} \qquad (29)$$

At shear stresses exceeding this critical value, all grain sizes are transported at rates in proportion to their presence in the bed material (Powell, 1998), although the entrainment of bed particles is sporadic and only a small portion of the available sediment is in motion at any given time (Andrews and Erman, 1986). Lower transport rates and lower excess shear stresses require a greater degree of surface coarsening in order to equalize the mobility of different grain-size fractions (Parker, 1990).

On the other hand, work by Komar (Komar, 1987a, 1989; Komar and Shih, 1992; Shih and Komar, 1990a,b) and Ashworth and Ferguson (1989) supports *selective entrainment* by grain size. Entrainment experiments conducted with variously shaped particles indicate that the likelihood of grains of differing size being entrained at the same incident flow depends on the packing and grain-size distribution of the bed material (Carling et al., 1992). Wilcock (1993) suggested that equal mobility may apply to unimodal and weakly bimodal sediment distributions, whereas critical shear stress increases with grain size for strongly bimodal sediments. Studying mountain rivers with high sediment loading resulting from the 1991 eruption at Mount Pinatubo, Montgomery et al. (1999) suggested that equal mobility and selective entrainment represent end-member concepts that apply to channels with low (or intermittent) and high (or continuous) sediment supply, respectively.

Field studies indicate variability in the mode of sediment entrainment as a function of discharge, time, and grain size distribution (Table 3.3). Sand becomes mobile along pool-riffle channels at lower values of shear stress than does gravel, but equal mobility is approximated at the higher measured values of shear stress and when bedload transport is integrated over longer timespans of an entire flow season (Church et al., 1991; Kuhnle, 1992a). Similarly, selective transport best describes ordinary snowmelt high flows (1-2 year recurrence interval) along Squaw Creek, Montana, USA (step-pool, pool-riffle, and pool-alternate bar), although equal mobility may occur during extreme flows that also drastically change channel morphology (Bunte, 1996). Wathen et al. (1995) found that gravel transport in a pool-riffle channel was slightly size-selective, whereas sand transport was close to equal mobility. Sand and gravel transport at discharges of 0.1-1.0 m^3/s along a stable, bouldery step-pool channel in Colorado approximated equal mobility (Blizard and Wohl, 1998).

Kuhnle (1992b) made an important distinction between *equal entrainment mobility*, where all sediment sizes in the bed begin to move at the same strength of flow, and *equal transport mobility*, during which all sediment sizes are transported according to their relative abundance in the bed material. One does not imply the other. Kuhnle (1992b) did not detect equal entrainment mobility, but equal transport was approached at high values of shear stress (at low shear stress, fines were over-represented). The tendency to either equal mobility or selective entrainment appears to depend on local conditions, and may be influenced by the manner in which entrainment is defined in the field (Richards, 1990).

Part of the variability in entrainment and transport may also be associated with supply-limited versus capacity-limited conditions. Two-phase bedload transport has been described during which the initial phase is supply-limited, with finer fractions of the bed material in transport over an armored surface, whereas the bed is disrupted and all grain sizes are in transport during the later phase (Jackson and Beschta, 1982; Bathurst, 1987a). During the initial phase, fine sediment may infiltrate into the bed, but during the later phase the bed may become a source of suspended sediment.

Table 3.3. Equal mobility versus selective entrainment of clasts.

Equal mobility (Parker et al., 1982; Andrews, 1983)	Selective entrainment (Komar, 1987a, 1989; Ashworth & Ferguson, 1989; Shih & Komar, 1990a,b
* the exposure of large grains compensates sufficiently for their greater submerged weight, and all grain sizes are entrained at approximately the same shear stress	* grains are selectively entrained as a function of size * critical shear stress depends on grain size * as shear stresses exceed critical, increasingly larger grains are transported
* critical shear stress is independent of a grain's size, but dependent on substrate median size	
* at shear stresses exceeding critical, all grain sizes are transported in proportion to their presence in the bed material	
may apply to unimodal and weakly bimodal sediment distributions Wilcock, 1993	applies to strongly bimodal sediments
applies to low or intermittent sediment supply Montgomery et al., 1999	applies to high or continuous sediment supply
approximated at higher shear stress and when bedload transport is integrated over the entire flow season Church et al., 1991 Kuhnle, 1992a	sand mobile along pool-riffle channel at lower values of shear stress than gravel
extreme flows that substantially change channel morphology Bunte, 1996	ordinary snowmelt high flows (1-2 year recurrence interval)
sand transport in pool-riffle channel Wathen et al., 1995	gravel transport in pool-riffle channel

[distinguish *equal entrainment mobility* (all sediment sizes in bed begin to move at same strength of flow) from *equal transport mobility* (all sediment sizes transported according to relative abundance in bed) Kuhnle, 1992b]

Observed differences may largely be related to two-phase bedload transport -- initial phase is supply-limited, with fine particles transported over stable coarse surface, and second phase is capacity-limited, with bed disrupted and all grain sizes in transport (Jackson & Beschta, 1982; Bathurst, 1987a)

Fine sediment may also be incorporated into the flow by a gradual winnowing process to a depth equivalent to the d_{50} of the armor layer (Beschta and Jackson, 1979; Carling, 1984b). Successive flows that disrupt the bed may eventually deplete the supply of fine sediments and change the suspended sediment rating curve (Milhous, 1982).

Bunte (1990) hypothesized a similar alteration in bedload transport during a high discharge to explain the variable transport rates observed at Squaw Creek. During rising discharge selective entrainment and transport of the fine sediments creates a bed load distribution that increases regularly with discharge. When the removal of fines sufficiently exposes the cobbles on the bed, a threshold is crossed and the entire bed becomes mobile. This is a temporary condition, however, because of interactions between grain sizes (e.g. hiding, clustering) and a decrease in shear stress associated with local deposition, which promote pulses of bedload transport (Bunte, 1990).

Empirical observations of magnetically tagged gravels indicate that some areas of gravel-bed channels have little, if any, bed activity even during floods. Haschenburger (1999) used the exponential density function to describe frequency distributions of scour and fill depths along gravel-bed channels. She found that this function provides a plausible model of these channels, in which a limited area of the bed scours or fills relatively deeply (for a 15-m wide channel, up to 1 m vertically of scour or fill during the highest discharges observed). In general, there is an increasing depth of activity over an increasing proportion of the channel bed as peak discharge increases (Haschenburger, 1999).

Both field and flume studies indicate the importance of form drag as an influence on sediment entrainment in gravel-bed rivers (Brayshaw, 1985; Petit, 1989, 1990; Hassan and Reid, 1990; Reid et al., 1992; Best, 1993). For a given particle size, the greater the bed roughness, the greater will be the shear stress required to initiate motion. This may be incorporated into shear stress equations using the roughness length y_o, which is the height of zero velocity obtained by extrapolation of the law of the wall fitted to field velocity profile data:

$$\theta_{ci} = 0.069 \ (d_i/y_o)^{-0.699} \qquad \text{(Richards, 1990)} \qquad (30)$$

Most sediment transport equations predict increasing transport rates with increasing stage. The effect of form roughness, however, is such that changes in relative protrusion of bed particles may result in a decline in transport rates with increasing depth (Bagnold, 1977; Reid et al., 1985). Because of the many stochastic variables influencing particle critical shear stress, Powell (1998) suggests that critical shear stress be characterized by a probability distribution, rather than a single value.

A final important point with respect to shear stress and sediment entrainment comes from studies on Turkey Brook in the United Kingdom (Reid et al., 1985): the bed shear stress at entrainment averages three times the shear at the cessation of motion, an effect analogous to that described by Hjulström (1935) with respect to velocity.

Mechanics of Bedload Transport

Once the bed material grain-size distribution has been characterized, and the conditions under which entrainment occurs have been specified, another basic requirement for predicting bedload transport along mountain rivers is empirical data. It is important to distinguish between bedload discharge, which refers to instantaneous transport rates (e.g. kg/s, m³/s), and bedload yield, which refers to amounts of sediment (e.g. tons, m³) moved over longer time periods of floods or a seasonal cycle (Carson and Griffiths, 1987). In the following discussion, bedload is equivalent to bed material load, and is that part of the sediment load composed of grain sizes represented in the bed and moving by rolling, sliding, or saltating. In contrast, dissolved load moves in solution, and wash load is that part of the sediment load moving in suspension and composed of grain sizes finer than those of the bed.

Bedload transport along steep, gravel-bed rivers is notoriously difficult to directly measure (Ryan and Troendle, 1997). Any sampler placed in the flow may perturb local hydraulics sufficiently to create anomalously high or low transport conditions. The Helley-Smith sampler is commonly used either hand-held on a rod or by lowering from a boat or bridge. Efficiency ratings for the Helley-Smith sampler have been calculated as sampler efficiency and hydraulic efficiency. Sampler efficiency is a ratio of sediment collected to sediment that would have passed the nozzle area without the sampler present (Glysson, 1993). A field calibration of the Helley-Smith sampler demonstrated sampler efficiencies of 90-100% for particles 0.5-16 mm in diameter (Emmett, 1980). Sampler efficiency dropped below 70% for particles greater than 16 mm, although the reduction may have been caused by the small number of particles in motion. Hydraulic efficiency is the ratio of water discharge through the sampler orifice to discharge through the same area without the sampler (Kuhnle, 1992b). Calculated hydraulic efficiencies range from 1.43 to 1.53 (Hubbell, 1987; Kuhnle, 1992b). Because this does not create a sampler efficiency greater than 100%, it is not regarded as a problem. U.S. Geological Survey protocol recommends a sampling time of 30-60 sec so as to account for instantaneous transport variations, but not clog the sampler bag (Glysson, 1993). Sampler efficiencies drop off after the sampler is 40% full (Emmett, 1980), but sampling times of up to 10 minutes may be appropriate under low-flow conditions (Ashworth and Ferguson, 1989).

One of the challenges of using a point sampler such as the Helley-Smith is that bedload movement commonly varies by an order of magnitude or more across a channel cross section (Carling, 1994b). Because of this, Gomez and Troutman (1997) suggest that sampling errors decrease as the number of samples collected increases, and the number of traverses of the channel over which samples are collected increases. They also recommend that sampling be conducted at a pace which allows a number of bedforms to pass through the sampling cross section.

An alternative to point sampling of bedload is to use some type of sediment trap and to measure filling rates. In 1973 a portion of the East Fork River in Wyoming, USA was temporarily diverted so that a concrete trench could be emplaced across the bed. Hydraulically operated horizontal gates opening to 15-cm wide and flush with the bed, allow bedload to be trapped in individual sections or across the whole channel. A conveyor belt transports trapped sediment to the bank for measurement (Leopold and Emmett, 1976; Bagnold, 1977). Laronne et al. (1992) and Ergenzinger et al. (1994b) describe slot samplers set at intervals across other channels. A Birkbeck-type pressure pillow is located in the slot and the system is fully automated to sample at 0.25-sec intervals. The slots have a capacity of 0.25-0.4 m^3, and usually fill before the cessation of bedload transport. Klingeman and Milhous (1970) adapted a vortex-tube, which utilizes vortices that develop in slots perpendicular to flow to trap sediment, to Oak Creek in Oregon, USA, and Hayward and Sutherland (1974) used a similar design on the Torlesse Stream catchment in New Zealand. The main limitation to these techniques is the width of the channel (at 15m the East Fork River is the widest channel so instrumented to date) and the capacity of the sampler.

A sediment trap may also take the form of a storage area such as a large pit excavated at the downstream end of a reach, which can be monitored for volume of sediment fill following a single flood or an entire flow season (Lenzi et al., 1990). Using a sediment trap as the reference, Warburton (1990) found that a bedload rating curve constructed from a series of Helley-Smith samples overpredicted yield by 36% on a small, steep (0.07 m/m) boulder channel in Switzerland. Loads calculated with the Schoklitsch formula overpredicted yield by 111%. Warburton (1990) concluded that the Helley-Smith and Schoklitsch methods did not account for temporal and spatial variation in transport rates. In contrast, comparison of more than 30 years of weir pond data and more than 1500 Helley-Smith samples from mountain channels in Colorado indicated that the values of total bedload from each method were comparable (Troendle et al., 1996).

Bedload movement may also be estimated from a subset of marked tracer particles that are assumed to represent some proportion of total movement. Markers may be miniature radios, magnets, paint, or radioactive injections (Hassan et al., 1984; Chacho et al., 1994; Ergenzinger and de Jong, 1994; Michalik and Bartnik, 1994; Thompson et al., 1996).

Rickenmann (1994b) describes the use of hydrophones, sensors installed in the channel bed that measure the acoustic signals resulting from the impact of bedload grains transported over the measuring cross section. Several investigators (e.g. Richards and Milne, 1979; Bänziger and Burch, 1990) have attempted to indirectly measure bedload using acoustic collision meters, but have been unable to adequately calibrate the meters, particularly for high flows. A pressure-pillow placed on the channel bed may be used to calculate the thickness of overlying sediment as a function of the difference between the internal pressure of the pillow and the hydrostatic pressure (Kurashige, 1999). Gomez (1987) reviews bedload measurement techniques.

Numerous studies using each of these types of bedload measurement have demonstrated that bedload movement is episodic along a given channel reach (Schick et al., 1982; Lekach and Schick, 1983; Reid et al., 1985; Kuhnle and Southard, 1988; Whiting et al., 1988; Hassan et al., 1991; Bunte, 1992; Hoey, 1992). This episodicity has been explained in terms of number of channels and sediment storage along braided rivers (Hoey and Sutherland, 1991; Young and Davies, 1991; Warburton and Davies, 1994). For single flow-path channels, the migration of bedforms (Reid and Frostick, 1986; Gomez et al., 1989; Young and Davies, 1991), longitudinal sediment sorting (Iseya and Ikeda, 1987), and the lateral shifting of bedload streets (Leopold and Emmett, 1976; Ergenzinger et al., 1994a) have been invoked to explain episodic bedload transport. Other investigators have noted the presence of different stage-bedload discharge rating curves in adjacent channel reaches, which causes downstream changes in sediment transport that may develop by a feedback mechanism into bed waves (Griffiths, 1989). Carling (1994b) found that the passage of bedload sheets through a reach was accompanied by selective deposition of fine bedload in the coarse surface armor. This caused physical and hydraulic smoothing of the bed and associated adjustment of hydraulic parameters. As the sheet passed, reentrainment caused further readjustment to hydraulically rougher conditions. Changes in the sorting of mixed-size sediment may also affect bedform dimensions and dynamics (Wilcock, 1992a).

Bedload sheets are migrating slugs of bedload one to two grain-diameters thick that alternate between fine and coarse particles (Whiting and Dietrich, 1985; Iseya and Ikeda, 1987). The sheets form when bedload segregates into alternating mobile zones of low grain roughness and high grain roughness. The larger grains move rapidly across the smooth areas of finer grains, and then accumulate downstream where other large grains create high grain-to-grain friction (Lisle, 1987). When the coarse grains trap sufficient fine particles in their interstices, they become mobile again (Whiting et al., 1988). This process has been described as an alternation between a smooth bed in which sand controls the mobility of the sediment mixture, and a congested bed in which gravel controls mobility (Ikeda, 1984; Ikeda and Iseya, 1986,1988). Features such as longitudinal slope discontinuity and alternating repetition of scour and fill have been attributed to processes associated with heterogeneous sediment transport.

Cross-sectional to reach-scale heterogeneity of bed structure and relief may be responsible for some of the spatial and temporal heterogeneity of bedload movement (Laronne and Carson, 1976). Clusters of bed particles (Brayshaw et al., 1983) may impede particle entrainment because larger particles shield smaller particles. Transverse ribs formed by lines of large clasts across the channel (Koster, 1978), and bed steps with an associated plunge pool (Whittaker and Jaeggi, 1982), commonly form in steep channels and create hydraulic jumps and other flow heterogeneities. Bars and pools are associated with diverging and converging flow that promotes deposition and scour, respectively (Ashmore, 1982; Thompson, 1986). These bars and pools may be fixed by bedrock outcrops, channel bends, or large woody debris (Lisle, 1986; O'Connor et al., 1986). Large woody debris may temporarily store a wedge of sediment upstream and, when the debris breaks or is mobilized, the sediment is released suddenly (Beschta, 1987; Adenlof and Wohl, 1994).

Heterogeneous bedload movement along mountain rivers may also be associated with differing sediment supply developing in response to progressive bed armoring (Gomez, 1983), or associated with hillslope mass movements and/or debris flows along the channel (Hack and Goodlett, 1960; Lisle, 1987; Benda, 1990; Wohl and Pearthree, 1991; Cenderelli and Kite, 1994). Because of the close coupling between hillslope and channel processes, and the difficulty in directly measuring downstream sediment movement over longer time periods, sediment transport and routing for mountain rivers are sometimes estimated using mathematical models that incorporate topography, lithology, climate, and sediment transfer and storage through a series of reservoirs at the drainage-basin scale (Pickup et al., 1983; Kelsey et al., 1986; Lisle, 1987; Mizutani, 1987).

Bedload movement may also vary in a manner analogous to the hysteresis curve commonly used to describe suspended sediment transport during a flood (Schöberl, 1991; Rickenmann, 1994b). Kuhnle (1992a) describes greater bedload transport rates during rising stage and hypothesizes that they may be caused by a lag in the forma-tion and destruction of bedforms and/or the bed pavement relative to flow. Moog and Whiting (1998), in a ten-year study of six gravel-bed mountain rivers in Idaho, USA, also found a hysteresis effect in bedload transport. At a given flow rate, more bedload was carried by discharges preceding the first annual occurrence of a "threshold" rate because readily moved sediment supplies that accumulated in the channels during low-flow periods from late summer to early spring were removed by rising spring-time discharges up to the threshold. The threshold discharge is greater than mean annual discharge and about one-half bankfull discharge.

Hysteresis in bedload transport may also be related to an effect described by Schick et al. (1987a,b). They note that ephemeral desert channels have less well developed coarse surface layers than perennial channels, perhaps because the brief and violent desert floods cause disruption of the coarse surface layer at a rate faster than it can form during the relatively short and less geomorphically effective periods of hydrograph recession. Desert channels with a cobble-pebble-sand size distribution have coarse clasts present in both the surface and subsurface. Tracer particles indicate that these coarse clasts are intermittently buried and re-exposed from one flood to the next in an equilibrium vertical exchange. Clasts which have an inter-event buried phase move significantly farther in their subsequent move than those which do not, suggesting that rising limb bed-scour may be an important control on bedload trans-port rate along some channels.

Bedload transport may also be related to suspended sediment concentrations. Studies of sand moving in suspension and as bedload over an open-work gravel bed indicated that the depositional rate for the sand infilling the gravel was strongly lin-early correlated with the suspended sediment concentration, although turbulent resus-pension of sediment prevented deposition in a surface layer of gravel of thickness approximately equal to the mean grain size of the gravel (Carling, 1984a).

Downstream Bedload Transport Patterns, Rates, and Frequency

In addition to the episodic pulses of bedload movement that have been measured along many different types of mountain rivers, bedload transport may vary downstream because of differential erosion and deposition associated with bedform sequences. Carling and Glaister (1987) and Carling (1990) describe segregation of gravel from sand in the flow separation zone downstream from a negative step or bar-front. Using painted tracer particles in a pool-riffle channel, Petit (1987) and Thompson et al. (1996) both found higher sediment-transport competence in pools than in riffles at high flow. Riffles contained significantly smaller deposited tracer particles than pool centers, pool exit-slopes, and runs (Thompson et al., 1996). Along North St. Vrain Creek, Colorado, riffles provided the most stable high-flow deposi-tional sites for particles 16-90 mm in size; larger particles were usually deposited on runs or pool exit-slopes (Thompson et al., 1996). These grain-size trends reflect hydraulic controls. A central jet of high velocity flow present in the pool during high discharge scours the pool thalweg, leaving only very coarse particles. This jet dissi-pates in upwelling and boil formation at the pool exit-slope, promoting deposition of sediment transported through the pool center. As flow continues beyond the pool into the next downstream riffle, shallower flow depths and high bed roughness further decrease flow competence (Thompson et al., 1996). Riffles and alternate bars are thus sites of sediment deposition during high flows (Andrews and Nelson, 1989; Harvey et al., 1993). During low flows, the steepened water-surface gradients over riffles and bars may promote bar dissection and the removal of finer particles (Harvey et al., 1993), which are then stored in pools until the next high flow (Lisle and Hilton, 1992, 1999). Pool-riffle channels may thus have downstream sorting in sediment size in association with bedforms, causing trends of sediment entrainment and deposition to reverse between high and low flow conditions.

Step-pool channels show similar trends; clasts in the pools have the highest prob-ability of entrainment during the rising limb of floods, and pools are also favored locations for deposition during the falling limb (Whittaker, 1987b; Schmidt and Gintz, 1995). The large, step-forming clasts remain stable except during infrequent (approximately 50 yr recurrence interval) large flows (Grant et al., 1990). Comparing step-pool and pool-riffle reaches of channels in the mountains of Colorado, Ryan (1994a,b) found that pool-riffle channels were partially mobile as the more readily entrained partices (d_{50} = 4-40 mm) moved across a static bed. In contrast, transport was minimal in step-pool channels, where sands and small gravels (d_{50} = 1mm) moved in pulses during the falling limb of the hydrograph. Using magnetic tracer par-ticles along ephemeral channels with pools and alternate bars, Hassan et al. (1991) found that when mean particle travel distance approaches the scale of bar spacing, trapping in the bars interrupts particle movement.

Ergenzinger et al. (1994a) describe similar bedload-channel bed interactions along a channel with pools and alternate bars. Bedload pulses are preferentially gen-erated during smaller floods when sediment that has accumulated in local deposits (bars) is entrained again. Roughness elements that protrude into the flow cause local-ly increasing vertical velocities which in turn drive vortex cells that are important to initiating entrainment from a bar. As the flow cells are enlarged and displaced local-ly, differential erosion, deposition and transport occur across the cross section, and bedload pulses are created and magnified. The probability of a bedload pulse occurring thus depends on the magnitude and duration of discharge, and the organization of secondary flow. As the pulse moves downstream, it is unlikely to maintain a constant volume because of continuing interactions with the flow and channel-bed topography. During large bedload pulses, the vortex cells may be replaced by a more chaotic two-layered flow (Ergenzinger et al., 1994a).

In addition to cross-sectional or reach-scale pulses of bedload movement, large volumes of coarse sediment introduced to a channel from a point source or during a relatively short time interval may move downstream along the drainage basin in discrete waves of bedload. Examples of this phenomenon come from studies of dispersal of mine tailings (Knighton, 1989; James, 1993); sediments contaminated by plutonium released from the nuclear facility at Los Alamos, New Mexico, USA (Graf, 1996); and sediments from hillslopes destabilized by timber harvest and heavy rains in northern California, USA (Wohl et al., 1993; Madej and Ozaki, 1996). The sediment wave may be dispersive or transgressive, and may move passively along a channel or interact with the channel boundaries such that the boundaries are eroded locally (Wathen and Hoey, 1998). Flume experiments indicate that variations in longitudinal slope will initially be the dominant influence on wave evolution, and the sediment wave will decay in amplitude and increase in wavelength without significant migration along the channel (Lisle et al., 1997). After the sediment wave has delayed sufficiently, it may migrate downstream as a persistent and coherent feature. Needham and Hey (1992) describe a one-dimensional, physically-based model developed for predicting the initiation and propagation of bed waves and the associated morphological response of the river.

Bedload transport rates and the distances that bedload clasts are transported vary widely among mountain rivers as a function of channel morphology, grain-size distribution, magnitude and frequency of discharge, and other factors. The bedload transport rates and distances listed in Tables 3.4 and 3.5 commonly include variation at a site of 1-2 orders of magnitude. This variability undoubtedly reflects the complex interactions among the three sets of variables which control bedload movement; channel-bed sedimentology (texture, packing, armoring, bedforms), hydraulics, and grain characteristics (size, shape, density).

Einstein (1937) initiated the use of statistical distributions to describe particle movements along a channel. Subsequent similar studies have used exponential or gamma distributed step lengths, either of which leads to a compound Poisson distribution of total path length during a flood, when each particle may move repeatedly (Hassan et al., 1991; Hassan and Church, 1992). Using several hundred magnetically tagged clasts in two gravel-bed streams in Israel, Hassan et al. (1991) tested the compound Poisson model. They found that the model fits the data relatively well for movement during low flows, when the shear stress is only slightly above the threshold of particle movement and most particles move a relatively small number (1-2) of steps. During high flows most particles move in several distinct phases that are not adequately described by a homogeneous random process, and the measured data differ signifi-

Table 3.4. Bedload transport rates.

Channel type	Gradient	Discharge during sampling (m³/s)	Bedload discharge	Bedload D_{50} (mm)	Source
braided	0.018[1]	3 - 30	8.5-2630 Mg/day	8	Emmett et al., 1996
pool-riffle	0.008-0.033[2]	80 - 164	0.0004-165.9g/ms	> 8	Wilcock et al., 1996a
---	0.0083-0.0108[3]	0.015 - 2.83	0.004-156 g/s	1-4	Williams and Rosgen, 1989
---	0.0163[3]	2.6 - 9.5	0.51-32.1 g/s	1-2	Williams and Rosgen, 1989
---	0.039[3]	0.2 - 1.5	0.29-28.2 g/s	1-4	Williams and Rosgen, 1989
step-pool	0.2[1]	0.15 - 0.3	600-3000 g/s	1-2	Ashida et al., 1976
pool-riffle	0.030-0.035[1]	55 - 300	0.8-11 kg/ms (ch. 19-43 m wide)	80-300	Inbar and Schick, 1979
pool-riffle	0.008[1]	3.70	26.87 kg/min	32	Billi and Tacconi, 1987
pool-riffle	0.6-1.2%[1]	4 - 36	0.09-9.7 kg/s	16-180	Haschenburger and Church, 1998

1. bed gradient; 2. energy gradient; 3. water-surface gradient

Table 3.5. Bedload transport distances.

Channel type	Gradient	Discharge (m³/s)	Flow duration	Mean distance of movement (m)	Grain size (mm)	Drainage area (km²)	Source
step-pool	0.02	3.4-165	0.5-66.8 h	4-451	30-170	---	Gintz et al., 1996
braided	0.018	3-30	6-8 wks	500-2000	90	---	Emmett et al., 1996
pool-riffle	0.007	4.1-11.3	2.5 months	0 to >50	30-100	84	Thompson, 1997
pool-riffle & braided	0.05	0.12-2.75	4 h	15-100	1-80	---	Schick et al., 1982
pool and alternate bars	0.008-0.014	5.7-49.8	hours	11.7-65.3	6-64	---	Hassan et al., 1991
---	0.1		1 yr	30-50	---	23	Nakamura et al., 1987
---	0.08		1 yr	10-20	---	11	Nakamura et al., 1987
---	0.04		1 yr	10-20	---	65	Nakamura et al., 1987
---	0.004		1 yr	105-155	---	1345	Nakamura et al., 1987
---	0.09		1 yr	45-70	---	21	Nakamura et al., 1987
pool and alternate bars	0.008	3-17	7-48 h	100-300	16-128	40	Cencetti et al., 1994
pool-riffle	---	0.1-4	6 days	44-65	100	50	Keller, 1970
pool-riffle	0.02-0.002	5-20	2 yrs	44-191	16-256	---	Ferguson and Wathen, 1998
regime bed (sand)	0.002	97 90	1 yr 1 yr	837 263	18-90	615	Hassan et al., 1999
pool and alternate bars	0.016 0.014	9-50 6-37	hours hours	12-65 14-146	1-100 1-100	250 90	Hassan, 1993

cantly from the fitted curves (Hassan et al., 1991). Carling and Hurley (1987) found a good match between a Poisson distribution and bedload transport during short, discrete flows on two upland streams in the United Kingdom. Ergenzinger and Schmidt (1990) also found that a Poisson distribution best described the travel length of cobbles in a step-pool channel in Bavaria.

The frequency at which clasts of varying size are entrained is of importance when attempting to determine the dominant discharge or the minimum flows required to maintain some aspect of a channel (such as flood conveyance or salmonid spawning habitat). Working on five ephemeral gravel streams with gradients of 0.014-0.030, Begin and Inbar (1984) estimated that frequent flows with a probability of 0.9-0.7 of being equalled or exceeded produced the median grain size (0.1-46 mm) along the channels. Pitlick (1994a) found that flows about 3.5 times the mean annual discharge initiate motion of cobble and gravel bed material along the upper Colorado River, which is close to a threshold between braiding and meandering (S= 0.0015). Flows equivalent to at least a 5-year flood are necessary to create significant movement of the bed material in this system (Pitlick, 1994a). Similarly, a study of 24 non-braided gravel-bed rivers (S = 0.0009-0.026; d_{50} = 23-120 mm) in the Colorado Rocky Mountains found that transport of bed-material particles was a relatively frequent occurrence that began at flows slightly less than bankfull that were equaled or exceeded on average several days each year (Andrews, 1984). A later study on 23 headwater gravel-bed streams in snowmelt-dominated portions of Idaho found that flows between mean annual discharge and bankfull discharge move 57% of the bedload, whereas flows above bankfull discharge move only 37% of the bedload (Whiting et al., 1999). (Bankfull discharge on these rivers has a 2 year recurrence interval.) The bedload effective discharge on these rivers, defined as the discharge that transports more sediment than any other flow over the long term, averages 80% of bankfull discharge, and has an average recurrence interval of 1.4 years. The ratio of effective discharge to bankfull discharge is independent of basin size, grain size, and gradient, but does increase with the relative magnitude of large, infrequent flows (Whiting et al., 1999). Using six years of data from two small upland streams in the United Kingdom, Carling and Hurley (1987) found that 90% of the total bedload was transported by 29% of the floods in one case (drainage area 11.7 km[2]), and 38% of the floods in the other case (drainage area 2.2 km[2]).

In contrast to these findings, long-term research in the small, high-relief catchment of Nahal Yael, Israel has demonstrated that bedload transport along this ephemeral channel occurs primarily during high-magnitude, low-frequency flows (Schick et al., 1982). Studies on a bouldery step-pool subalpine channel have also found that the channel bed remains stable during the peak flow of average years, with only much finer sediment (sand and gravel) mobilized (Adenlof and Wohl, 1994; Blizard and Wohl, 1998). The duration of near-bankfull flows (approximately 1.5 year recurrence interval) correlates well with sand and cobble transport along these snowmelt channels, however (Troendle, 1992).

As might be expected, the frequency of bedload movement will be a function of the ratio between hydrologic driving forces and channel resisting forces. Very coarse grained or poorly sorted mountain rivers may require extreme flows that recur infre-quently before substantial mobilization of the coarsest sediment occurs. A portion of the finer (sand to gravel/cobble) fraction may be mobilized annually, however. Clasts in mountain rivers with more uniform and finer grains (cobble or smaller) may be mobilized annually or every few years.

Issues of bedload transport magnitude and frequency are important in regions such as the Colorado Rocky Mountains, where increasing flow diversions from mountain rivers and flow regulation below dams necessitate definition of flows necessary to main-tain channel conveyance or desirable aspects of aquatic and riparian habitat (Jowett, 1997). Work on the Gunnison River (drainage area 20,534 km^2, S of 0.0019 to 0.0084) in Colorado indicates that monthly mean discharge during the snowmelt season has decreased 63% since the construction of upstream reservoirs in the mid-1960s; bankfull discharge and the 10-year and 25-year floods have decreased to approximately half of pre-reservoir levels (Elliott and Parker, 1992). As a result, bed-material entrainment has decreased. Channel reaches that formerly had periodically entrained coarse beds are now paved and stable, particularly downstream from tributary confluences with periodic sup-plies of coarse debris-flow sediments (Elliott and Parker, 1992). Concerns about main-taining populations of the endangered Colorado squawfish (*Ptcyhocheilus lucius*) along the Yampa River, Colorado led to minimum streamflow hydrograph recommendations for baseflow, rising and recessional limbs, and peak discharge based on field observa-tions and experimental and computer simulations of sediment entrainment and transport (O'Brien, 1987). In this case, the issues of concern were (1) ensuring a relatively sand-free cobble substrate during the summer spawning period, (2) providing backflooded slackwater habitat for juvenile fish, and (3) maintaining the pool-riffle sequence. As water diversions from mountain rivers increase, there will be growing pressure to pre-cisely specify the minimum flow regime required to maintain characteristics such as spawning habitat for squawfish. Such specifications in turn rely on mathematical descriptions of the hydraulic conditions under which bedload transport occurs (e.g. Pitlick and Van Steeter, 1998).

A related concern is that of predicting the likely impacts of climate change on mountain rivers. The EROSLOPE project, for example, evaluates the effects of varying scenarios of climate change by determining probabilities of hillslope and channel-bed erosion in Alpine drainage basins (Ergenzinger, 1994).

Bedload Transport Equations

Several bedload transport equations have been developed from empirical data col-lected on steep, coarse-grained channels. Because these equations are empirical, their applicability is limited to the specific conditions of sediment, hydraulics and channel morphology under which the data were collected. The data from which the equations were developed may also be too limited to adequately characterize the range of bedload transport conditions present at a specific site, or the transport equations may over-sim-plify the variability present in bedload transport. After reviewing several bedload transport equations developed for gravel-bed channels, Carson and Griffiths (1987) conclude that there may be no simple, readily predictable relationship between instantaneous coarse sediment transport rates and channel flow parameters. Limits on sediment supply, bed roughness, hydraulics, and bed-sediment packing and sorting may be so stochastic and site-specific that generalized bedload transport equations never adequately approximate actual bedload movement.

Bedload transport equations tend to focus on grain tractive stress (e.g. Einstein, 1937, 1942; Brown, 1950; Meyer-Peter and Muller, 1948; Baker and Ritter, 1975; Parker et al., 1982); on stream power per unit area (e.g. Bagnold, 1977, 1980); on stream discharge (e.g. Schoklitsch, 1962; Bathurst, 1987a); or on stochastic functions for sediment movement. The Einstein-Brown formula is based on uniform grain size and plane-bed conditions, which are seldom present along mountain rivers. Although the Meyer-Peter and Muller equation does take into account particle roughness, it either grossly underpredicts (if d_{50} for the surface layer is used) or overpredicts (d_{50} for the subsurface layer) relative to actual transport in gravel-bed channels (Parker et al., 1982; Carson and Griffiths, 1987). The Parker formula, developed from the low unit transport rates of the Oak Creek data set, may not apply well to channels with higher transport rates. This equation is based on the assumption that, in gravel-bed streams with pavement, all bedload sizes experience equal mobility beyond a threshold. Bedload relations developed empirically for each of 10 grain-size ranges in the Oak Creek data are collapsed into a single curve described by:

$$W^* = 0.0025^{[14.2(\phi - 1) - 9.28(\phi - 1)]} \tag{31}$$

where W^* is the dimesionless total bedload, defined by

$$W^* = rq_B/[g^{0.5}(HS)^{1.5}] \tag{32}$$

where r is the submerged specific gravity of the sediment, q_B is the volumetric total bedload per unit width of gravel bed, S is the downstream slope of the energy grade line, and

$$\phi_{50} = \tau^*_{50} / \tau^*_{r50} \tag{33}$$

τ^*_{50} is the Shields stress for the median diameter of the subpavement, defined by

$$\tau^*_{50} = \tau / \rho rgd_{50} \text{ (where } d_{50} \text{ is subpavement median grain size)} \tag{34}$$

$$\tau^*_{r50} = 0.0876 \tag{35}$$

This equation is valid only for ϕ_{50} less than 1.65. An extension equation beyond $\phi_{50} = 1.65$ is:

$$W^* = 11.2 [1 - (0.822/\phi_{50})]^{4.5} \tag{36}$$

Dawdy and Wang (1993) note the need for a protocol governing determination of surface and subsurface grain-size distributions, local energy slope, cross section location, and data collection when using this formula.

Although Carson and Griffiths (1987) concluded that the Bagnold equation tends to overpredict transport, Gomez and Church (1989) found that the Bagnold formula was the most successful of 12 sediment transport formulae that they tested against gravel-bed channel data (Table 3.6). The success rate for this formula was 25%, however, and it did contribute a "spectacular failure" (Gomez and Church, 1989).

Studies prior to that of Gomez and Church (1989) compared theoretical and actual results by either (1) plotting calculated bedload discharge versus actual water discharge in a sediment rating curve, and then comparing the rating curve from actual bedload discharge, or (2) using a discrepancy ratio of observed/calculated bedload discharge. Gomez and Church (1989) combine both methods as

$$Y_j = X_j + E + E_j + e_j \qquad (37)$$

where Y = observed bedload, X = calculated bedload, j = a set of values, E = mean bias

Table 3.6. Tests of bedload transport equations against empirical data for mountain rivers.

Equations evaluated (preferred equations in bold)	Reference
Meyer-Peter; Meyer-Peter and Muller; Schoklitsch; Parker; duBoys-Straub, Einstein, Yalin, Ackers, **Bagnold**	Gomez and Church, 1989
Schamov, Schoklitsch; Egiassaroff; Meyer-Peter and Muller; Levi; Smart	Georgiev, 1990
Schoklitsch; Ackers-White; Meyer-Peter and Muller; Smart; Mizuyama; Bagnold	Bathurst et al., 1987
Yalin; Baker-Ritter; Shields	Carling, 1983
Bagnold	Hayward, 1979
Bagnold	Carling, 1989a
Smart	Whittaker, 1987a,b
Einstein-Brown; **Ackers-White**; Smart-Jaeggi; Bagnold; **Schoklitsch (two forms)**	Blizard, 1994
Yang; Meyer-Peter and Muller; **Laursen; Einstein**	Johnejack and Megahan, 1991

of the computational procedure (E = Y(mean) - X(mean)), E_j = the local bias of the procedure for the jth case, and e_j = the random error contributing to empirical variance.

Using this procedure, most of the formulae (Meyer-Peter, Schoklitsch, Meyer-Peter and Muller, Parker, duBoys-Straub, Einstein, Yalin, Ackers, Bagnold) characteristically overpredict, perhaps because they do not account for surface coarsening or variations in sediment supply rate (Gomez and Church, 1989).

Other tests of bedload formulae against data from mountain rivers have favored different equations: Georgiev (1990) favored equations by Schamov and by Schoklitsch (1962); Bathurst et al. (1987) favored Schoklitsch; Carling (1983) favored Yalin (1963); Hayward (1979) favored Bagnold's (1966) concept of stream power and the proportion of stream power utilized in bedload transport; and Carling (1989a) favored Bagnold. The Schoklitsch formula is:

$$q_{sb} = [2.5/(\rho_S/\rho)]S^{1.5} (q - q_c) \tag{38}$$

where q_c is the critical discharge at which bedload transport begins:

$$q_c = 0.26 [(\rho_S/\rho) - 1]^{1.67} \quad (d_{40}^{1.5}/S^{1.17}) \tag{39}$$

For steep channels, Bathurst et al. (1987) modified q_c:

$$q_{*c} = q_c/ (g^{0.5}D_{16}^{1.5}) = 0.21 \ S^{-1.12}, \tag{40}$$

for S = channel slope (0.25-10%).

The great majority of bedload transport equations, even those developed specifically for gravel-bedded or mountain rivers, are not based on data from step-pool channels. Exceptions include equations by Suszka (1991), and the equation of Smart (1984), developed for channels steeper than 5%:

$$q_b = [4/ (s - 1)](d_{90}/d_{30})^{0.2} q_r \ J^{1.6} [1 - (\theta_{cr} (s-1)d_m/y_m J] \tag{41}$$

where q_b = bedload discharge per unit width, q_r = water discharge per unit width, s = relative density of sediment to water, d_m = median grain size, θ_{cr} = critical Shields parameter, J = slope, and y_m = mean flow depth.

Whittaker (1987a,b) has found that this equation best describes sediment transport in supply-limited step-pool systems where sediment moves along the channel in waves not controlled by bed and hydraulic variables. By contrast, Blizard's (1994) comparison of 7 bedload transport formulae (Einstein-Brown, Ackers-White, Smart-Jaeggi, Bagnold, 2 forms of Schoklitsch equation) to data from a subalpine step-pool channel demonstrated that both forms of the Schoklitsch formula and the Ackers-White equation were most successful, although even these tended to overpredict bedload discharge by up to three orders of magnitude. Another comparison of four equations (Yang, Meyer-Peter-Muller, Laursen, and Einstein) to empirical data from step-pool channels in Idaho used an "effective" slope, which removed all vertical drops from the profile and more accurately modeled the energy slope in the pools (Johnejack and Megahan, 1991). Under these conditions, the Laursen and Einstein equations predicted transport within an order of magnitude, but did not adequately predict the gradation of the transported sediment, or the percentages of suspended and bedload. The threshold of incipient motion was not exceeded with the Yang and Meyer-Peter-Muller equations (Johnejack and Megahan, 1991).

The results summarized here support Carson and Griffith's (1987) conclusion that a simple, readily predictable, and widely applicable equation for bedload transport probably cannot be developed. What may be the most efficient approach is to develop a series of equations, with each equation having a narrow range of applicability that is defined by the most important controlling parameters, including channel gradient, relative roughness, grain size distribution (e.g. Armanini, 1992), bedforms present, and velocity distribution. In the absence of such predictive equations, bedload transport is often extrapolated from records of multi-year sediment yield or sediment budgets.

Bedload Yield and Sediment Budgets

Bedload yield may have large seasonal or interannual variations as a result of changes in sediment supply or sediment storage. Sediment supply along mountain rivers is strongly influenced by both drainage basin and channel processes. Drainage basin sediment inputs include hillslope, valley bottom, and tributary channel sources that may be gradual (e.g. slope wash, average tributary inflows, soil creep) or abrupt (e.g. debris flows, rockfalls, tributary flash floods). These inputs may also be seasonally driven (e.g. Wetzel, 1994) or aperiodic. Bogen (1995) noted that one of the primary difficulties when attempting to generalize with respect to processes of erosion and sediment transport in mountain areas is the dominant influence and spatial variability of the bedrock geology and the thickness and nature of the regolith. A typical mountain river is essentially a number of local erosion and sedimentation subsystems (see also chapter 4), and downstream sediment yield records may not accurately characterize the system as a whole (Bogen, 1995).

Studies along the Fall River of Colorado and the Colorado River in the Grand Canyon illustrate how tributary sediment inputs may be re-worked by flow in the main channel. In July 1982 the earthen-fill Lawn Lake Dam in Rocky Mountain National Park, Colorado failed catastrophically. Drainage of 740,000 m^3 of water from Lawn Lake generated a flood that peaked at 500 m^3/s along the steep ($S = 0.10$), narrow Roaring River that drains the lake (Jarrett and Costa, 1986). The floodwaters eroded a large quantity of glacial till from the channel margins of the Roaring River. A fan 17 ha in area and containing 280,000 m^3 of sediment (Blair, 1987) was deposited where the Roaring River joins the meandering Fall River ($S = 0.002$) in a broad glacial valley. During the succeeding years, several investigators studied the resulting pulse of sand and gravel transport along the previously cobble-bedded Fall River. Within a year of the dam failure, large snowmelt floods moved much of the sediment downstream from the junction of the two rivers to an undisturbed, highly sinuous reach about 2 km long on the Fall River (Pitlick and Thorne, 1987). Within this zone, the channel aggraded approximately 0.7 m, to the level of the floodplain. Subsequent lower snowmelt discharges gradually transported sediment downstream such that the upper end of the storage zone was eroded to the pre-flood bed while the downstream end still had abundant flood sediment, producing large spatial variations in bedload transport along the channel (Pitlick and Thorne, 1987).

Debris flows and flash floods along channels tributary to the Colorado River in Grand Canyon repeatedly introduce large volumes (peak discharge averages 100-300 m^3/s) of sediment to the river in the form of debris fans (Melis et al., 1995). These fans constrict the main channel, creating steep rapids. During large discharges on the Colorado River (exceeding approximately 1400 m^3/s) the constriction creates supercritical flow that facilitates erosion of the debris constriction until it is approximately half the upstream width, at which point erosion decreases and the fan becomes fairly stable (Kieffer, 1989). Coarse clasts eroded from the constriction may be deposited 2-3 channel widths downstream, where the high velocity jet through the constriction dissipates (Kieffer, 1987; Kieffer et al., 1989).

The rate of sediment supply from hillslopes to mountain rivers is a function of geology (lithology, structure, tectonics) and climate as these control rates of weathering and erosion. Comparing sediment yields from 21 sites (drainage area 3-75 km^2) in the mountains of central Japan, Mizutani (1987) found that Quaternary volcanic rocks yielded twice as much sediment as intrusive rocks, and ten times the sediment from mixed Paleozoic lithologies. Working on the semiarid Ash Creek drainage basin in Arizona, USA, Harvey et al. (1987) found that differences in weathering characteristics between the granodiorite in the upper basin and granite in the lower basin, combined with a strong elevation-precipitation gradient, resulted in the upper basin producing most of the runoff and the lower basin most of the sediment. A study of twenty mountain streams in central and southern California found that a period of dry climate (1944-1968) had consistently low annual river sediment flux, whereas a subsequent period of wet climate (1969-1999) had a mean annual suspended sediment flux approximately five times greater (Inman and Jenkins, 1999).

Sediment supply to mountain rivers from drainage basin sources differs from this supply to low-gradient alluvial rivers in that the proximity of steep hillslopes to many mountain rivers commonly results in large volumes of coarse-grained sediment being introduced from the hillslope directly into the channel. Ackroyd and Blakely (1984) describe the catastrophic removal of a 600 m^3 sieve deposit along a mountain channel in New Zealand. The deposit had accumulated in the channel from landslides on perched scree fields, and was stable for 30 years until a flood mobilized it, causing bedload transport rates at least four times average transport rates. Mizutani's (1987) study of mountain rivers in central Japan found an inverse correlation between sediment yield and drainage density, suggesting the more efficient transfer of sediment from hillslopes to headwater channels. Also, mountain rivers commonly have a lower ratio of valley-bottom to channel width than lower-gradient rivers. As a result, flood-plains along mountain rivers tend to be poorly developed and to store minimal sediment relative to low-gradient systems. Nakamura et al. (1987, 1995) compared four drainage basins (drainage area of 11 of 1345 km², S of 0.1 to 0.004) in a mountainous area of northern Japan. Using the ages of riparian trees to determine the time of sediment deposition, they found that sediment residence time and average transport distance increase downstream. The upper portions of the catchments had more frequent slope failures and landslides which produced sediment that was quickly transported downstream from the steep, narrow portions of the channels.

In-channel sediment inputs may also contribute to sediment yields. Along mountain rivers these inputs come from bed and bank erosion of storage sites such as riffles and bars (erosion during low flows), and pools (erosion during high flows). The strongest correlation in the Mizutani (1987) study was between sediment yield and channel mean gradient. Because steep channel gradients tend to be associated with direct hillslope sediment inputs, minimal valley-bottom storage, and high values of shear stress and unit stream power, it is difficult to know which factor(s) best explains this correlation. Ultimately, bedload yield reflects the balance between hydraulic driving forces and sediment availability.

Glacial dynamics may strongly influence sediment supply to mountain rivers in alpine glacier basins, as reviewed by Gurnell (1995). The presence of bedrock under a glacier can result in sediment yields that are an order of magnitude lower than for glaciers of similar size underlain by till. The size of the glacier and the volume of discharge strongly control total annual sediment yield for glaciers underlain by sediment, and the level of activity of the glacier influences the amount and timing of sediment yield. Major conduits within the glacier are more stable in their position, and are likely to be associated with lower and less variable production of suspended sediment than are smaller conduits. Transitions among small, linked conduits and major conduits during the ablation season are likely to result in major changes in sediment availability to the changing drainage network. Discussing rivers draining glaciers in the Norwegian mountains, Bogen (1995) notes that the relationship between water discharge and sediment transport is subject to continuous change through the season and from year to year as the subglacial drainage system changes. The weak correlations between water discharge and sediment transport during rising discharges may reflect the erosion of spatially variable sediment sources as subglacial tunnels expand and sediments are entrained from the glacier bed or released by the melting of debris-loaded ice. The stronger correlations during falling discharges may reflect a stronger control by hydraulic variables on the amount of sediment remaining in transport.

Sediment yields from drainage basins with only relict (Pleistocene) glacial deposits may also be influenced by the glacial history. Owens and Slaymaker (1992) found that catchments larger than 1 km² (up to 3 X 10⁴ km²) had higher unit sediment yields than smaller catchments. Sediment yields from the larger catchments are dominated by secondary remobilization of Pleistocene sediments stored along valley bottoms, whereas smaller catchments may still be storing sediment eroded from hillslopes.

Volcanic activity may also strongly influence sediment supply to rivers in some mountainous regions. Nearly twenty years after the 1980 eruption of Mount St. Helens in the Cascade Range of Washington, for example, annual sediment yield below the massive avalanche deposit created by the eruption remained 1-2 orders of magnitude (10^3-10^4 Mg/km^2) greater than pre-eruption yield ($\sim 10^2$ Mg/km^2) (Major et al., 1999). Recovery time and magnitude of increase varied in relation to eruption effect on each drainage basin (eg. lahar deposits versus deforestation from the blast).

Sediment yields reported from mountainous drainage basins around the world vary by four orders of magnitude (Table 3.7) as a result of interactions among the various factors controlling sediment yield. Sediment yield may be highly variable even within a specific region. Spreafico and Lehmann (1994) reported specific sediment yields (m^3/km^2) that varied by three orders of magnitude for a given catchment size in Switzerland. Consistent characteristics, however, are that all rivers with large sediment loads originate in mountains, and that the majority of the sediment load within a river basin will come from the mountainous portion (Milliman and Syvitski, 1992). For example, more than 80% of the sediment load in the Amazon River basin comes from the Andes, which constitute only about 10% of the river basin area (Meade et al., 1985). Although Dedkov and Moszherin (1992) reported the highest suspended sediment yields from glacial and subnival zones in a comparison of 1,872 mountain rivers, climate does not appear to exert an important influence on global sediment yield patterns outside of glaciated regions; equatorial rivers and higher-latitude mountain rivers of similar size do not have significantly different sediment yields (Milliman and Syvitski, 1992). Land use does appear to be important; Milliman and Syvitski attribute high erosion rates in mountainous regions throughout much of southern Asia to poor soil conservation, deforestation, and over-farming. In general, global sediment budgets consistently underestimate sediment fluxes from small mountainous rivers, many of which discharge directly onto active margins (Milliman and Syvitski, 1992).

One of the most commonly used methods of calculating sediment yield for a drainage basin is that of measuring sediment accumulation in natural or artificial reservoirs (e.g. Khosrowshahi, 1990; Fujita et al., 1991; Schick and Lekach, 1993; Valero-Garcés et al., 1999). Lisle and Hilton (1992) describe a more localized, reach-based approach that uses V^* (the fraction of scoured residual pool volume that is filled with sand and fine gravel) as an index of the supply of mobile sediment in a stream channel. Wathen et al. (1997) used magnetic tracer particles to characterize sediment fluxes and quantify storage at the reach scale of a gravel-bed river.

Other methods of estimating sediment yield rely on equations to predict (1) upland sediment supply (e.g. various modifications of the Universal Soil Loss Equation (Wischmeier and Smith, 1978; Renard et al., 1991); the USDA Forest Service's WATSED model (USFS, 1992); EPIC, designed by Klaghofer and Summer (1990) for alpine catchments; (2) bedload transport along the channel (e.g. HEC-6 model (Hydrologic Engineering Center, 1977)); or (3) integrated hillslope-channel processes (e.g. the Stanford Model (Crawford and Lindsley, 1962), the Colorado State Model (Simons et al., 1975; Simons and Li, 1976; Li, 1979), Benda and Dunne, 1997a).

Table 3.7. Sediment yields.

Location	Gradient	Drainage area (km²)	Sediment yield	Timespan	% bedload	Source
Romania	---	5 - 10	> 4,000 m³/km²/yr	20 yrs	---	Ichim and Radoane, 1987
central Japan	0.4 - 0.7	3 - 75	150-10,000 m³/km²/yr	14 yrs	65	Mizutani, 1987
s. Israel	0.05	0.6	40.6 m³/km²/yr	20 yrs	20	Schick and Lekach, 1993
Iran	0.03	691	1320 m³/km²/yr	15 yrs	1-33	Khosrowshahi, 1990
N. Island, New Zealand	0.0009 - 0.008	14 - 6643	50-28,000 t/km²/yr	20 yrs	---	Adams, 1979
Snowy Mts., Australia	---	0.18 - 1098	2.4-213 t/km²/yr	<10 yrs	(susp. only)	Yu and Neil, 1994
Bolivian Andes	---	64 - 59,800	260-11,600 t/km²/yr	3 yrs	---	Guyot et al., 1994
New Zealand	---	122 - 3430	45-8750 t/km²/yr	---	---	Thompson and Adams, 1979
s. Germany	---	0.0002 - 0.021	0.01-78.6 t/ha	2 yrs	2	Wetzel, 1994
Spitsbergen	---	5	24-46 t/km²/yr	2 yrs	---	Barsch et al., 1994a
s. Germany	17%	0.74	815 m³/km²/yr	11 yrs	---	Rickenmann, 1997
	5%	1.38	50	22 yrs	---	
	5%	1.66	83	25 yrs	---	
	11%	0.54	78	51 yrs	10	
w. Canada	---	66,000 - 300,000	106-300 t/km²/yr	---	---	Slaymaker, 1972
	---	780 - 8350	8-382	---	---	
	---	6 - 38	6-1333	---	---	

Table 3.7. Sediment yields (continued)

Location	Gradient	Drainage area (km²)	Sediment yield	Timespan	% bedload	Source
n. California	--	1.74	24-2,074 t/km²/yr	4 yrs	--	Lehre, 1981
glacierized basins, Norway	--	12.5 - 65	263-738 t/km²/yr	2 yrs	30-56	Gurnell, 1987a
glacierized basins, Switzerland	--	4.8 - 80	200-1,770 m³/km²/yr	2 yrs	19-82	Bezinge, 1987
margins of Mediterranean Sea	--	390 - 40,000	260-4200 t/km²/yr	--	--	Woodward, 1995
Philippines	--	19	1.3-40 t/ha	3 yrs	--	White, 1995
	--	2040	4-33 t/ha	3 yrs	--	
Idaho	0.004	381	15.7 t/km²/yr	54 yrs	(bedload only)	Whiting et al., 1999
	0.011	280	2.1 t/km²/yr	9 yrs	"	
	0.010	106	1.3 t/km²/yr	13 yrs	"	
	0.030	46	4.4 t/km²/yr	4 yrs	"	
	0.075	1.3	7.6 t/km²/yr	9 yrs	"	
California	--	281	4.1 t/yr/ha	5 yrs	--	Inman and Jenkins, 1999
		940	10.8 t/yr/ha	5 yrs		
		2640	17.9 t/yr/ha	5 yrs		
		8400	8.3 t/yr/ha	5 yrs		
		10,890	8.9 t/yr/ha	5 yrs		
New Zealand	--	352	17,000 t/km²/yr	--	(susp. only)	Nezat et al., 1999
Yugoslavia	0.032	96	1228-6124 t/yr	10 yrs	(susp. only)	Djorovic, 1992

Short-term (less than 10 years) estimates of sediment yield may also vary great-ly as a function of fluctuations in controlling parameters. Working in the wet tropics of Australia, Yu (1995) found that the 1% of the total rainfall with the highest inten-sity contributed 9% of the transported sediment; for 30% of the total rainfall with the highest intensity, the figure rose to 87% of the transported sediment. Decadal varia-tions in precipitation characteristics can thus greatly influence short-term sediment yields.

Sediment budgets may be developed by identifying and quantifying the sources, storage, and transport of sediment, commonly on an average annual basis. This iden-tification and quantification may use field mapping; aerial photographs; measure-ments of hillslope erosion using sediment fences or erosion pins; mapping and chronology of sediment storage sites; soil isotopic ratios influenced by nuclear weapons tests; naturally occurring radionuclides; or reservoir sedimentation rates (LaMarche, 1968; Caine, 1974; Dietrich and Dunne, 1978; Griffiths, 1980; Lance et al., 1986; Roberts and Church, 1986; Sutherland, 1991; Froehlich and Walling, 1992; Bradley and Williams, 1993; Richards, 1993; Foster et al., 1994; Olley and Murray, 1994; Saynor et al., 1994; Wallbrink et al., 1994; Loughran and Campbell, 1995; Oguchi, 1997b; Hill et al., 1998).

Processes of Deposition

As mentioned in the previous sections, bedload in transport along a mountain river commonly moves in episodic steps when considered at the timescale of an indi-vidual flow, an annual hydrograph, or a longer period of time. Coarse sediment deposits along mountain rivers may take many forms as a function of sediment sup-ply, channel morphology, and hydraulics. Examples include alternate bars, lateral gravel berms, transverse bars, point bars, steps, and lobate deposits across the chan-nel (Cenderelli and Cluer, 1998). Once a bar has been formed, it functions as a sedi-ment storage area and influences local hydraulics and sediment transport (Jaeggi, 1987). The clasts actually creating surface roughness for the bar also influence local depositional patterns. Clifford et al. (1993) proposed that the scale and intensity of turbulence create a turbulence template under which only clasts large enough to tol-erate the local turbulence are deposited.

Studies of coarse-sediment deposition along high-gradient channels have focused on hydraulic thresholds for deposition (Bordas and Silvestrini, 1992). Attention has also been given to the use of depositional patterns to infer flow hydraulics (Elfström, 1987). The locations of coarse-grained deposits may reflect sites of declining or minimum unit stream power during large discharges (O'Connor et al., 1986; Wohl, 1992a; O'Connor, 1993), for example. Differences in morpholog-ic, sedimentologic, and fabric characteristics of deposits may also reflect changes in flow processes along a flood route (Cenderelli, 1998; Cenderelli and Wohl, 1998). Studies focusing on the mechanics of deposition (Ashworth et al., 1992; Ashworth, 1996) have used both field observations and flume experiments, with flume experiments facilitating detailed process observations. In one of the early studies, Lewin (1976) examined re-adjustment of the gravel-bed River Ystwyth, Wales ($S = 0.004$) following artificial straightening in 1969. Primary mid-channel transverse bars formed rapidly at a fairly regular downstream spacing during infrequent high flows. This in turn led to bank erosion, and the primary bars became the cores of point bars, with additional lateral and tail accretion and chute formation, until the channel became sinuous.

Baumgart-Kotarba's (1986) work on the braided Bialka River in the Carpathian Mountains of Poland indicated that channel bars formed only when flow velocity was sufficient to transport cobbles and simultaneously scour the pools. Large discharges (recurrence interval > 4 years) significantly widened the channel and formed new bars, with the major sediment supply for the bars coming from bank undercutting. Coarse clasts deposited at zones of flow divergence formed the nucleus of the bar, which then accreted downstream or laterally with smaller clasts. The dip angles of the clasts on the bars increased with current velocity, and were highest on the distal portions of the bars (Baumgart-Kotarba, 1986). In general, processes of deposition and channel adjustment in braided rivers are among the most difficult to measure and to model because of the huge quantity of field data necessary to describe the distributions of depth, slope, velocity and sediment in these intrinsically variable systems (Davies, 1987), and because of the continual feedbacks and adjustments between channel morphology and sediment movement (Ferguson and Ashworth, 1992; Laronne and Duncan, 1992; Ashworth, 1996).

Flume studies have largely focused on the conditions that initiate and maintain bar formation. Carling's flume studies indicate that clast deposition may be initiated at the sites of energy loss associated with flow transitions such as hydraulic jumps (Carling, 1995) or the shear zone of flow separation (Carling, 1989b). The resultant accretionary gravel and boulder berms take the form of (1) simple berms that consist of a well-defined single curvilinear ridge parallel or oblique to flow; (2) complex berms of one curvilinear ridge with an integral series of lobes or re-curved ridges; and (3) compound berms of two or more independent subparallel berms (Carling, 1989b). These berms minimize energy losses and ensure that high flows are transmitted efficiently through channel transitions.

Iseya et al. (1990) observed lobate coarse clast deposits along the Higashi-Gochi (S of 0.09 to 0.11) tributary of the Oi River, Japan following a flood with a recurrence interval of approximately 30 years. These lobate deposits had a unit of massive coarse clasts overlain by a stratified unit that included layers of open-work, matrix-fill, and matrix-supported clasts. Flume experiments suggested that a high frequency of coarse clasts develops at the downstream end of bedload pulses. These clasts rapidly aggrade along portions of the channel with high grain and form roughness. The later stages of the bedload pulse then aggrade more slowly, allowing stratification and a finer matrix to develop (Iseya et al., 1990). A similar process produced stationary alternate bars that diverted flow across the experimental channel and caused pool scour, leading to alternate sequences of bars and pools (Lisle et al., 1991).

A transverse negative step in the channel bed, such as that present downstream from a bed step, large clast, woody debris, or bar front, creates flow separation in the form of a transverse roller eddy. At the point of flow separation, sand may be carried downstream in suspension trajectories in the main flow, while gravel traveling by rolling or sliding is deposited immediately below the step as the flow separates. The initial gravel deposit has an open-work structure with poorly developed fabric, but increasing volume of deposition creates a depositional slope with grading and a sand matrix. Distinct facies can thus be produced while flow remains steady (Carling and Glaister, 1987; Carling, 1990).

Suspended Sediment

Although more attention has been devoted to bedload processes in mountain rivers, suspended sediment may also exert an important influence on channel processes and morphology, water quality, and the availability of aquatic habitat. The sources and transport of suspended sediment have received some attention, with more attention being given to the effects of fine sediment on aquatic habitat.

Mountain rivers are commonly regarded as having low suspended loads relative to lower gradient channels, although suspended load may exceed bedload along some mountain channels (Barsch et al., 1994a). The high-gradient channels in Williams and Rosgen's (1989) compilation of sediment data for 93 streams in the U.S. had suspended sediment concentrations of 1-2,840 mg/L, although channels affected by the 1980 eruption of Mt. St. Helens had concentrations up to 29,100 mg/L for several years after the blast. By comparison, low-gradient channels listed in this compilation had concentrations of 14 to 15,700 mg/L (Williams and Rosgen, 1989). Worldwide, mountain catchments plot above the mean line on Walling and Kleo's (1979) suspended sediment yield-catchment area graph (Gurnell, 1987b).

Mountain rivers in arid and semiarid regions may carry appreciable suspended sediment (e.g. Barsch et al., 1994b). Lekach and Schick (1982) report concentrations up to 285,800 ppm along Nahal Yael, Israel. The silt-clay fractions of this load are derived by wash from underneath the stony surface layer on the basin slopes, and reach a maximum of 30,000 ppm, beyond which the additional suspended sediment is all sand supplied by the channel.

Mountain river basins subject to recent disturbances may also have a substantial increase in suspended sediment load. During a four-year period following the 1988 forest fire in the Yellowstone region of Wyoming, USA, a headwater catchment experienced suspended sediment increases of up to 473%, whereas lower channel reaches had only 60% increases (Ewing, 1996). These types of increases may be moderated by accumulations of debris on hillslopes and in small channels that form debris dams and trap sediment (Gellis, 1993).

Mountain rivers draining alpine glaciers may also have seasonally high suspended sediment concentrations. Bogen (1995) found that Norwegian proglacial rivers had low concentrations (< 40 mg/L) during early snowmelt, higher concentrations

(50-100 mg/L) as glacier melting progressed, and the highest concentrations (> 500 mg/L) during floods generated by both rain and glacier melting. For the braided channel network downstream from the glacier, suspended sediment concentration depends both on sediment supply from upstream and on the amount of sediment deposited in, or eroded from, the braided river system. The highest concentrations are reached during a rapid increase in water discharge and when discharge during the preceding period is of intermediate size (Bogen, 1980). Swift flow during high discharge restricts sedimentation, as does low sediment supply during low discharge.

In contrast to subglacial suspended sediment supply to basal channels in temperate glaciers, suspended sediment may be acquired principally via subaerial sediment supply to ice-marginal channels at non-temperate glaciers (Hodgkins, 1996). Arctic glaciers may have seasonal trends in diurnal hysteresis between suspended sediment concentration and discharge, with progressive changes from a suspended-sediment-concentration-lead to a suspended-sediment-concentration-lag. The ice-marginal channels have a continuing sediment supply from heavily debris-covered ice-cored moraines, and the hysteresis probably results from a delaying effect, because of sediment circulation in low-velocity water adjoining the channel, which varies with discharge (Hodgkins, 1996).

Work on headwater channels in Japan indicates that suspended sediment concentration may peak before or during peak water discharge, depending on whether the suspended sediment is coming primarily from the channel bed, or from the hillslopes (Kurashige, 1994, 1996). The amount of fine sediment entrained from the channel bed will depend on whether the coarse surface layer remains stable, thus limiting the supply of fines, or the whole bed surface is mobilized so that the greater supply of fine sediment in the subsurface can also be accessed by flow (Diplas and Parker, 1992). Because the sources of suspended sediment may not be uniformly distributed throughout the watershed, predicting suspended sediment in relation to precipitation may be difficult (Banasik and Bley, 1994). The contribution of suspended sediment from specific source areas can be directly measured using traditional field monitoring techniques, or indirectly estimated using models or physical reasoning (He and Owens, 1995). Source areas can also be identified via "fingerprinting" one or more of the diagnostic properties of suspended sediment and potential source materials. Diagnostic properties include sediment mineralogy, color, or chemistry, mineral magnetics, heavy-metal content, or radionuclide activity (^{137}Cs, ^{210}Pb, ^{7}Be, ^{226}Ra) (He and Owens, 1995).

Suspended sediment has been observed to move in clouds or waves. On a proglacial stream in Switzerland, these waves were associated with the progressive encroachment of the stream across its floodplain during glacier melt (Gurnell and Warburton, 1990). On the Torlesse Stream, New Zealand, these waves are of 1-3 hour durations and are related to a sudden influx of sediment into the channel as a result of bank collapse (Hayward, 1979). When suspended sediments are being transported along the Torlesse they may account for up to 90% of the sediment yield, but during most stormflows there are prolonged periods of no suspended sediment transport. As a result, suspended sediment contributes less than 10% of the annual sediment yield from the catchment (Hayward, 1979). Measurements of suspended sediment transported in meltwaters from a Swiss glacier indicated that considerable variations in seasonal and interannual sediment transport result from drainage basin instabilities associated with initiation of the drainage network in spring, from temporary flow constrictions in subglacial channels, and from precipitation-enhanced high discharges (Collins, 1990). Studies on the River Exe in the United Kingdom also support the idea that suspended sediment transport may be more strongly influenced by sediment supply than by transport energy (Walling and Webb, 1987).

As with bedload, actual sampling of suspended load may be problematic. A standard procedure in the United States is to use a DH-48 sampler to obtain samples of the flow that are either point-integrated (sampling at a specific flow depth until the sampler is full) or depth-integrated (lowering and raising the sampler at a constant rate from the flow surface to just above the channel bed) (Leopold et al., 1964). The data for Nahal Yael, Israel come from Hayim 7 multiple stage automatic samplers, which abstract several 1-liter samples during the rising stage of flow (Lekach and Schick, 1982). The filling of a particular container begins when the stage rises to approximately 3 cm above the container's intake, and lasts approximately 1 minute. By arranging several samplers at varying height above the channel bed, point-integrated samples can be obtained for successive stages of the rising limb. Comparing samples collected from the water surface with those collected from close to the bed using a vacuum pump, Carling (1984a) found that the suspended sediment load in shallow rough-bedded streams is fully mixed, with an insignificant depth-dependent concentration gradient. In contrast, narrow and deep streams carry proportionally more suspended sediment close to the bed as discharge increases because the efficiency of turbulent transfer to the surface is reduced.

The effect of high suspended sediment concentrations on flow processes is poorly understood. Vertical velocity and sediment profiles, frictional resistance and sediment transport cannot yet be accurately predicted for high-concentration flows (Bradley and McCutcheon, 1987). When sediment exceeds 20% by volume, standard descriptions such as the log velocity profile for the law of the wall or the Manning resistance equation often do not adequately describe flow conditions (Bradley and McCutcheon, 1987).

The effects of suspended sediment on aquatic habitat commonly become of concern when the supply of suspended sediment to a channel increases to the level that fine sediment deposition alters the grain-size distribution of the channel-bed material. Land-uses such as timber harvest (Corn and Bury, 1989; Madej and Ozaki, 1996), mining (Wagner and LaPerriere, 1985; Van Haveren, 1991), construction (Wolman, 1967; Boon, 1988), agriculture (De Boer, 1997), or grazing (Trimble and Mendel, 1995; Myers and Swanson, 1996a) may result in increased fine sediment entering a mountain river. This may in turn cause infilling of pools (Lisle and Hilton, 1992), or of spawning gravel frameworks (Harvey et al., 1993; Kondolf and Wilcock, 1996; Wilcock et al., 1996b), and consequent loss of aquatic habitat for macroinvertebrates and fish. It may also cause reduction of instream photosynthesis (Cuker et al., 1990), change in nutrient availability (Farnworth et al., 1979), and effect sight feeding, respiration, and orientation of fish (Karr and Schlosser, 1977; ASCE Task Committee, 1992). Most stream organisms can withstand short-term exposure to elevated levels of suspended sediment, but chronic exposure is more detrimental (ASCE Task Committee, 1992).

In summary, the entrainment, transport, and deposition of all grain sizes present along a mountain river are strongly influenced by hillslope processes, and by in-channel interactions between flow and substrate. One aspect of channel substrate that is unique to mountain rivers is the presence of large woody debris. Although large debris accumulations were historically present along many lowland rivers, these accumulations have been removed to a much greater extent than along mountain rivers. In addition, single pieces of debris or very small accumulations can exert a significant control on channel processes along a small headwater channel in which flow is not capable of mobilizing the debris.

Large Woody Debris

Large woody debris (logs, limbs, and rootwads greater than 10 cm in diameter) exerts an important control on channel processes in many mountain rivers. This debris increases boundary roughness and flow resistance; deflects flow toward the channel bed and banks and thus accentuates local boundary erosion; produces a stepped channel profile where single pieces or debris jams span the channel; creates sediment and organic material storage sites and provides cover for fish; and enhances substrate diversity (Keller and Swanson, 1979; Keller and Tally, 1979; Naiman and Sedell, 1979; Harmon et al., 1986; Covich and Crowl, 1990; Montgomery et al., 1996a; Wohl et al., 1997; Buffington and Montgomery, 1999b) (Figure 3.9). Large woody debris (LWD) may reach a specific in-channel site directly from the channel banks and valley walls, or by transport from upstream. The likelihood and importance of transport from upstream increase for higher-order channels, as does the likelihood that LWD will move as individual pieces rather than as debris jams (Baudrick et al., 1997). The relative immobility of LWD in small streams is reflected in the higher proportion of LWD oriented perpendicular to flow in small streams (Bilby and Ward, 1989; Richmond and Fausch, 1995). Much of the movement that does take place in these channels may occur during high discharge years (Lawrence, 1991; Berg et al., 1998). Meleason et al. (1999) developed a computer simulation model of LWD dynamics in small headwater streams of the U.S. Pacific Northwest which reflects these downstream trends. A study of spatial and temporal patterns of LWD retention and transport in first- to seventh-order streams in Oregon indicated that less than 30% of debris volume occurs within the active channel; the majority of LWD is retained along channel margins and floodplains (Gregory, 1991). No more than 10% of the LWD in this study was redistributed in any year, and debris longer than the active channel width rarely moved (Gregory, 1991).

Figure 3.9. (a) Looking downstream to bed-step created by LWD jam along East St. Louis Creek, Colorado, USA. Channel is approximately 4 m wide. (b) Looking upstream in the same reach of East St. Louis Creek. Note the sediment stored at middle left of photograph, above LWD jam.

Total debris loading along a channel reach reflects geology as this controls valley-side slope and the occurrence of mass movements, as well as channel width, discharge, and drainage area (Keller and Tally, 1979; Robison and Beschta, 1990; Rosenfeld, 1998). Small streams tend to have high debris loading because they have narrow valleys, steep side slopes, numerous mass movements, narrow channels, and small upstream drainage areas (Keller and Tally, 1979). Working on a headwater channel in Vermont, Thompson (1995) interpreted the relations among volume of standing timber adjacent to the channel, LWD, and sediment storage behind LWD to indicate that LWD is involved in a negative feedback such that channel degradation leads to increased standing timber recruitment and LWD sediment-storage sites until the channel once again becomes stable.

The majority of LWD research in the United States has been conducted in the Pacific Northwest, where old-growth coniferous forest produces large quantities of LWD that may reside in streams for more than a century (Swanson et al., 1976). High-gradient rivers in this region commonly have sediment stored upstream from the LWD, with plunging flow over the debris and a scour pool at the base (Bilby and Ward, 1989). In this situation, 30-80% of the vertical drop of the stream is influenced by debris (Keller and Swanson, 1979), and much of the stream's energy is dissipated at LWD-created falls and cascades that occupy a fairly small proportion of total channel length (Heede, 1972; Thompson, 1995). In one study using sediment tracer particles on first- and second-order step-pool channels in Idaho, approximately seventy percent of the tracer material remaining in the study reaches was deposited behind LWD jams (Ketcheson and Megahan, 1991). Similar patterns have been noted in headwater channels in Europe (Piégay and Gurnell, 1997).

While LWD is stable, sediment stored in low-velocity zones associated with the debris has a longer residence time than it would likely have in a uniform gradient channel, and the increase in substrate stability and heterogeneity provides more diverse habitat for aquatic organisms (Keller and Swanson, 1979). The LWD itself also provides substrate diversity (Bisson et al., 1987; ASCE Task Committee, 1992), and stores organic matter. A study of mountain rivers in New Hampshire, USA indicated that 75% of the standing stock of organic matter in first-order streams is contained in LWD dams; this drops to 20% in third-order streams (Bilby and Likens, 1980). Experiments with marked woody debris along a second-order channel in Puerto Rico indicated that LWD is commonly associated with debris dams and large amounts of organic litter (Covich and Crowl, 1990). When the LWD breaks or is mobilized, it may release a pulse of sediment that moves downstream to the next depositional site, resulting in bed degradation at the site of LWD removal (Bugosh and Custer, 1989; Adenlof and Wohl, 1994). The stored sediment and LWD may also be periodically flushed from the channel by a debris flow that scours the channel to bedrock (Swanston and Swanson, 1976) and creates a massive debris jam at a lower gradient reach downstream (Kochel et al., 1987). Such jams may effectively trap sediment for decades until the debris decomposes (Keller and Swanson, 1979; Abbe and Montgomery, 1996). By increasing hydraulic roughness, LWD may also promote deposition of finer bed material throughout a channel reach (Buffington and Montgomery, 1999b).

The relative importance of LWD in affecting flow energy dissipation and sediment storage decreases as channel gradient decreases (Keller and Swanson, 1979). LWD is deposited along channel margins in lower gradient, wider streams (Bisson et al., 1987), and associated sediment storage and boundary scour occupy a smaller proportion of the channel (Bilby and Ward, 1989). At the upstream end of a basin, steep, bedrock-confined streams seldom contain appreciable LWD because large pieces remain above the flow and small pieces are rapidly transported downstream (Nakamura and Swanson, 1993).

The pools associated with LWD have received particular attention because of their importance to salmonid fish (Dill et al., 1981; Fausch, 1984; Sullivan et al., 1987). Bisson et al. (1982) described plunge pools, backwater pools, dammed pools, and lateral scour pools associated with either root wads or large debris as being among the types of pools enhanced by LWD. Other studies have indicated that up to 75% of all pools along mountain rivers may be associated with LWD (Robison and Beschta, 1990; Young et al., 1990). Pool volume has been found to be inversely related to stream gradient and directly related to amount of LWD (Carlson et al., 1990). Flume experiments (Beschta, 1983) indicate that, for debris suspended above the streambed (as opposed to buried in the bed), larger diameter pieces create longer and deeper pools. Maximum scour depth and surface area scour occur when LWD is perpendicular to flow (Cherry and Beschta, 1989). Pool area also correlates positively with the debris volume at the pool (Bilby, 1985).

Timber harvest in a mountain drainage basin may impact hillslope water and sediment yield and the supply of LWD to channels (Heede, 1991b). Comparison of logged and unlogged basins in western Washington, USA revealed that although the number of LWD pieces was similar, logged basins had smaller LWD (Ralph et al., 1994). Other studies have shown fewer LWD pieces in logged than in old-growth basins (Murphy and Hall, 1981; Richmond and Fausch, 1995). Numerous studies comparing logged and old-growth basins have consistently demonstrated that channels in logged basins have reduced pool area and depth, and increased riffle area (Murphy and Hall, 1981; Hogan, 1986; Bisson et al., 1987; Ralph et al., 1994; Richmond and Fausch, 1995). During much of the 20th century, LWD has been removed from stream channels to improve flood conveyance, enhance fish passage, or for timber salvage. Rivers from which LWD has been directly removed are less sinuous, wider, shallower, and have less pool volume and overhead cover than comparable undisturbed rivers (Klein et al., 1987; Schmal and Wesche, 1989; Fausch and Northcote, 1992).

Disturbance in the form of forest fire may also affect LWD characteristics. Young (1994) compared adjacent burned and unburned watersheds 2 and 3 years after the 1988 Yellowstone, USA fire. Although the mean diameter of riparian trees was less along the burned channel, the mean diameter of LWD in the channel was greater. LWD in the burned channel was also more mobile (Young, 1994). These comparisons illustrate the control that LWD exerts on hydraulics, sediment transport, and channel stability.

Channel Stability and Downstream Trends

As with beauty, channel stability may be in the eye of the beholder. As first explained by Schumm and Lichty (1965), physical factors that control channel morphology, such as hillslope gradient, may be independent of channel processes at timescales less than a hundred years, but dependent on channel processes at longer timescales. And a channel that appears to be rapidly changing and unstable during a two-year period that includes a large debris flow, may demonstrate quasi-equilibrium when considered over a century. Numerous definitions could be proposed for channel stability as a result of considering differing timespans or differing magnitudes of fluctuation in such channel characteristics as width/depth ratio or bedform configuration. Brunsden and Thornes (1979) defined a transient form ratio,

$$TF = \frac{\text{mean relaxation time}}{\text{mean recurrence time of events,}} \qquad (42)$$

such that TF > 1 for unstable systems with transient forms (that is, because the recurrence interval of events capable of producing change is shorter than the time necessary for the channel to equilibrate, the channel is constantly changing), and TF < 1 for stable channels with characteristic forms (the channel remains fairly constant because the system reaches equilibrium long before the next event capable of producing change; because only very infrequent events are capable of changing channel form; or because frequent, moderate events produce little change). The mean recurrence time of events capable of producing substantial change along mountain channels varies widely as a function of geology, tectonic regime, climate, and land use. Hey (1987) characterized headwater channel reaches, particularly in tectonically active mountain belts, as being inherently unstable relative to lowland rivers or to rivers in tectonically stable or unglaciated regions. In general, debris flows and floods are the primary natural agents of change along mountain rivers.

Debris Flows

Debris flow is used here as a general term for a mass movement of sediment mixed with water and air that flows readily on low slopes (Johnson and Rodine, 1984). This usage of debris flow thus subsumes debris slide, mud flow, mudslide, earth flow, debris torrent, lahar, and several other terms. Debris flows may be triggered by seismic activity; intense or long duration rainfall or snowmelt; rainfall following a forest fire, timber harvest, or road construction; landslides; rapid drainage of a glacial lake or a volcanic crater lake; or the impact of a high-speed stream of water from a cliff or channel knickpoint (the "firehose effect") (Swanston and Swanson, 1976; Innes, 1983; Costa, 1984; Johnson and Rodine, 1984; Weirich, 1987; Wells et al, 1987; Gavrilovic and Matovic, 1991; Jacobson et al., 1993; Inbar et al., 1998). The presence of abundant unconsolidated material, steep slopes, a large but intermittent source of moisture, and sparse vegetation renders many of the world's mountainous regions particularly susceptible to debris flows (Costa, 1984). And progressively smaller and steeper drainage basins have the potential to transport an increasingly larger percentage of sediment by debris flows because of their proportionally larger volume of rainfall or snow, and steeper slopes (Costa, 1984).

Portions of drainage basins that serve as sediment storage sites may be particularly important for debris flow initiation. Several investigators have described this role for zero-order basins or hollows in humid mountain regions (Dietrich and Dunne, 1978; Iida and Okunishi, 1983; Marron, 1985). The underlying bedrock geometry of the hollows conforms fairly closely to the surface topography, with the thickest colluvium in the axis of the hollow (Dengler et al., 1987). The form of the hollow may be a function of the size and durability of boulders supplied to slopes, rather than of the underlying bedrock (Mills, 1989). In the central Appalachians, deep v-shaped hollows are present where smaller boulders may be mobilized by surface water flow. Hollows are shallow and u-shaped where boulders are too large to be mobilized even by floods (Mills, 1989). Colluvium is likely to be saturated in the upper to middle portions of the hollow (Dengler et al., 1987), facilitating failure during precipitation events.

Naef et al. (1990) describe an interesting situation in the Swiss Alps, where retreat of the Pleistocene glaciers left oversteepened and unsupported valley walls that lead to "sackung," the downslope movement of bedrock by slow gravitational collapse. The fissures created during this collapse produce high infiltration and permeability, and large subsurface water storage capacity. These characteristics in turn prevent flooding along rivers draining the region, but may facilitate debris flows (Naef et al., 1990).

Flow conditions may vary among debris flow, hyperconcentrated flows, and water floods both downstream and with time during a flow (Takahashi, 1991b; Cenderelli and Wohl, 1998; O'Connor and Costa, 1993; Walder and O'Connor, 1997; Berti et al., 1999; Cronin et al., 1999). A water flood is a turbulent, Newtonian flow of water which carries relatively small amounts of sediment (1-40% by weight) and has a bulk density in the range of 1.01 to 1.3 g/cm^3 (Costa, 1984). A hyperconcentrated flow is a stream flow enriched with a large amount of sediment (40-70% by weight), and a bulk density of 1.3-1.8 g/cm^3 (Beverage and Culbertson, 1964; Costa, 1984). A debris flow is a flow of sediment and water moving together as a single visco-plastic body that may be up to 90% sediment by weight, with a bulk density of 1.8-2.6 g/cm^3 (Costa, 1984). Bedload transport rate and maximum clast size may increase with increasing fluid density, if the flow around the grains is not laminar (Rickenmann, 1991). Debris flows in particular are notable for being able to transport enormous clasts that may exceed 100 m^3 (Gavrilovic and Matovic, 1991). Differentiation of sediment deposits produced by each of the three types of flow is very difficult, but generally rests on clast fabric (orientation of clast long axis with respect to flow); deposit morphology; and grain-size, sorting and stratification. Of the three flow types, debris flows tend to produce deposits in which the long axes of cobbles and boulders show no preferred orientation, whereas hyperconcentrated and water flows produce deposits in which the clast long-axes dip upstream (Innes, 1983; Waythomas and Jarrett, 1994; Cenderelli and Kite, 1998; Cenderelli and Wohl, 1998). Debris flows commonly have multiple steep-sided lobate boulder deposits and coarse grained, poorly sorted, sharp-crested levees, in contrast to the flat-topped, better sorted boulder berms produced by water floods and hyperconcentrated flows (Sharp, 1942; Costa and Jarrett, 1981). Debris-flow deposits are likely to be matrix supported, with minimal sorting and stratification. Hyperconcentrated flows and water flows in mountainous regions may also produce relatively poorly sorted deposits, but these deposits are more likely to be clast supported and to have some stratification and grading (Blackwelder, 1928; Hooke, 1967; Scott, 1971; Bull, 1977; Janda et al., 1981).

Debris flows may erode steep or confined portions of headwater channels to bedrock (Benda, 1990; Wohl and Pearthree, 1991), removing sediment that had been stored along the channel for decades to millennia. Benda (1990) calculated that debris flows removed an average of 5-10 m^3 of sediment per meter length of channel along headwater streams in western Oregon, USA. Erosion by debris flow in these channel networks continued a short distance into third-order channels. Many headwater channels may be primarily depositional sites between the occurrence of debris flows because the catchment area of these low-order channels is not large enough to generate discharge sufficient to mobilize the large woody debris and coarse clasts introduced to the channel from the surrounding hillslopes. Benda (1990) estimated that 80% of the sediment delivered to first- and second-order channels in western Oregon accumulated during the time between successive scouring debris flows; fluvial transport removed only 20%. Working on mountain channels in Arizona, Wohl and Pearthree (1991) found that 10-year-old debris flow deposits in second-order channels had been very little modified by subsequent water flows. Along channels with more abundant sediment supply and more frequent debris flows, passage of a debris flow may disrupt the stable, coarse surface layer of a channel, initiating channel incision (Zicheng and Jing, 1987), or a complex response of aggradation and degradation (Shimazu and Oguchi, 1996). Occurrence of a debris flow may also alter rainfall-runoff relations for a basin (Agata, 1994).

The geomorphic effectiveness of a debris flow in terms of transporting sediment and altering channel morphology will be a function of debris flow recurrence interval (Table 3.8) in relation to sediment supply. Wohl and Pearthree (1991) describe varying geomorphic effects among several mountain channels in southeastern Arizona, USA that had debris flows following a forest fire in 1988. Channels that had also been subject to debris flows in 1977 showed little change after the 1988 flows, whereas channels that had experienced only water flow for at least several decades prior to 1988 were substantially altered.

Debris flows may deposit substantial volumes of sediment in lower gradient or less confined reaches of a channel (Benda, 1990; Wohl and Pearthree, 1991) (Figure 3.10). They may also be a significant source of coarse clasts to the channel and flood-

Table 3.8. Debris flow recurrence intervals in mountainous regions (after Costa, 1984, Table 3).

Location	Recurrence interval (yrs)	Reference
United States of America		
w. Washington	600 - 800	Crandell, 1971
n. California	1 - 25	Osterkamp et al., 1986
w. Oregon	750 - 1500	Benda and Dunne, 1987
e. California	300 - 350	Beaty, 1990
s. Arizona	500 - 1000	Wohl and Pearthree, 1991
s. California	>300 - 600	Florsheim et al., 1991
n. Arizona	20 - 50	Webb, 1987
New York	10 - 70	Renwick, 1977
Virginia	3,000 - 6,000	Kochel et al., 1982
Colorado	150 - 400	Curry, 1966
Colorado	10	Simons Li & Assoc., 1982
China	$10^1 - 10^2$	Zicheng and Jing, 1987
French Alps	10 - 40	Van Steijn et al., 1988
Norway	50 - 60	Rapp and Strömquist, 1976
Japan	0.2 - 0.4	Okuda, 1978
Japan	300	Iso et al., 1980
Sweden	50 - 400	Rapp and Nyberg, 1981
Lappland	8	Rapp and Strömquist, 1976
Canada	$10^1 - 10^2$	Broscoe and Thomson, 1969
Pakistan	> 30	Wasson, 1978
Canada	15 - 25	Gardner, 1982
Italian Alps	9	Strunk, 1992

Figure 3.10. (a) Junction of a tributary channel with South Fork Ash Creek, Arizona, USA. The tributary had a debris flow about 3 months before the photograph was taken, and the debris flow sediment created a large fan at the junction of the two channels, temporarily damming the South Fork Ash Creek, which flows from left to right. (b) Upper portion of tributary channel, showing scour to bedrock that occurred during the debris flow.

Figure 3.1l. (a) Debris flow scars on debris flow cones, Tatra Mountains, Poland. The debris flow channels are highlighted by snow. (b) Debris flow cone with recent debris flow channel scar at left, Langtang Valley, Himalaya, Nepal.

plain (Rutherfurd et al., 1994). Debris-flow deposition has been predicted as a function of channel slope and tributary junction angle (Benda and Cundy, 1990); past depositional sites; boundary roughness (Mizuyama et al., 1987); grain-size distributions and hydrographs of debris flow and channel (DiSilvio and Peviani, 1991); and the flow hydrograph (yield strength, flow viscosity, discharge) (Whipple, 1992).

Debris flow deposits take the form of debris fans at tributary channel junctions or mountain fronts (Figure 3.11), and levees and terraces along the channel (Osterkamp et al, 1986; Benda, 1990; Hewitt, 1998). The ability of subsequent water flows to re-work the debris flow deposits is directly proportional to drainage area. Larger channels (third-order or higher) may not preserve distinct debris-flow deposits more than a few years after the debris flow, although they may have a non-uniform

Figure 3.11b

longitudinal distribution of coarse clasts as a result of tributary debris flow inputs (Wohl and Pearthree, 1991). These larger channels receive increasingly greater proportions of sediment from debris flows; Benda (1990) estimated that 40% of the sediment delivered to second-order channels came via debris flows (compared to 20% via stream transport), and debris flows delivered 70% of the sediment to third-through fifth-order channels. This debris-flow-delivered sediment causes aggradation at the tributary junctions of the higher channels, with the debris flow deposit subsequently eroding to a boulder lag. Debris flows thus drive cycles of aggradation and degradation along mountain rivers of varying size, with the timespan of the cycle varying at 10^2 to 10^3 years as a function of debris flow recurrence interval and sediment supply (Benda and Dunne, 1987; Bovis and Dagg, 1987; Okunishi et al, 1987; Wieczorek et al., 1989). These cycles of aggradation and degradation in turn control channel and valley-floor geometry, disturbance regime, riparian vegetation structure and composition, and gradient of side slopes and channels (Swanson et al., 1987; Florsheim et al., 1991; Hewitt, 1998).

Channels with periodic debris flow inputs may develop a debris fan or debris cone where the channel flows out from the mountain range (Figure 3.11). These fan-shaped accumulations of poorly-sorted debris have gradients of 12-25° (Brazier and Ballantyne, 1989) and form a continuum with fans containing some fluvial deposits, wholly alluvial fans (Brazier et al, 1988; Harvey, 1992), and paraglacial fans created through the resedimentation of glacial deposits by fluvial and mass movement processes (Ryder, 1971a,b; Owen and Sharma, 1998). Episodic deposition may dominate the morphology and sedimentology of these fans in both humid temperate (Williams and Guy, 1973; Pierson, 1980) and arid and semi-arid regions (Blackwelder, 1928; Hooke, 1967; Beaty, 1990). Fan size and morphology are directly related to drainage-basin climate, lithology, tectonic setting, and sediment supply mechanisms (Bull, 1964; Oguchi and Ohmori, 1994; Whipple and Trayler, 1996; Sorriso-Valvo et al., 1998). Fans with a substantial input from high-sediment-concentration debris flows tend to have a steeper gradient and rougher surface than fans with low-sediment-concentration flows (Hooke and Rohrer, 1979; Beaty, 1989; Whipple and Dunne, 1992; Ikeda et al., 1993). Debris flows are likely to be primarily depositional on fans, whereas water floods may incise fanhead trenches (Beaty, 1990; Scott and Erskine, 1994).

Floods

Gallino and Pierson (1985) describe a landslide on the flank of Mount Hood, Oregon that was transformed rapidly into a debris flow. The debris flow eroded and incorporated large volumes of channel fill as it surged down Polallie Creek, and created a large debris fan that temporarily dammed the East Fork Hood River at the confluence of the two channels. Within 12 minutes, a lake of 104,600 m^3 formed behind and then breached the dam, sending a flood wave down the East Fork Hood River (Gallino and Pierson, 1985). Similar cases of hillslope mass movement temporarily damming a channel and facilitating an outburst flood have been described from British Columbia, Canada (Russell, 1972), and from Japan (Ouchi and Mizuyama, 1989).

The sediment supplied from hillslope mass movements may also strongly influence total sediment load along a channel during a flood (Williams and Guy, 1973; Mizuyama, 1991; DiSilvio, 1994), and the spatial patterns of erosion and deposition along the channel (Jacobson et al., 1993; Miller, 1994; Cenderelli and Kite, 1998). Nolan and Marron (1985) described contrasting channel responses to major storms in two mountainous areas of western California. Channels in northwestern California have pervasive, long-lasting widening and filling of intermediate- and high-order channels during regional storms with recurrence intervals in excess of 50 years. Sediment delivery to these channels by landslides from the structurally weak rock units of the Mesozoic Franciscan assemblage overwhelms transport capacities throughout much of the channel network. Streamside hillslope failures are less common in the Tertiary sedimentary and volcanic units of the Santa Cruz Mountains of west-central California, and channel sediment transport capacity is exceeded only locally during large storms. Widespread bedrock control along the channel banks limits channel widening. As a result, there is only moderate scour in steep low-order channels and moderate fill in high-order channels in the Santa Cruz Mountains (Nolan et al., 1984).

Drainage area and channel gradient, as well as magnitude and frequency of hill-slope failures, will also strongly influence how hillslope sediment affects channel morphology. Debris flows in the central Appalachians during Hurricane Camille in 1969 caused scour in drainage areas less than 1 km^2 and channel gradients steeper than 0.1; mixed erosion and deposition with continuous reworking of the valley floor along streams draining up to 65 km^2; and localized, discontinuous valley-floor reworking along basins larger than 100 km^2 (Miller, 1990a).

Floods along mountain rivers may be generated by various types of rainfall, rain-on-snow, snowmelt, or the failure of either natural or artificial dams. The magnitude-frequency differences between the largest floods and more frequent floods will be a function of the mechanisms that produce the floods. Pitlick (1994b) compared floods in five mountainous regions of the western United States. He found that in semi-arid regions where floods are produced by intense thunderstorms, the 100-year flood may be more than ten times the mean annual flood. For regions where flooding is caused by large-scale frontal storms, the 100-year flood may be three to six times the mean annual flood, and in regions dominated by snowmelt the 100-year flood is less than two times the mean annual flood. Pitlick (1994b) also compared various measures of basin physiography and drainage area, but concluded that variability in precipitation amount and intensity was most important in controlling variation in flood frequency distribution. In glaciated basins, extreme floods can occur when a late afternoon thunderstorm coincides with maximum meltwater from the lower part of a glacier (Gerrard, 1990).

Dam failure may produce a flood peak discharge more than an order of magnitude larger than precipitation-generated floods along a channel. Such a failure may be associated with an artificial dam (Jarrett and Costa, 1986), failure of a caldera lake (Houghton et al., 1987; Waythomas et al., 1996), or a landslide dam (Reneau and Dethier, 1996), but many mountain outburst floods originate from glacier lakes. Thirty-five outburst floods have occurred during the past 200 years in the Karakoram Himalaya (Hewitt, 1982), for example. Approximately 230 supra- or proglacial lakes are present in the Cordillera Blanca of Peru, and a widespread glacier recession beginning in the 1920s initiated a series of damaging floods (Lliboutry et al., 1977). At least eleven outburst floods occurred in the Nepalese and Tibetan Himalaya between 1935 and 1991 (Cenderelli, 1998).

The meltwater that supplies a glacier-outburst flood may be trapped where a glacier occupies the main valley and the tributaries are ice-free, or where a recessional moraine across an alpine valley dams meltwater released as the glacier continues to retreat. Meltwater may also be trapped in the angle between two confluent glaciers; where small lakes develop on the collapsing margin of a retreating glacier; or where water pockets develop within or beneath a glacier (Gerrard, 1990). When the pressure of accumulated water becomes sufficient, the water is released rapidly through or under the ice dam. This is most likely to occur in late summer and autumn.

The Icelandic term jökulhlaup is used to describe the sudden and rapid release of water impounded by, within or under, or on the surface of a glacier. This water can drain through subglacial tunnels, by overtopping the dam at the contact of the valley margin and glacial ice, or by rupture of the ice dam (Costa and Schuster, 1988; Driedger and Fountain, 1989; Walder and Costa, 1996), although subglacial drainage is most common (Walder and Costa, 1996). Once the ponded water begins to drain, energy dissipated by the flowing water melts the ice and enlarges the subglacial channels until the water is drained (Clarke, 1982). The subglacial channels are then blocked by roof collapse or plastic flow of the ice (Björnsson, 1992), allowing the water to accumulate once more. This cycle repeats on an annual or irregular basis as a function of glacier dynamics (Cenderelli, 2000).

Because jökulhlaup discharges are commonly much larger than rainfall- and snowmelt-generated floods occurring in a given drainage basin, jökulhlaups may perform substantial geomorphic work (Post and Mayo, 1971; Hewitt, 1982; Haeberli, 1983). A 1984 jökulhlaup from Ape Lake in British Columbia, Canada widened the alluvial reaches of the upper Noeick River (562 km^2 drainage area) from a preflood average of 75 m to almost 200 m, and caused up to 0.75 m of aggradation along the floodplain (Desloges and Church, 1992). At least nine large, well documented jökulhlaups occurred along mountain channels in western Canada from 1850 to 1997 (Clague and Evans, 1997).

Water ponded behind a moraine dam is catastrophically released only once, in contrast to jökulhlaup floods. Numerous moraine-dammed lakes are present in glaciated mountainous regions because of the retreat of glaciers since the Little Ice Age circa 1500 to 1850 AD (O'Connor and Costa, 1993; Cenderelli, 2000). These moraine dams are prone to failure because their steep, unvegetated slopes are unstable; the dams consist of poorly sorted sediment that may be uncompacted and noncohesive; and the moraine may have only a thin veneer of sediment over a melting ice core (Costa and Schuster, 1988). The dam may overtop and breach, the ice core may melt and collapse, or the dam may be weakened by seepage and piping erosion (Yesenov and Degovets, 1979; Fushimi et al., 1985; Costa and Schuster, 1988). As with jökulhlaups, catastrophic drainage of the ponded water produces a rapid rise in discharge and a flood peak that commonly exceeds those associated with other types of floods in the drainage basin. This in turn may cause substantial geomorphic change along downstream channel segments (Blown and Church, 1985; Vuichard and Zimmermann, 1987).

Outburst floods in mountainous regions commonly also occur from the failure of landslide dams blocking the main valley drainage. If these dams fail, it is usually within one year of formation (Costa and Schuster, 1988). Although seepage may be present, most dams fail from overtopping of impounded water (Costa and Schuster, 1988). The hydrograph of the resulting flood depends on the erosion rate of the breach and the water volume released (Walder and O'Connor, 1997), and is commonly steep and geomorphically effective. Outburst floods from landslide dams have been reported from mountains in many regions, including western Canada (Evans, 1986), south-central China (Tianche et al., 1986), the Karakoram Himalaya (Code and Sirhindi, 1986), the western United States (Gallino and Pierson, 1985; Costa and Schuster, 1988), and the Andes (Snow, 1964).

In general, sediment transport rates may be substantially increased during the years immediately following an outburst flood as sediment deposited along the channel during the waning stages of the flood is re-mobilized by subsequent lower flows and as channel banks eroded during the flood continue to supply sediment after the flood (Bathurst et al., 1990; Bathurst and Ashiq, 1998).

The erosional and depositional features produced by floods along mountain rivers vary widely as a function of flood hydraulics, channel boundary resistance, and sediment supply. Erosional features in cohesive substrates include potholes, longitudinal grooves, pool scour, inner channels, knickpoints, plucking of jointed rock, and flute marks (Baker, 1973, 1988a; Baker and Pickup, 1987; Miller and Parkinson, 1993; Tinkler, 1993; Wohl, 1993, 1998). Erosional features formed in unconsolidated materials take the form of longitudinal grooves, channel widening and incision, stripped floodplains, anastomosing erosion channels, cutoff chutes, and erosion of impinging tributary fans (Stewart and LaMarche, 1968; Baker, 1988a; Miller and Parkinson, 1993). Changes during a single flood may be dramatic, as when the active bed width of the armored Reuss River, Switzerland more than doubled (35 to 75 m) during an August 1987 flood with an estimated recurrence interval between 250 and 700 years (Naef and Bezzola, 1990). Another example comes from the 1996 failure of an artificial dam on the Ha!Ha! River in Quebec, Canada (Lapointe et al., 1998). The resulting peak discharge of 1100 m^3/s was eight times the 100-year flood. More than 9 million cubic meters of sediment were eroded from the river valley, and portions of the channel incised up to 16 m and widened by up to 250 m.

Depositional features associated with floods along mountain rivers include channel gravel bars, gravel splays, gravel and sand sheets, wake deposits, slackwater deposits (Figure 3.12), terrace-like boulder berms, in-channel aggradation, and a change from a single channel to braiding or bifurcating (Scott and Gravlee, 1968; Stewart and LaMarche, 1968; Baker and Kochel, 1988; Miller and Parkinson, 1993; Hasegawa and Mizugaki, 1994; Warburton, 1994; Cenderelli and Cluer, 1998). Describing floods with 50-100 year recurrence intervals in the Italian Alps, DiSilvio (1994) noted that these floods are invariably characterized by high sediment transport and extreme channel aggradation. This aggradation decreases downstream; a July 1987 flood on the Adda River produced up to 4.5 m of bed aggradation in the upper reaches (bed slope 1.2%, bed width 30 m), and 1.5 m of aggradation in the lower reaches (bed slope 0.25%, bed width 90 m). DiSilvio found that in-channel flood aggradation was most serious in channels with bed slopes between 2% and 0.2%.

In many of the world's mountainous regions, high-magnitude low-frequency floods may be the dominant geomorphic events because only these floods generate the high driving forces necessary to alter the resistant channel boundaries of mountain rivers. Wolman and Miller (1960) defined dominant discharge as the flow which transports the most sediment. Using suspended-load gaging station records from rivers throughout the United States (drainage areas of 358,500 to 26 km^2), they interpreted the dominant discharge to be relatively frequent (approximately 1-2 year recurrence interval) flow of moderate magnitude for most streams. Wolman and

Figure 3.12. Interbedded tributary channel gravels and fine-grained slackwater sediment back-flooded from the main channel, mouth of channel tributary to the Verde River, Arizona, USA. Dark circle at center of photograph is 35-mm camera lens cap for scale.

Gerson (1978) expanded the concept of geomorphic work and dominant discharge to geomorphic effectiveness, defined as the modification of channel morphology. They noted that a flood could significantly alter channel and floodplain morphology without transporting extremely large quantities of suspended sediment, and they emphasized that effectiveness also depended on the rate of recovery of channel morphology to the form that prevails between successive floods, versus flood recurrence interval. Subsequent studies in a wide variety of geomorphic settings have sought to delineate the conditions under which either extreme or relatively frequent floods dominate channel morphology. Kochel (1988) summarized the drainage basin factors (basin morphometry, climate, lithology) and channel factors (sediment load, channel boundary material) that control channel and floodplain response to large-magnitude floods. Many mountain channels have the characteristics of high relief, thin soils, sparse vegetation, hillslope failures, coarse bedload, high channel gradient, flashy hydrograph, and resistant channel boundaries which, using Kochel's (1988) criteria, lead to major geomorphic response to large floods. Support for the idea that extreme floods are geomorphically more important in highland than in lowland channels comes from several studies comparing highland and lowland channel responses to floods (Froehlich and Starkel, 1987; Gupta, 1988; Patton, 1988b; Miller, 1990a; Grant and Swanson, 1995).

De Jong's (1994) study of flood features in the Schmiedlaine catchment (Bavarian Alps) illustrates the controls on the localized geomorphic effectiveness of floods. Extreme floods (150 year recurrence interval) along the Schmiedlaine reorganize the channel and deposit the largest scale features, such as megaclusters, step-pool sequences and log jams. The persistence of these features is controlled by position along the channel. Those at the apex of a bend are likely to remain unaltered, whereas those at the entrance or exit to a bend are more likely to be re-worked by normal flood flows (de Jong, 1994).

What becomes clear when reviewing these studies is that the geomorphic influence of a given flood on a mountain channel will be largely a function of the balance between flood driving forces and channel-boundary resisting forces (Baker, 1977, 1988a; Pitlick, 1988; Miller, 1990b). This balance may vary rapidly with time and along the channel because of variations in (1) flood hydraulics resulting from the flood hydrograph at a site, downstream changes in flood discharge, or channel morphology in terms of width/depth ratio and gradient (Miller, 1994), and (2) channel-boundary resistance as a function of bedrock characteristics and exposure, and sediment characteristics, storage, and supply (Scott and Gravlee, 1968; Froehlich and Starkel, 1987; Harvey et al., 1987; Warburton, 1994; Miller, 1995). Bull (1979, 1988) emphasized the importance of thresholds between driving and resisting forces in controlling channel aggradation versus degradation at a site. An example comes from a study of glacier-lake outburst floods (GLOFs) along mountain rivers in the Khumbu Himal region of Nepal (Cenderelli, 1998; Wohl et al., in press; Cenderelli and Wohl, 1998). Wider, lower gradient channel reaches (w of 150 to 200 m, $S = 0.046$) had abundant deposition during a 1985 GLOF, whereas narrow, steeper channel reaches (w of 15 to 60 m, $S = 0.074$) with channel boundaries formed in glaciofluvial outwash had extensive erosion. Narrow, steep channel reaches formed in bedrock had minimal channel change during the flood because of the much greater channel-boundary resistance. Similar patterns of channel change on steep rivers during large floods have been described from the Colorado Front Range (Shroba et al., 1979; Jarrett and Costa, 1986), the southern Appalachian Mountains (Miller and Parkinson, 1993), the Klamath Mountains of northern California (Stewart and LaMarche, 1968), and the Alps of southern Germany (Schmidt, 1994).

Several authors have proposed unit stream power thresholds for substantial channel modification during floods. Magilligan (1992) used data from five floods on low gradient, alluvial channels to identify a minimum threshold of 300 W/m^2 for substantial erosional modification. Working on a steeper, confined channel, Lapointe et al. (1998) also identified a 300 W/m^2 threshold for major scouring of the alluvial valley bottom. Summarizing flood data from six canyon rivers, Wohl et al. (in press) proposed a lower threshold value for substantial flood modification (erosion or deposition) of channel boundaries in the form

$$y = 21 \ x^{0.36} \tag{43}$$

where y is stream power per unit area (W/m^2) and x is drainage area (km^2).

The specific channel morphology produced during flooding will also depend on antecedent conditions, and on the magnitude of the flood relative to earlier floods. Thompson (1987) described an upland channel in the United Kingdom that had alternated during the preceding 150 years between meandering and braided as a function of the magnitude and frequency of flooding. A series of moderate floods produced gradual change as processes of bar dissection and channel division led to braiding. Periods of more frequent and severe flooding produced a meandering planform. Upland channels in northwestern England have been categorized as stable, sinuous channels in areas of low sediment supply, and unstable, braided channels in catchments of high sediment input (Harvey, 1987). In contrast to the example from Thompson (1987), a 1982 storm with a return period in excess of 100 years produced massive erosion and sediment input that caused two of the stable channels to become braided (Harvey, 1987). Returning to the 1985 glacier-lake outburst flood in the Khumbu Himal, the geomorphic effects of the flood decreased dramatically downstream. This resulted from a combination of (a) peak discharge attenuation with distance from the damburst source (from approximately 2300 m^3/s at 7 km downstream, to 1400 m^3/s at 27 km downstream), (b) a decreasing ratio of outburst-flood peak discharge to seasonal snowmelt peak discharge (ratio of 60 at 7 km, to 6 at 27 km), and (c) the passage of a comparably-sized glacier outburst flood down the lower channel reaches in 1977 (Cenderelli, 1998).

The concept of channel stability, as applied to mountain rivers, is largely a function of the magnitude of channel change caused by debris flows and large floods, and the frequency of these events, in relation to channel change that occurs between successive events. A channel may be largely unchanging or stable between disturbances when considered at graded or steady time spans, with either a steady-state or a very gradual trend of aggradation or degradation (TF < 1). The higher the channel boundary resistance, and the more extensive the bedrock or very coarse substrate controls on width/depth ratio and gradient, the more likely the channel is to have stable patterns of erosion, deposition, and channel morphology, and to be substantially altered only by infrequent events. Alternatively, a channel may continually alternate between differing morphologies and rates of sediment transport because of frequent disturbances (TF > 1) (Figure 3.13a). This situation could also be described as one in which a threshold of channel operation is frequently crossed.

Bull (1979) expressed the threshold of critical stream power as a ratio between driving and resisting forces that governs whether a channel will be aggrading or degrading.

A

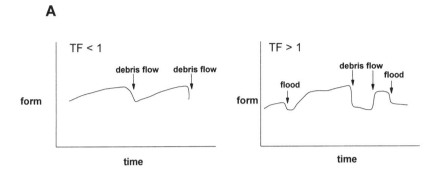

(A) Transient form ratio applied to channel-bed elevation and considered during graded or steady time. For TF < 1, sediment gradually accumulates along channel and bed aggrades to constant level until infrequent debris flow strips channel to bedrock. For TF > 1, channel-bed elevation and material are continually changing as floods and debris flows alternately erode and deposit sediment along channel. (After Brunsden and Thornes, 1979).

B

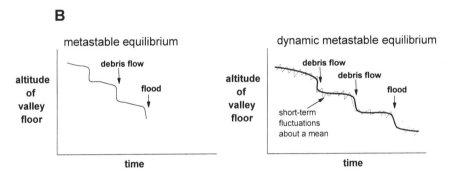

(B) When considered over cyclic time, the channel-bed has net degradation, with most of the work being accomplished during infrequent debris flows and floods. (After Chorley and Kennedy, 1971; Schumm, 1977).

Figure 3.13. Schematic representation of channel stability and instability. (a) Transient form ratio applied to channel-bed elevation and considered during graded or steady time. For TF < 1, sediment gradually accumulates along channel and bed aggrades to constant level until infrequent debris flow strips channel to bedrock. For TF > 1, channel-bed elevation and material are continually changing as floods and debris flows alternately erode and deposit sediment along channel. (After Brunsden and Thornes, 1979). (b) When considered over cyclic time, the channel-bed has net degradation, with most of the work being accomplished during infrequent debris flows and floods. (After Chorley and Kennedy, 1971; Schumm, 1977).

For the scenario of TF > 1 in Figure 3.13a, the first debris flow strips the channel to bedrock, creating a very efficient conveyance system that continues to transport sediment out of the channel reach, increasing degradation. In this case the erosion accompanying the debris flow has caused the channel to cross a threshold from aggradation to degradation. The second debris flow deposits sufficient sediment along the channel to increase boundary roughness and decrease channel conveyance, and causes the channel to cross another threshold from progressive degradation before the debris flow to progressive aggradation after the debris flow. This is an example of Schumm's (1973) extrinsic threshold, or a channel response driven by an external influence.

Schumm (1973) also describes intrinsic thresholds inherent in the operation of a system. Intrinsic thresholds have been described for the operation of steep arid or semiarid drainages where localized deposition over a period of time may result from downstream loss of transport capacity because of evaporation and infiltration. Eventually the valley-floor becomes over-steepened and the channel incises, even though the water and sediment yields from the basin side slopes have not changed (Schumm and Parker, 1973; Patton and Schumm, 1975; Womack and Schumm, 1977).

Depending on the time interval of observation, a channel undergoing complex response could be described as stable or unstable. Of course, when considered over the longer timespan of cyclic time, the channel will be steadily eroding. At this timescale, a mountain river dominated by infrequent floods or debris flows may be best represented as having metastable or dynamic metastable equilibrium (Chorley and Kennedy, 1971; Schumm, 1977; Figure 3.13b). The crossing of either an extrinsic or intrinsic threshold may also trigger the type of complex response whereby channel behavior alternates between aggradation and degradation both downstream and with time. And finally, lag times up to tens of thousands of years may produce long-term trends in channel stability. As a result, any attempt to describe channel stability must be strictly defined with respect to temporal and spatial scales, and the magnitude of channel change or variability (e.g. Ritter et al., 1999). Within these constraints, individual mountain channels may unstably alternate between aggradation and degradation at a timescale of decades (e.g. Froehlich et al., 1990), or have a transient form ratio less than 1 at a similar timescale (e.g. Harvey et al., 1979; Nakamura and Swanson, 1993).

The balance among driving forces, resisting forces, and sediment supply, and the consequent stability of a channel, has predictable downstream trends. Channel morphology and sediment transport along steep, headwater channels are more likely to be largely controlled by debris flows and floods (Seidl and Dietrich, 1992; Shimazu, 1994). As channel gradient decreases and width/depth ratio and valley-bottom width increase downstream, the magnitude of change caused by extreme events relative to changes induced by moderate events decreases, and frequently recurring fluvial processes become more effective at modifying debris flow and extreme flood features (Heede, 1981; Patton, 1988b; Wohl and Pearthree, 1991; Miller and Parkinson, 1993). These changes are commonly associated with a decrease in the portion of bed roughness caused by individual clasts or large woody debris; a decrease in very localized turbulence and an increase in larger-scale persistent secondary flow such as eddies; a decrease in stream power per unit area and an increase in total stream power; an increase in bed sediment mobility and consequently channel responsiveness to varying flow conditions; an increase in width/depth ratio; and a decrease in channel and valley-bottom gradient. These downstream trends in physical channel characteristics partly control downstream trends in channel morphology (chapter 4) and in aquatic and riparian biota (chapter 5).

Summary

The hydrologic regime of a mountain catchment may be dominated by runoff from glacier melt, snowmelt, rain-on-snow, rainfall, or some combination of these processes. Runoff-generating mechanisms commonly change with elevation, so that drainage area-discharge relations are unlikely to be linear in mountain regions. Runoff is generally strongly seasonal and spatially variable at scales from a single hillslope to an entire drainage basin.

Discharge records tend to be sparse for mountain rivers. Floods along these systems may be brief, unsteady, and debris-charged, and critical and supercritical flow are more common than along low gradient channels. These conditions may make indirect discharge estimation difficult and relatively inaccurate. Despite these limitations, historical, botanical, paleocompetence, paleohydraulic, and paleostage records have all proven useful in supplementing systematic discharge records in mountain regions.

Mountain channels characteristically have steep gradients, large grain and form roughness, and highly turbulent flow with non-logarithmic velocity profiles. Research efforts have focused on: (1) trying to predict resistance coefficients as a function of gradient, relative submergence, flow depth, particle size distribution, or some other parameter; (2) quantifying the contributions of grain and form roughness; and (3) characterizing the distributions of velocity, lift force, bed shear, and unit stream power. Several methods have been developed for estimating the resistance coefficient, although these are mostly not designed specifically for steep channels. At present, no consensus exists on the method most applicable to mountain rivers. The relative importance of different sources of roughness changes throughout a drainage network (eg. grain roughness may be more important in the headwater channels, form roughness becomes more important downstream), and with channel type (eg. grain roughness may dominate boulder bed channels, whereas form roughness dominates gravel bed channels). Although vertical velocity distributions commonly do not approximate a logarithmic curve, both velocity profiles and mechanisms of turbulence generation vary widely as a function of boundary roughness. Bed shear stress has proven difficult to measure, and there is no consensus on the best method of measurement. Most investigators use temporally and spatially averaged conditions or probability distributions to characterize bed shear.

The grain size distribution of the channel bed may be characterized by bulk sampling or, most commonly, by in situ clast measurements. Several methods have been used for the latter, but these do not necessarily produce consistent results. The channel bed of mountain rivers commonly has a coarse surface layer which may be either mobile or static. There is no consensus at present on how this layer develops, at least in part because mechanisms of formation and maintenance probably vary throughout a channel network and with time.

Clast entrainment is commonly characterized by physically based stochastic models that treat velocity fluctuations and variations in grain size and pivoting angle. The alternative models of equal mobility and selective entrainment both seem to apply as a function of differing conditions of discharge and sediment supply, and as a function of differing locations within a catchment.

Very few good datasets of bedload transport exist for mountain rivers. Bedload transport consistently demonstrates high spatial and temporal variability, and this has been attributed to progressive bed armoring, heterogeneity of bed structure and associated hydraulics, the sediment storage associated with LWD, the migration of bedforms, and other factors. Bedload transport equations focus on grain tractive stress, unit stream power, discharge, or stochastic functions for sediment movement. Although many equations have been developed, no single equation has been found to consistently outperform the others when applied to mountain rivers. It will probably be most effective to develop several different equations, each of which applies to a specific channel type and sediment supply. At present, a compound Poisson distribution of total path length seems to best approximate bedload transport along coarse-grained channels.

Coarse sediment may enter mountain rivers directly from adjacent hillslopes, and there is relatively little storage of sediment along valley bottoms. Sediment yields vary by four orders of magnitude among mountain drainages, but are consistently higher than yields from lowland drainages. Sediment production and yield in a mountain catchment may be strongly influenced by climate, tectonics, lithology, contemporary glacial processes, or the legacy of Pleistocene glaciation. Suspended sediment loads from mountain rivers tend to be relatively low except in arid or glaciated catchments, or following a disturbance such as a volcanic eruption or forest fire.

Large woody debris exerts a significant influence on many mountain rivers. LWD alters boundary roughness and flow resistance, promotes localized scour, creates bed steps in higher gradient channels and islands or bars in lower gradient channels, stores sediment and organic material, and increases substrate and habitat diversity. Single, largely immobile pieces of LWD in headwater channels give way to greater LWD mobility and the creation of debris jams downstream.

Channel stability along mountain rivers is largely a function of the magnitude and frequency of debris flows and floods. Because these extreme flows can more effectively overcome the high boundary resistance of mountain channels, erosional and depositional features created by these flows tend to dominate channel and valley morphology. Debris flow recurrence intervals vary widely in mountain catchments, from less than one year to more than 5,000 years, as a function of climate, lithology, and tectonics. Floods may result from precipitation or from dam failure. The geomorphic importance of any debris flow or flood will be influenced by the ratio of hydraulic driving forces to substrate resisting forces, by antecedent conditions, and by the magnitude of the flow relative to the magnitude of earlier flows.

4

CHANNEL MORPHOLOGY

Morphologic Variability

The morphology of an ideal alluvial channel flowing across a homogeneous, weakly resistant substrate would reflect only the hydraulic and sediment transport processes occurring within the channel. This is what Leopold and Langbein (1962) described as a channel that is the author of its own geometry. In practice, most alluvial channels are subject to some morphologic constraint in the form of differing substrate resistance or tectonic movement (Ouchi, 1985; Schumm, 1986). However, alluvial channels do tend toward the smoothly concave upward longitudinal profile characteristic of a graded stream (Mackin, 1948). Mountain rivers, in contrast, are likely to have strongly segmented longitudinal profiles that may be straight or convex upward, as well as concave (see also chapter 3). These profile characteristics may result from one or more of the following controls.

(1) The stream power in the headwater portion of a drainage is low relative to substrate resistance, and the channel is unable to incise at a rate equal to tectonic uplift (Merritts and Vincent, 1989).

(2) In a bedrock-dominated system, lithologic and structural variations downstream may strongly influence substrate resistance and sediment supply. The Poudre River, Colorado provides an example of structural controls. Where the channel follows the course of a Precambrian shear zone, the river valley is broad (300-500 m) and lower in gradient (0.014). The valley is much narrower (50-100 m) and steeper (0.028) where the channel moves away from the shear zone (Figure 4.1). As another example, Harden's (1990) work on incised meanders on the Colorado Plateau (USA) indicated that channel gradient, channel cross-sectional shape, and bend symmetry correlated strongly with bedrock type.

(3) The glacial or climatic history of a region may have produced downstream variability in sediment supply to the channel, thus affecting channel morphology differently along a downstream gradient. Glaciated drainages, in particular, may have channel gradients that are independent of both discharge and drainage area (Day, 1972; Ferguson and Ashworth, 1991). For example, the terminal moraine of late-Pleistocene glaciation in the Poudre River valley effectively created a local baselevel. The 10 km of valley upstream from the moraine are filled with finer-grained alluvium, creating a 0.2% gradient along which the Poudre River meanders. The valley segments immediately up- and downstream have a steep, narrow, coarser-grained morphology (Figure 4.2). Phillips and Harlin (1984)

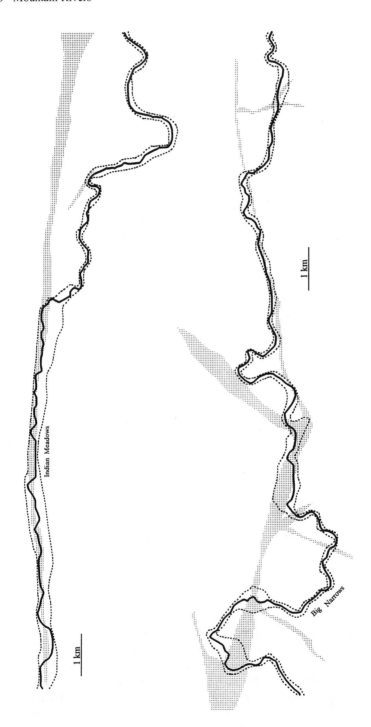

Figure 4.1.   Plan view of portions of the Poudre River in the Colorado Front Range. Solid line denotes the path of the river, dashed lines are the edges of the valley bottom, shaded areas represent a Precambrian-age shear zone. The river valley is most narrow and sinuous where it diverges from the shear zone.

Figure 4.2. View upstream along the Poudre River at the Big Narrows reach; channel is approximately 15 m wide and closely constrained by bedrock valley walls.

describe appreciable variations in downstream hydraulic geometry exponents for a subalpine stream where it crosses a meadow occupying a former lake bed in the Sangre de Cristo Mountains of southern Colorado, USA. Another example of downstream variability in the effects of climate change on mountain rivers comes from Bull's (1991) work in the New Zealand Alps. An increase in temperature and precipitation would result in a decrease of hillslope sediment yield for portions of the drainage basin below 1200 m in elevation, because of an increase in soil thickness and vegetation density. Above 1200 m elevation (above present treeline), the same climatic change would result in an increase in erosion, decreased soil thickness, and an increase in sediment yield (see also chapter 2).

(4) Bedrock-dominated channels in a variety of tectonic, lithologic, and climatic environments tend to have downstream alternations between relatively steep, narrow reaches and lower gradient, wider reaches. This characteristic, which has been noted for channels with a catchment less than 1 km², to major river systems draining tens of thousands of square kilometers, apparently is not controlled by systematic variations in lithology or structure (Wohl, 1998). Because most mountain valleys are bedrock-dominated, valley and channel morphology may be expected to vary substantially and abruptly downstream, regardless of lithology, tectonic regime, and climate history.

(5) Other factors such as human land use, forest fires, floods, and mass movements may also affect sediment supply and thus channel morphology. Wohl and Pearthree (1991) described a progression in channel morphology following forest fires and debris flows in the Huachuca Mountains, Arizona, USA. Debris flows stripped the steeper portions of ephemeral tributary channels to bedrock, creating a trapezoidal channel that then gradually filled with sediment during the next few decades until it became a vegetated swale. The tributary debris flows caused local aggradation and non-uniform distribution of coarse sediments in the perennial main channels, with the effects becoming less pronounced with distance downstream from the tributary, and with time. The details of channel morphology along any given reach of these mountain channels would thus partly reflect the recent history of forest fires and debris flows. Ryan and Grant (1991) found a 30-fold increase in open riparian canopies on low-order tributaries of the Elk River basin, Oregon between 1956 and 1979. These openings were caused by hillslope mass movements associated with clearcuts and roads. Channel response to the increased sediment supply included formation of gravel bars, bed and bank erosion, and loss of LWD. Hewitt (1998) describes "naturally fragmented river systems" in the Karakoram Himalaya where rockslide barriers have created alternating gorges and aggraded valley reaches at a scale of tens of kilometers along each river.

One of the primary characteristics of mountain channel morphology is thus pronounced and abrupt variations in gradient, valley width, channel pattern, and grain size as these reflect substrate resistance and climatic and tectonic history. Wider valley segments are likely to have a lower gradient channel formed in coarse alluvium, whereas narrower valley segments are likely to have a steep bedrock channel. These steep, narrow channel reaches limit the response of intervening alluvial reaches to base level lowering or decreased sediment supply. The erosional resistance of the bedrock reaches allows these reaches to act as local baselevels that limit incision of upstream alluvial reaches.

In contrast to this spatial variability, mountain channels in many regions of the world maintain relatively stable channel morphologies through time. Because of the high channel-boundary resistance, only extreme and relatively infrequent events substantially alter the channel boundaries. Following these extreme events, the channel may again be stable for decades to centuries (see also chapter 3). For example, a 1985 glacier-lake outburst flood along the Langmoche Khola in the Nepalese Himalaya eroded approximately 2,600,000 m³ of sediment, including boulders up to 2.7 m in diameter, from 26 km of a valley that ranged from 10 m to 200 m wide (Vuichard and Zimmermann, 1987). Doing field work in the region 10 years later, Cenderelli and Wohl (1998) observed that the longitudinal boulder bars created by the 1985 flood remained in pristine condition, with no re-working of clasts by subsequent flows. Flows following the 1985 flood had incised a channel approximately 10 m wide and 2 m deep into the outburst-flood deposits, which spread across a valley that was more than 100 m wide at some locations. Another example comes from Kite and Linton's (1993) study of the 1985 flood on the Cheat River in West Virginia (USA). This flood was the only event during at least a century capable of transporting the large boulders that strongly influence channel morphology along the Cheat Narrows and Cheat Canyon.

Proglacial and other braided mountain channels provide an exception to the general rule of stability between extreme events. These braided channels commonly change substantially during the summer melt season or between years in response to fluctuations in glacier mass balance (Fenn and Gurnell, 1987; Gregory, 1987), or to fluctuations in sediment yield from adjoining hillslopes.

The temporal variability of mountain channel morphology will be a function of disturbance frequency. In some regions, channel morphology may essentially be relict from Pleistocene deglaciation. Some investigators have argued, for example, that the coarse clasts forming step-pool sequences along alpine and subalpine channels of the Colorado Rocky Mountains can no longer be mobilized by lower, post-glacial discharges (Gordon, 1995). Larger channels at lower elevations in this same region may have much shorter recurrence intervals for substantial disturbance. The 1976 flood along the Big Thompson River in the Colorado Rocky Mountains created dramatic erosional and depositional features in the coarse-grained alluvium overlying the resistant bedrock substrate (Figure 4.3). Channel reaches steeper than 2% gradient generally were scoured, especially on the outsides of bends and where the channel was constricted. Deposition occurred along reaches of channel with a gradient less than 2%; boulders as large as 3.6 m in diameter were moved (Shroba et al., 1979). Floods of similar magnitude occurred in this region in 1864, 1935, and 1965. Starkel's (1972) description of the geomorphic effects from a flood produced by intense rainfall in the Darjeeling Himalaya provides another example of frequently disturbed channels. Widespread slope failures contributed massive amounts of coarse sediment to the rivers, and even small channels carried boulders 3-5 m in diameter. Headwater channels were deepened up to 2-3 m in bedrock, and channel width increased greatly. Starkel (1972) estimates a recurrence interval of 20-25 years for such events in the Darjeeling Himalaya.

The nature of channel adjustment to an abrupt disturbance or to a prolonged change in water and sediment yield will depend on the magnitude and duration of the external change, and on the channel boundary resistance. Very rapid adjustments may occur in the channel width/depth ratio or bed configuration, whereas changes in chan-

Figure 4.3. (a) Aerial view of July 1976 flood deposition around houses along the margin of the Big Thompson River, Colorado. Photograph courtesy of Stanley A. Schumm. (b) Aerial view of July 1976 flood erosion of road crossing along Big Thompson River. Photograph courtesy of Stanley A. Schumm.

nel planform and reach or basin gradient occur over decades or longer (Knighton, 1984). As the grain size of the channel substrate decreases downstream, boundary resistance decreases and channel width/depth ratio and bedforms become more responsive to short-term changes in controlling variables. This is well illustrated by comparing the response of step-pool versus pool-riffle channels to flow diversion, for example (Ryan, 1994b).

Channel Classification Systems

Channel classification may be particularly challenging for mountain rivers because of the pronounced spatial variability in morphology. There are numerous channel classification systems that may be at least partially applicable to mountain channels. At the drainage basin scale, channels may be classified in terms of (1) sequence with respect to structure (consequent, subsequent, resequent, etc); (2) sequence with respect to time (superimposed, antecedent; see Powell, 1875, 1876) and evolution (youthful, mature, old; see Davis, 1899); (3) spatial pattern (dendritic, radial, rectangular, etc; see Howard, 1967); or (4) hierarchy within a stream ordering

Figure 4.3 (b)

network. This last method is commonly used today. Following the stream-order system of Strahler (1952), a first-order channel has no tributaries, and two equal-order channels must join to create the next highest order. Channels are most commonly interpreted from dashed or solid blue lines on topographic maps, although they may also be defined in terms of the degree of contour crenulation.

Mountain channels are also commonly classified at the reach scale, where a reach is defined as a segment of uniform channel morphology that is at least several channel widths in length. Reach classifications may be based on hydrology, channel planform, bedforms, or some combination of these characteristics (Table 4.1). Mountain channels most commonly fall into the step-pool, plane-bed, or pool-riffle categories of Montgomery and Buffington (1997), or into one of the bedrock cate-

Table 4.1. Examples of reach-scale channel classification systems applicable to mountain rivers.

Basis of system	Types of channels and description of system	Reference
Hydrology	Ephemeral -- temporally discontinuous flow Intermittent -- spatially discontinuous flow Perennial -- continuous flow	
Hydrology	Losing stream -- infiltration to subsurface Gaining stream -- infiltration from subsurface	
Hydrology	Snowmelt dominated -- annual peak flow produced primarily by snowmelt Glacier-melt dominated -- annual peak flow produced by melting of glacier ice Rainfall dominated (subdivided based on type of rainfall) Rain-on-snow	
Channel planform	Straight -- sinuosity < 1.5, commonly have wandering thalweg, pool-riffle sequences Meandering -- sinuosity > 1.5 Braided -- channel divided around alluvial bars and islands	Leopold and Wolman, 1957
Bedforms	Cascade -- longitudinal and laterally disorganized bed material; high gradient Step-pool -- discrete channel-spanning accumulations of steps separated by pools Plane bed -- lack well-defined bedforms; long stretches of relatively planar channel bed Pool-riffle -- undulating bed defines sequence of bars, pools and riffles Dune ripple -- variety of mobile bedforms provide primary flow resistance	Montgomery and Buffington, 1997
Sediment transport and channel stability	Suspended load -- 85-100% suspended load, 30-100% silt-clay in channel perimeter (M) Mixed load -- 65-85% suspended load, 8-30% M Bedload -- 30-65% suspended load, 0-8% M Stable Depositing Eroding	Schumm, 1963a
Combined characteristics	Seven channel types (A-G) based on gradient, bankfull width to depth ratio, and entrenchment ratio Bedrock channel reaches classified on single vs. multiple flow path, sinuous vs. non-sinuous planform, uniform vs. variable bed gradient, and uniform vs. variable across cross section 42 channel types based on 3 levels of information: degree of hillslope interaction with channel as defined by (1) channel gradient vs. 1/factor of safety or 5.0 valley-side gradient, (2) channel width vs. valley width, and (3) medium sediment size vs. average channel depth times channel gradient -- the idea is to categorize process domains 5 channel types as a combination of sediment transport, channel pattern, and relative stability	Rosgen, 1994 Wohl, 1998 Whiting and Bradley, 1993 Schumm, 1981

gories of Wohl (1998, 1999). Montgomery et al. (1996a) note that the occurrence of bedrock and alluvial channels can be described by a threshold model relating local sediment transport capacity to sediment supply. Valley-spanning logjams may create alluvial channels in what would otherwise be bedrock reaches.

The next three sections focus on three types of reach-scale channel morphology that commonly occur in a downstream progression. The bedforms most characteristic of these channel morphologies are part of a continuum from disorganized large clasts to regularly spaced pools and riffles. This continuum reflects downstream changes in channel gradient, grain size/substrate, and the expenditure of flow energy. The presence of specific bedforms and channel morphologies may thus be used to infer reach-scale stability and response to disturbance.

Step-Pool Channels

Step-pool channels are characterized by a regular downstream alternation between steps composed of clasts, large woody debris, and/or bedrock, and plunge pools that form at the base of each step (Figure 4.4) (Chin, 1989). Hayward (1980) distinguished among boulder steps composed of a group of boulders arranged in a straight or curved line across the channel; riffle steps formed by a collection of larger-than-average clasts that steepen the channel, and occur at slopes less than 0.05; and rock steps where the channel is confined by bedrock. To these may be added debris steps of large woody debris (pieces longer than 1 m and wider than 10 cm). Step geometry is commonly defined in terms of step height and step spacing. Although relatively little attention has been given to pools in step-pool sequences, these features can be described similarly to pools occurring in pool-riffle sequences, using residual pool volume, pool infill ratio, and simple length and depth measurements (Figure 4.5).

Step-pool sequences have been described for various lithologies, in climatic regimes from cold temperate (Grant et al., 1990) to hyperarid (Wohl and Grodek, 1994), and at step spacings from tens of centimeters (Abrahams et al., 1995) to tens of meters (Bowman, 1977). Wohl (1992b) proposed that alternating steep and gentle gradient channel reaches at a scale of hundreds of meters may be large-scale step-pool sequences. Montgomery and Buffington (1997) noted that step-pool sequences are most common at reach gradients of 0.03 to 0.10.

Most studies of step-pool channels have sought correlations between step characteristics and the potential control variables of reach-scale gradient, discharge, and sediment supply and grain size. Step-pool channels are commonly hypothesized to indicate a supply-limited system (Whittaker, 1987b), and are most common along reaches where relatively immobile coarse clasts or large woody debris can trap sediment in a wedge that tapers upstream. Flow plunging over the immobile obstacle scours a pool at the obstacle's base, creating a step-pool sequence. Laboratory experiments with a poorly sorted mobile gravel bed have demonstrated that steps may originate as antidunes (Whittaker and Jaeggi, 1982; Ashida et al., 1984; Grant and Mizuyama, 1991; Grant, 1994; Hasegawa and Kanbayashi, 1996; Parker, 1996). In

Figure 4.4. View upstream of step-pool bedform sequence along a small mountain river in northwestern Montana, USA. Channel is approximately 5 m wide.

these experiments, larger particles that came to rest under the crests of standing waves trapped other smaller particles and created a step of imbricated grains. On the other hand, studies of steps formed by coarse clasts along ephemeral tributaries with flows insufficient to submerge the clasts (Wohl and Grodek, 1994), and steps formed in bedrock (Duckson and Duckson, 1995), suggest that other mechanisms may also operate in step formation. Chin (1999a) suggests that, although field data on Froude number, flow depth, and step wavelength from the Santa Monica Mountains, California are consistent with the antidune origin of step-pool formation, true antidunes may be difficult to maintain in steep headwaters where large, less mobile roughness elements may disturb the regularity of flow and sediment transport.

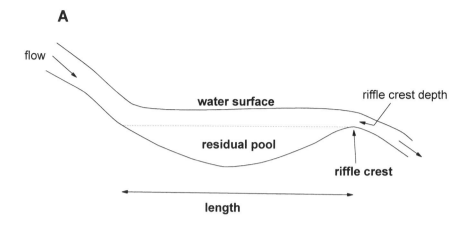

A

flow

water surface

riffle crest depth

residual pool

riffle crest

length

B

water surface

water depth

buried armor layer

fine sediment
depth

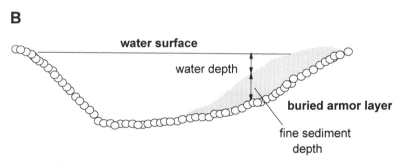

Figure 4.5. Definition of pool geometry measurements. (a) Longitudinal view of pool, show-ing pool residual depth as defined by the depth of water remaining in the pool if flow in the channel ceased. (b) Cross sectional view of pool, showing pool infill ratio, as defined by the depth of fine sediment overlying the buried armor layer in the pool. Both views after Hilton and Lisle, 1993, Figure 1.

Grant et al. (1990) suggest that flows of a magnitude sufficient to form steps have a recurrence interval on the order of 50 years in the western Cascade Mountains of Oregon. In contrast, studies of a small (6.5 km²) basin in the Japanese Alps indicated that debris flows that occurred approximately once each year thoroughly destroyed the exist-ing channel and deposited extensive sediment to create a uniform channel-bed gradient (Sawada et al., 1983). Subsequent water flows re-created a step-pool sequence nearly identical to that existing prior to the debris flow and as the bed once again became armored, sediment transport decreased substantially until passage of the next debris flow. Studies on the Lainbach River, Germany indicate that minor floods, with a discharge less than 10 m³/s (average discharge is approximately 2 m³/s) maintain the step-pool system (Ergenzinger, 1992). During an extreme flood of 200 m³/s in 1990 the channel rapidly changed from step-pool to braided, but subsequently resumed a step-pool morphology.

In general, the mobility of steps is a function of particle size (Chin, 1998), as well as hydrologic regime in the channel. Steps tend to be stable when considered at small temporal and spatial scales, so that the steps function as independent variables that dissipate stream energy and regulate channel hydraulics (Chin, 1998). At larger scales, steps become dependent variables that reflect changes in water and sediment discharge.

Several studies have demonstrated a consistent correlation between step spacing and height, and channel gradient (Heede, 1981; Whittaker, 1987b; Wohl and Grodek, 1994). Channel gradient is interpreted as an indicator of rate of flow energy expenditure. Step characteristics in relation to gradient do not differ significantly between substrate types along channels with mixed alluvial and large woody debris steps (Wohl et al., 1997), mixed alluvial and bedrock steps (Grodek et al., 1994; Wohl and Grodek, 1994), and mixed lithology bedrock steps (Duckson and Duckson, 1995), suggesting that flow energy expenditure strongly controls step characteristics. Chin (1999b) interprets step geometry to reflect a mutual adjustment between flow, sediment, and energy conditions, with particle size as the direct control on step height, and discharge as the primary control on step wavelength.

Step characteristics represent a means of adjusting boundary roughness, and step-pool bedforms appear to evolve toward a condition of maximum flow resistance because maximum resistance implies maximum stability (Abrahams et al., 1995). In a series of flume experiments, Abrahams et al. (1995) demonstrated that maximum flow resistance occurs when steps are regularly spaced and have a ratio of mean step height:mean step length:channel slope between 1 and 2, a condition observed along many natural step-pool channels. These authors also noted that their results were inconsistent with the antidune model of step formation because the Froude numbers at which flow resistance was maximized are well below those values usually associated with antidunes.

Little is known of the hydraulics and sediment transport of step-pool channels relative to pool-riffle channels. Working with rigid, concrete stepped chutes and spillways, Chanson (1994, 1995) described nappe flow and skimming flow. Nappe flow consists of a succession of free falls at low discharges, with the free-falling jet followed by a hydraulic jump at the downstream end of the step tread. With increasing flow rates or decreasing step length, the hydraulic jump disappears and a skimming flow regime develops. In skimming flow the water flows as a coherent stream, with recirculating vortices occurring at the base of each step riser (Chanson, 1996). Egashira and Ashida (1991) noted that the rate of energy dissipation in this separation zone downstream from the step crest plays an important role in flow resistance. In natural channels the occurrence of nappe vs. skimming flow would presumably be influenced by the more irregular step geometry associated with plunge pool erosion (Abrahams et al., 1995). It may be that step geometry is partly controlled by the presence of step-forming clasts large enough to withstand the erosional energy of hydraulic jumps present during nappe flow except during the largest discharges.

Working on a step-pool channel in Bavaria, Stüve (1990) found that energy loss and roughness were extremely variable between successive cross sections at low discharges. As discharge increased, there was a tendency toward more uniform energy loss between cross sections.

Wohl and Thompson (2000) measured velocity profiles and velocity fluctuations over steps and pools throughout the snowmelt hydrograph. They found that flow became more turbulent (as judged by coefficient of variation of velocity) as stage increased, particularly at lower-gradient reaches with less variable bed roughness. Flow also became more turbulent as gradient increased, and as bed roughness increased. Velocity profiles suggest that pools immediately downstream from steps have wake turbulence from mid-profile shear layers. Locations immediately upstream from steps, at step lips, and in runs are dominated by bed-generated turbulence. Adverse pressure gradients upstream and downstream from steps may be enhancing turbulence generation, whereas favorable pressure gradients at steps are suppressing turbulence (see also chapter 3). The wake-generated turbulence leads to higher energy dissipation in step-pool reaches relative to more uniform-gradient reaches.

Field studies using tracer particles indicate that particle shape, size, and position on the channel bed influence transport frequency and length for bedload along step-pool channels. Elongated pebbles have longer transport distances than platy (disc) shaped particles (Schmidt and Ergenzinger, 1992; Moore and Diplas, 1994). Shear forces dominate erosion when the particle is exposed, but lift force becomes much more important when the particle is level with neighboring particles (Ergenzinger and de Jong, 1994). Particles located in pools are much more likely to be entrained and will be transported longer distances than those on steps or riffles (Schmidt and Ergenzinger, 1992). Sediment transport is episodic during a flood, with alternating transport steps and non-movement intervals (Schmidt and Ergenzinger, 1992). Attempts to predict sediment transport along step-pool channels using some of the standard sediment relations developed for coarse sediments and steep gradients (e.g. Ackers-White, Bagnold, Einstein-Brown, Schoklitsch, Smart-Jaeggi) indicated that these relations tended to overpredict actual measured bedload transport by more than three orders of magnitude (Blizard, 1994; see discussion, chapter 3). Actual bedload transport is highly temporally and spatially variable. Although bedload discharge may correlate with hydraulic variables in these channels, bedload movement is strongly influenced by such factors as woody debris location and stability, and by local bed gradient and step height and spacing (Adenlof and Wohl, 1994; Busskamp, 1994; Trayler, 1997; Blizard and Wohl, 1998; Trayler and Wohl, 2000).

Montgomery and Buffington (1997) characterize step-pool sequences as transport reaches that are relatively insensitive to changes in water and sediment yield caused by human activities. Examining the effect of flow diversion on mountain streams in Colorado, Ryan (1994b, 1997) found no change in the width of step-pool channels after 20-100 years of flow diversion, in contrast to the 30-50% decrease in width of similar pool-riffle channels. Madsen's (1995) assessment of channel response to increases in water and sediment yield associated with timber harvest in northwestern Montana indicated that step-pool channels were much less sensitive than pool-riffle channels. The only response of the step-pool channels was a fining of pool particle sizes with increased sediment yield. This was in contrast to the pool-riffle channels in the study, which served as response reaches (Montgomery and Buffington, 1997) in which substantial channel change was observed.

Plane-Bed Channels

Plane-bed channels lack the well-defined, rhythmically-occurring bedforms that characterize both step-pool and pool-riffle channels (Montgomery and Buffington, 1997). Plane-bed channels, which are most common at channel gradients of 0.01 to 0.03, may have a surface layer of coarse clasts, or may be formed on bedrock. Long stretches of relatively planar channel bed may be punctuated by occasional channel-spanning rapids (Figure 4.6). These channels lie at the boundary of Montgomery and Buffington's (1997) transport and response reaches, and may function as either sources or storage sites for sediment as water/sediment ratios change. Although the characteristics of plane-bed channels indicate supply-limited conditions during most discharges, correlation of bedload transport rate and discharge during higher flows that mobilize the bed (Jackson and Beschta, 1982; Sidle, 1988) suggests that during high discharge these channels are transport-limited. The presence of sufficient large woody debris may increase flow convergence and divergence to the level that pool scour and bar deposition transform the channel to a forced pool-riffle morphology (Montgomery and Buffington, 1997).

Pool-Riffle Channels

Keller and Melhorn (1978) published one of the early systematic examinations of pool-riffle channel morphology and the processes which create and maintain this morphology. They described pools and riffles as meandering in the vertical dimension, produced by the occurrence of regularly spaced deeps (pools) with intervening shallows (riffles), and noted that these features are found in both bedrock and alluvial channels. The regular spacing of pools has been related to channel width (Keller and Melhorn, 1978) and to channel gradient (Wohl et al., 1993), although variability of channel-boundary resistance associated with bedrock (Roy and Abrahams, 1980), large woody debris (Montgomery et al., 1995), or other obstructions (Lisle, 1986) may also influence pool spacing. The regularity of pool spacing along channels has led several investigators to interpret the undulating bed topography of pools and riffles as a means of regulating flow energy dissipation, and specifically of maintaining quasi-equilibrium (Dolling, 1968); minimizing potential energy loss per unit mass of water (Yang, 1971); or minimizing power expenditure (Cherkauer, 1973).

Gilbert (1914) and Keller (1971) proposed the velocity-reversal hypothesis to explain the maintenance of pool-riffle sequences. Using field data, Keller noted that as discharge increases, the near-bed velocity in a pool increases more rapidly than the velocity in an adjacent riffle. Keller hypothesized that the flow in pools might be more competent at high stage than the flow over riffles, thus explaining the common

Figure 4.6. View upstream along plane-bed channel formed on cobble substrate of small mountain river in northwestern Montana. Channel is approximately 10 m wide.

observation that pools scour at high flow and fill at low flow, whereas riffles are depositional sites at high flow and scour at low flow (e.g. Jackson and Beschta, 1982; Campbell and Sidle, 1985; Thompson, 1994; Sear, 1996; Thompson et al., 1996). Keller's (1971) data did not actually demonstrate a velocity reversal, however. Subsequent investigators proposed that velocity might instead become nearly equal at high flows (Richards, 1976; Carling, 1991); that shear stresses might vary differentially with discharge although a velocity reversal was unlikely (Teleki, 1972; Bhowmik and Demissie, 1982); that shear stress (Dolling, 1968) or unit stream power (O'Connor et al., 1986) in pools might exceed that over riffles because of greater depth; or that a competence reversal might occur in pools that are hydraulically rougher than riffles (Carling and Wood, 1994). Others (Andrews, 1979; Lisle, 1979; Keller and Florsheim, 1993) argued that velocity-reversal did indeed occur. Velocity profiles along a pool-riffle sequence indicated that the differences in near-bed velocities between pools and riffles decrease as discharge increases, suggesting a velocity reversal at or near bankfull flow (Robert, 1998).

Much of the uncertainty over the existence of a pool-riffle velocity reversal has been generated by the assumption that, to convey the same discharge at high flows, a lower velocity over a riffle must be compensated by a change in cross-sectional area, presumably by an increase in width (Richards, 1978). This assumption relied on cross-sectionally averaged velocity. Thompson (1994, 1997; Thompson et al., 1998, 1999) demonstrated that the presence of strong eddy flow along the margins of pools during high discharges permits the formation of a central jet of high velocity flow that does in fact exhibit velocity reversal with respect to riffle velocity.

Several investigators (Lisle, 1986; Clifford, 1993b; Smith and Beschta, 1994) have proposed that the vortex shedding associated with the channel constriction commonly present near the head of a pool is capable of substantially altering sediment-transport patterns. Pool formation has been attributed to vortex scour (Matthes, 1947; Lisle, 1986; Clifford, 1993b; Smith and Beschta, 1994), and the deepest parts of pools are often found immediately downstream from constrictions where vortex flow is strongest (Lisle, 1986; Clifford, 1993b; Thompson, 1997). Sediment deposition at the downstream end of pools has also been related to boil formation (Matthes, 1947; Lisle, 1986; Lisle and Hilton, 1992) and to deposition in recirculating-eddy systems (Kieffer, 1987; Schmidt, 1990; O'Connor, 1993; Carling et al., 1994; Thompson, 1994; Cluer, 1995).

Clifford (1993a) proposed that a velocity reversal was not necessary to explain pool and riffle formation and maintenance if riffles and pools are undulating components of a single coarse-grained bedform unit. In this case, pool-riffle sequences may result from kinematic waves (Langbein and Leopold, 1968) which in return require systematic spatial variation in clast arrival and departure probabilities capable of maintaining an undulating bed. Clifford (1993a) used field data to support the idea that such variation arose from (1) spatial differences in the structural arrangement of surface sediments (specifically, more microtopographic structuring on riffles than in pools), and (2) differences in the behavior of the turbulent velocity/stress field at riffles and at pools (greater turbulent kinetic energy over riffles for most of the flow range). The whole pool-riffle sequence could be initiated with the generation of roller eddies upstream and downstream from a major flow obstacle such as a very large clast, with the obstacle then being removed as part of the process of bed scour (Clifford, 1993b). Local scour of the pool creates deposition downstream, which then generates the next-downstream flow irregularity.

Lisle (1986), Wohl et al. (1993), and Thompson et al. (1996) proposed similar conceptual models for the initiation of pool scour, but emphasized the role of lateral constrictions rather than bed obstacles. Lisle (1986) presented the following equation for predicting the minimum width of an obstruction that will form a pool:

$$B = W_b - W_s \sec \beta - L_s \sin \beta \tag{1}$$

where B is width of obstruction (m), W_b is bed width of approach channel (m), W_s is width of scour hole measured perpendicular to the axis of the scour hole at the widest point of obstruction (m), L_s is length of scour hole (m), and β is the deflection angle of flow (degrees). Constrictions affecting 33-50% of the approaching flow tended to form pools, whereas small constrictions formed only local scour holes (Lisle, 1986).

Pool geometry along coarse-grained channels with lateral constrictions demonstrates consistent trends (Thompson and Hoffman, 1999). Pool depth is significantly correlated with average channel width, the pool expansion ratio (ratio of constriction width to downstream width), and the constriction gradient. Pool length correlates with average channel width and channel gradient, and the gradient of the pool exit-slope correlates with the constriction gradient and the total drainage area.

Sites of coarse sediment input have also been used to explain riffle locations (Webb et al., 1987; Wohl et al., 1993), and pools have been correlated with sites of lower boundary resistance along bedrock channels (Dolan et al., 1978). The fairly regular downstream spacing of pools and riffles suggests that whether obstacles, variability in boundary resistance, or coarse sediment input will initiate formation of a pool or a riffle is partly dependent on flow energy and on rates of energy expenditure.

Pool spacing in forested mountain drainage basins in Alaska and Washington depends on large woody debris loading and channel type, slope, and width (Montgomery et al., 1995). Mean pool spacing in pool-riffle channels with low LWD loading averages 2-4 channel widths, implying that channel morphology is very sensitive to the presence of LWD and other obstructions (Smith et al, 1993). Plane-bed channels with similar LWD loading have pools at 9-13 channel widths. Forced pool-riffle channels, which have higher LWD loading, have pools spaced less than 2 channel widths, and gradients that overlap pool-riffle and plane-bed channel types. In all channel types, however, less than 40% of LWD causes the formation of a pool. Montgomery et al. (1995) concluded that channel width strongly influences pool spacing in streams with similar LWD loading, but high LWD loading is likely to decrease pool spacing.

Attention has also been devoted to identifying and classifying pools and riffles. Criteria that have been proposed for distinguishing between pools and riffles include bed material size (Leopold et al., 1964); water surface slope (Yang, 1971); and the index v^2/d, where v is mean flow velocity and d is mean flow depth (Wolman, 1955). Because these criteria may depend on discharge or the history of previous discharge, other investigators (Richards, 1976; O'Neill and Abrahams, 1984; Takahashi, 1990) proposed using bed topography.

Pools may be subdivided on the basis of the primary erosional and depositional processes which create them (Bisson et al., 1982). Plunge pools form by scour associated with flow plunging vertically over an obstacle. Dammed pools form when debris spanning a channel ponds water upstream. A root wad protruding into the flow or large woody debris that directs the current along its length may form a lateral scour pool. A backwater or eddy pool can be formed by an eddy behind debris and other structures located at the channel margin (Bisson et al., 1982). Each of these types of pools has different patterns of flow, and sediment and nutrient retention.

Montgomery and Buffington (1997) characterized pool-riffle sequences as response reaches which exhibit channel change in response to changes in water and sediment discharges. Madsen (1995) found that increases in water yield associated with timber harvest in northwestern Montana caused bank erosion, sediment deposition, and substrate fining. In-channel scour triggered in part by increased peak flows appeared to be an important source of sediment in these channels. Ryan (1994b, 1997) found that flow diversions resulted in channel narrowing by 30-50% along pool-riffle channels in the mountains of Colorado.

Several studies (Lisle, 1982; Wohl et al., 1993; Madej and Ozaki, 1996; Wohl and Cenderelli, 2000) have demonstrated that a large increase in sediment load along a pool-riffle channel will cause preferential filling of the pools, effectively creating a more uniform reach gradient and flow depth. Lisle (1982) explained this response as leading to an increase in the effectiveness of moderate discharges (less than 2 year recurrence interval) to transport bedload and shape the bed because of a reduction in channel form roughness. As the excess sediment is removed from the channel reach, the pool-riffle sequence gradually re-forms. The proportion of V* residual pool volume filled with fine bed material can be used to monitor and evaluate the supply of excess fine sediment in gravel-bed channels (Lisle and Hilton, 1992, 1999).

Schumm's (1977) division of an entire drainage basin into source, transport, and depositional zones may also be applied to the mountainous portion of a drainage basin in that the steepest, low-order channels are likely to receive sediment directly from the hillslopes; the intermediate step-pool channels may mostly transport the sediment downstream; and the lower pool-riffle channels will respond to the sediment with increased storage and changes in channel configuration. Superimposed on this general downstream progression along a mountain river may be the presence of bedrock reaches with knickpoints and gorges, or reaches of braided channel.

Knickpoints and Gorges

A knickpoint is a step-like discontinuity in the longitudinal profile of a river channel. A knickpoint may be distinguished from a bed-step associated with a step-pool sequence in that knickpoints generally occur singly or in relatively small groups, and erode headward with time in contrast to the stationary bed-steps. Knickpoints may occur in unconsolidated or weakly consolidated alluvium, but they are best developed in bedrock or cohesive alluvium. Knickpoints may be stepped, buttressed, or undercut, and the headward erosion may take the form of parallel retreat or of rotation such that the angle of the knickpoint face with the vertical increases with time. The world's greatest waterfalls—such as the Sutherland (580 m) in New Zealand, the

Kjelfossen (792 m) in Norway, Angel Falls (979 m) in Venezuela, and Yosemite Falls (739 m) in USA—exemplify the vertical drop that may be associated with a knickpoint.

Knickpoints may be created when a baselevel fall, or uplift of the drainage basin, increases channel gradient and the stream's incisional capability so that a knickpoint originating at the channel mouth erodes upstream. Knickpoints may also migrate upstream along tributaries when incision in response to baselevel change or uplift occurs more rapidly along the main channel than along the tributaries (Seidl and Dietrich, 1992). The steep face of the knickpoint may be maintained during headward erosion in bedded substrates where a more resistant upper unit serves as a caprock that is continually undermined by erosion of the weaker units beneath (Holland and Pickup, 1976; Wohl et al., 1994a) (Figure 4.7). A steep face may also be maintained in jointed substrates where plucking of blocks from the knickpoint face occurs (Clemence, 1988; Bishop and Goldrick, 1992; Pyrce, 1995). A knickpoint eroding upstream in massive, homogeneous substrate is likely to become less pronounced with time as the knickpoint face decreases in slope and the incising reach above the knickpoint lip increases in slope (Gardner, 1983; Stein and Julien, 1993). As an illustration of this, a study comparing two nearby drainage basins in the mountains of Japan that were very similar except for lithology demonstrated that the river flowing over jointed granite had numerous knickpoints, whereas the river flowing over homogeneous sedimentary rocks had a smooth, straight profile (Tanaka et al., 1993). Comparison of numerous stepped- and straight-profile channels in Hawaii suggests that even channels on bedded and jointed rocks may have a straight longitudinal profile if they have a stable baselevel history (Seidl et al., 1994).

Knickpoints may also form as a result of an increase in the ratio of water/sediment discharge. This may occur during a single flood (Figure 4.8), or over a period of time as a result of land-use or other controls operating within the drainage basin. Finally, a knickpoint may form where a particularly resistant material is exposed in the channel-bed (Miller, 1991). A knickpoint of this type will either disappear or become a more gradually steepened knickzone once the river has incised an inner channel through the resistant unit (Biedenharn, 1989).

Although some of the world's largest waterfalls occur in low-relief continental shield provinces, knickpoints are also common in mountainous regions because of tectonic activity, the greater likelihood of finding resistant bedrock close to the surface, and the continuing fluvial adjustment to Pleistocene glacial erosion (Figure 4.9). Knickpoints are some of the sites of the greatest concentration of energy dissipation along a river (Young, 1985), and rates of knickpoint retreat may be two orders of magnitude greater than erosion rates elsewhere along the channel (Seidl et al., 1997). Reported rates of knickpoint migration range from 2 to 100 cm/kyr (Tinkler and Wohl, 1998; Wohl, 1999). The prevalence of knickpoints along mountain rivers formed in bedrock may indicate that other forms of channel incision cannot keep pace with uplift, resulting in steepening of the channel longitudinal profile until a knickpoint is formed and incision occurs fairly rapidly. The formation and headward retreat

Figure 4.7. Tchupala Falls, Queensland, Australia. Falls are formed where a massive basalt unit overlies a densely jointed basalt unit. Channel above falls is approximately 20 m wide.

Figure 4.8. Aerial view of headcut erosion along the alluvial channel of Dry Gulch, a tributary of the Big Thompson River, Colorado. Headcut formed during the July 1976 flood. Photograph courtesy of Stanley A. Schumm.

Figure 4.9. (a) Waterfalls, upper Amazon River basin, Ecuador. Main channel (at lower left) is approximately 20 m wide. (b) Waterfall in Yosemite Valley, California, USA associated with hanging valley left where a tributary glacier did not incise as deeply as the main glacier.

of a knickpoint may thus determine the extent to which a bedrock channel reach is serving as a local baselevel limiting incision along upstream alluvial reaches. As Stock and Montgomery (1999) note, two critical and unresolved questions with respect to the role of knickpoints in bedrock channel incision are: (1) what sets the frequency, amplitude, and decay rate of knickpoints? and (2) how do rivers with knickpoints in tectonically active regions evolve concave profiles?

The headward retreat of a knickpoint through a resistant substrate unit may leave behind a deep, narrow canyon with walls that are only slightly modified by slope processes. Such gorges form in erosional or tectonic escarpments, including the Ontario Escarpment of eastern Canada (Gilbert, 1896; Tinkler et al., 1994); and in mountain belts such as the Lachlan Fold Belt of southeastern Australia, where gorge extension and incision are a major mechanism of highland denudation (Nott et al., 1996). These gorges are commonly characterized by alternating pools and rapids. The pools have been interpreted as plunge pools formed during periods of slower upstream migration of the knickpoint, whereas the rapids represent either the plunge pool bars, or periods of faster recession that resulted in downstream deposition of eroded materials (Philbrick, 1970). Rapids may also result from localized inputs of coarse sediment associated with tributary junctions or fracture zones (Figure 4.10). Scheidegger (1995; Scheidegger and Hantke, 1994) has noted that many mountain-river gorges are oriented parallel to regional joint patterns and shear zones, suggesting that channel incision occurs more effectively along these zones of weakened rock. The maintenance of a deep, narrow channel cross section following knickpoint recession both reflects the erosional resistance of the canyon walls, and maximizes the shear stress and stream power per unit area for a given discharge and channel gradient.

Braided Channels

Braided channels have multiple flow paths separated by islands or bars. This channel morphology characteristically occurs along valley reaches of more erodible banks, steeper gradient, higher bedload supply, and highly variable discharge. These channels have high width/depth ratios and large bedloads, and may have large fluctuations in water and sediment discharge. They also tend to be laterally unstable, with substantial channel movement at timescales of a few hours to a single flow season. Braided channels are thus the exception to the rule that mountain channels are supply limited and stable. Braiding may be initiated by division of flow around a constructional bar formed within a single channel, by dissection of a transverse bar or point bar, or by avulsion and creation of a new braid channel (Germanoski, 1989). Braided channels may be found in proglacial to arid to tropical mountain environments. Braiding at the reach-scale is often associated with a large point source of sediment from a hillslope mass movement, or from a glacier. Braided channel reaches are relatively common in mountain environments because of the relative abundance of point sources of coarse sediment from adjacent hillslopes. These channel reaches are most likely to be viewed as "degraded" and targeted for restoration (see chapter 6).

Figure 4.10. Rapids controlled by inputs of tributary flood and debris-flow sediments, Badger Creek Rapids, Colorado River, Grand Canyon, USA. Colorado River flow is from right to left, and tributary enters from the left rear of the photograph.

Proglacial braided river systems are known as sandurs where the channel system expands freely, and valley sandurs where the development of the channel network is confined by valley walls (Krigstrom, 1962). Because the carrying capacity and competence of glacial ice and subglacial tunnels are often greater than the broad, shallow channels of the sandur, some of the coarse clasts deposited on the upper sandur are immobile (Bogen, 1995). The steep upper portion of the sandur is composed of the coarse-grained fractions of the sediment supplied. Channel bifurcation is common in this proximal zone, as is lateral channel shifting, and vegetation is absent. The number of channels reaches a maximum in the intermediate zone, where grain sizes in the channel bed and bars are smaller and some vegetation is present. Downvalley, in the distal zone, more abundant riparian vegetation stabilizes the channel banks and a layer of overbank sediments is deposited on the floodplain (Church, 1972). Because velocity in the secondary channels in particular may vary substantially with discharge, secondary channels may act as sediment traps during low discharges and as sediment sources as discharge rises (Bogen, 1995). The dynamics of braid bar formation and channel change are discussed in Lewin (1976), Davies (1987), Ferguson and Ashworth (1992), Laronne and Duncan (1992), Ashworth et al. (1992), and Ashworth (1996).

Summary

Mountain river channels are less likely than low-gradient alluvial channels to approximate the graded longitudinal profile and progressive downstream changes in channel morphology that are commonly regarded as the stable conditions toward which rivers trend. Mountain rivers may exhibit downstream trends of decreasing gradient and grain size, and greater channel stability, but these trends are likely to be interrupted as a result of changes in lithology and structure, glacial or climatic history, or coarse sediment input. Because of the relative lack of consistent downstream trends, mountain rivers are most appropriately classified at the reach scale. Using the Montgomery and Buffington (1997) classification, step-pool channels, plane-bed channels, and pool-riffle channels are the most common channel morphologies among mountain rivers. Step-pool sequences have received relatively little attention, but they tend to occur at high gradients where sediment supply is limited. Steps and pools influence boundary roughness, and tend to evolve toward a condition of maximum flow resistance. Step-pool sequences form transport reaches that are relatively insensitive to changes in water and sediment discharge, in contrast to pool-riffle sequences, which form response reaches. Pool volume and grain size are particularly sensitive. Differential velocity, shear stress and sediment movement through pools and riffles have been interpreted as reflecting a velocity reversal between pools and riffles at differing discharges. Bedrock gorges, which may include knickpoints, may interrupt the downstream trend of step-pool to plane-bed to pool-riffle channels. Knickpoints may result from a change in baselevel, substrate erodibility, or stream incisional capability. As the knickpoint erodes headward, it may leave behind a bedrock gorge. An increase in coarse sediment supply associated with a hillslope mass movement or a glacier may create a braided channel reach that also interrupts the general downstream trends in channel morphology.

Each type of channel morphology has characteristic distributions of substrate and hydraulics as well as characteristic stability. These characteristics provide the physical template for aquatic and riparian biota along the river.

5

MOUNTAIN CHANNEL BIOTA

River Ecology

Four basic dimensions must be considered when examining the river ecosystem: lateral, vertical, longitudinal, and temporal (Ward, 1989). Exchanges can occur along the three physical dimensions at different rates, and over different spatial scales. In the lateral dimension, for example, leaf litter stored along a channel-margin eddy may be flushed into the main channel during a high discharge, and overbank waters may spread from the channel onto the floodplain. Vertical exchange may occur within the water column, as when fine particulate matter stored in the interstices of the channel-bed gravel is brought into suspension during a flood. Vertical exchange may also occur between the channel and the hyporheic zone (the subsurface alluvium). Studies along Sycamore Creek, Arizona (USA), for example, demonstrate that hyporheic respiration is consistently higher in downwelling zones than in upwelling zones (Jones et al., 1995b), whereas algal standing crop in the channel is greater, and elevated concentrations of nitrate nitrogen occur, in upwelling zones (Valett et al., 1992).

The physical and chemical environment within the channel may be characterized by flow velocity and turbulence; sediment movement; substrate grain size, heterogeneity, and stability; water temperature, oxygen content, clarity, total dissolved solids, and nutrient availability; and magnitude and frequency of disturbance. These environmental factors partly govern the abundance and diversity of aquatic organisms (Ricklefs, 1987; Swanson et al., 1988; Allan, 1995). Seasonal or aperiodic exchanges of water, sediment, and nutrients between the channel and the adjacent floodplain (Junk et al., 1989), and between the channel and the subsurface water of the hyporheic zone (Stanford and Ward, 1988; Valett, 1993), may also strongly influence the physical and chemical conditions and nutrient availability of some channels, and hence aquatic and riparian communities (e.g. Boulton and Stanley, 1995).

Aquatic Communities

The energy resources of a river depend on both autochthonous and allochthonous production. Autochthonous production is primary production occurring within the river channel via photosynthesis by bryophytes (mosses and lichens), attached algae, and floating or rooted angiosperms (Ward, 1992). Periphytic algae attached to the channel substrate and non-vascular plants such as mosses constitute most of the primary producers in mountain rivers. These organisms are adapted to the specifics of substrate, nutrients, current, sunlight, and the presence of grazing organisms. Allochthonous production depends on detritus from outside the channel in the form of particulate and dissolved organic matter, much of which is derived from leaf litter and wood. Coarse particulate organic matter is broken down by fungi and by macroinvertebrate shredders. Large woody debris (LWD) exerts an important control on the retention of this particulate detritus at a given site in the channel. A study of mountain rivers in New Hampshire, USA demonstrated that 75% of the standing stock of coarse particulate organic matter (> 1 mm in diameter) was stored by LWD in first-order streams (Bilby and Likens, 1980). The importance of allochthonous organic matter to aquatic communities is reflected in the presence of organisms. Leaf litter often supports a higher abundance and diversity of organisms than do many inorganic substrates. (An interesting side note is that engineered LWD, structures consisting of an interlocking complex of small diameter poles, may play a similar role. Comparison of macroinvertebrate abundance, distribution, and taxa diversity between natural and engineered LWD and adjacent substrates found no statistically significant differences (O'Neal and Sibley, 1999).)

The primary consumers of organic matter are biofilm assemblages, macroinvertebrates, and fish. Biofilm is an organic layer that coats solid surfaces. This layer includes attached algae, bacteria, fungi, protozoans and micrometazoans (Lock et al., 1984). Dissolved organic matter is particularly important in supporting bacteria and fungi within the channel. Macroinvertebrates include aquatic insects, crustaceans, molluscs, leeches, amphipods, nematodes, and so forth. These organisms commonly constitute 98% of the stream biomass. Macroinvertebrates may be classified in terms of the physical niche they occupy within the channel, as benthic (closely associated with the channel bed); floating or swimming organisms residing in the open water; organisms associated with the air-water interface; or hyporheic organisms that inhabit the interstitial spaces between sediment grains below the channel-bed surface and laterally under the banks (Ward, 1992).

Benthic macroinvertebrates influence both energy flow through stream food webs and nutrient cycling (Covich et al., 1999). These organisms accelerate detrital decomposition (Wallace and Webster, 1996); release bound nutrients into solution through their feeding, excretion, and burrowing (Cummins et al., 1995); control the numbers, locations, and sizes of their prey (Crowl and Covich, 1990); supply food for both aquatic and terrestrial vertebrate consumers; and accelerate nutrient transfer to adjacent riparian zones (Naiman and DéCamps, 1997; Wallace et al., 1997).

Aquatic insects may also be classified via their feeding strategy as shredders, collector-gatherers, collector-filterers, grazers, and predators (Allan, 1995). Shredders feed on non-woody coarse particulate organic matter such as leaves and other plant parts. Collectors feed on finer organic matter which they gather from surface deposits or filter from the water column. Grazers scrape diatoms from the biofilm assemblage, and predators eat other organisms in the stream.

Aquatic insects, which originated from terrestrial insects, appear to have initially invaded freshwater in headwater streams, which are rich in dissolved oxygen. More than 90% of the benthos in high gradient temperate streams is aquatic insects. These insects also make up more than 80% of the benthos in high gradient tropical streams. Large rivers typically differ from one another in terms of their insect fauna, whereas the taxonomic composition of mountain rivers is similar in being dominated by Ephemeroptera (mayflies), Plecoptera (stoneflies), and Trichoptera (caddisflies). Exceptions to this similarity occur in some glaciated regions such as the Alps (Hynes, 1970).

All of the types of aquatic insects present in mountain rivers have adapted to the swift current and turbulent flow characteristic of these rivers (Hynes, 1970). Body morphology has been adapted via flattening, streamlining, and reducing projections off the body. Holdfasts in the form of suckers, friction pads, hooks and claws, or sticky secretions help the organism to maintain position, as does ballast such as the pebbles in caddisfly cases. Behavioral adaptations include movement into crevices or protected sites of reduced flow velocity, use of the current for downstream movement, and the creation of silk threads by Simuliidae larvae as "life lines" to regain original position if displaced or disturbed (Wotton, 1986; Ward, 1992). Physiologically, these species lack adaptations to survive low oxygen conditions and warm water (Ward, 1992). The number of generations per year and the timing of egg hatching and adult emergence into the atmosphere also reflect adaptations to the temperature and flow regime of a specific river.

Fish may be resident, or may be migratory species that spawn in the headwaters after living in lower riverine reaches, lakes, or the ocean (Ward, 1992). Fish may also be primarily bottom-dwellers, or may spend most of their time swimming in open water. Fish may be further classified in terms of their primary food source as detrivores, herbivores, planktivores, insectivores, piscivores, or omnivores. Like aquatic insects, fish in mountain rivers have morphologies suited to life in fast currents. Fish are dorsoventrally flattened or have an arched profile with a flat ventrum, have more muscular fins, eyes located more dorsally, gill openings more lateral, and mouths more ventral, reduced swim bladders and decreased buoyancy, and mouth suckers or hydraulics discs near the mouth that may be used for attachment to rocks (Ward, 1992).

As discussed in the next chapter, mountain rivers in North America have been extremely impacted by the activities of beaver (*Castor canadensis*). These large rodents build dams of LWD and sediment which affect water and sediment flow along a river and greatly increase habitat diversity for other organisms (Wright, 1999). Beaver historically colonized North American rivers from the arctic tundra to the deserts of northern Mexico, and the Atlantic to the Pacific coasts (Naiman et al., 1988), and were also widespread throughout Europe (Gurnell, 1998).

The geomorphic impacts on mountain rivers of other types of organisms are less well documented, but there is evidence that aquatic macroinvertebrates may locally alter channel-bed substrate; Statzner et al. (1996) documented sand erosion between cobbles in a mountain river in connection with bioturbation by stonefly (*Dinocras cephalotes*) larvae. Studies of salmonid habitat in the western United States have demonstrated that when the fish construct nests by excavating a hollow in the channel bed, finer sediments are selectively mobilized, leading to a coarser particle-size distribution than adjacent gravels not utilized for spawning (Chapman, 1988; Kondolf et al., 1989, 1993).

Riparian Communities

Adjacent to stream channels lie the zones of riparian (streamside) and floodplain vegetation. The actual species growing within these zones vary widely among rivers, but there is a general increase in tolerance for flooding, high water tables, and disturbance situated along a gradient from the floodplain to the channel. The species growing immediately adjacent to the channel tend to be herbaceous vegetation and shrubs, with small trees farther back from the channel, and larger trees in the floodplain forest (Hupp, 1988). In arid and semiarid regions, the floodplain vegetation may give way to upland species that are more tolerant of dry soils.

The controls on riparian vegetation pattern vary with climate and channel type (Osterkamp and Hupp, 1984; Harris, 1988; Hupp, 1988; Hupp and Osterkamp, 1996). In humid regions, these patterns may be largely controlled by the frequency, duration, and intensity of floods (Hack and Goodlett, 1960; Sigafoos, 1961; Walker et al., 1986; Kalliola and Puhakka, 1988). Harris (1987), for example, found that flood disturbance was the major environmental control on the spatial distribution of riparian communities along a sinuous alluvial channel in north-central California. Vegetation patterns in arid and semiarid regions may be most closely related to patterns of water availability (Auble et al., 1994; Tabacchi et al., 1996), particularly minimum and maximum flows, although mechanical disturbances associated with flooding may also exert a strong control (e.g. Baker and Walford, 1995). Vegetation along laterally mobile alluvial channels may be controlled by fluxes in sediment deposition and erosion. Channel stability, as reflected in channel narrowing, meandering, and flood deposition, also promotes a variety of spatial and temporal patterns of vegetation establishment (Scott et al., 1996b). During channel narrowing, vegetation becomes established on portions of the bed abandoned by the stream, and establishment is associated with a period of low flow lasting one to several years. During channel meandering, vegetation may become established on point bars following moderate or higher peak flows. Following flood deposition, vegetation may become established on flood deposits high above the channel bed (Scott et al., 1996b).

Differences in riparian vegetation as a function of channel dynamics can also be illustrated by comparing different meandering rivers. Along the meandering Beatton River in northeastern British Columbia, Canada, rapid sedimentation on surfaces adjacent to the channel favors the establishment of a dense, non-reproducing balsam poplar stand of uniform age (Nanson and Beach, 1977). As the active channel migrates further away and overbank sedimentation decreases (over a period of 50 years), white spruce colonize the soil beneath the poplar canopy and form a dense, relatively even-aged stand. As the surface reaches 100-150 years in age, the mature poplars die and the spruce develop into a mature, non-reproducing stand that persists until 350-400 years old. A second, less even-aged spruce stand develops on surfaces 500-550 years old, so that bands of differently-aged riparian species develop in regular patterns on the floodplain as a function of channel migration rate (Nanson and Beach, 1977). Similarly, small floods along low-gradient meandering rivers in the southwestern United States facilitate frequent (≤ 5 year) episodes of seedling establishment on point bars (Hughes, 1994). On less sinuous rivers in this region, cottonwoods establish in large numbers at infrequent intervals in synchrony with large floods (Stromberg et al., 1993).

In mountainous regions, climate as a function of elevation may produce fairly regular longitudinal patterns of riparian vegetation from the headwaters to the piedmont region. Working on the western slope of the Colorado Rocky Mountains, for example, Baker (1989) consistently found wetlands at treeline or at the top of the watershed, upper subalpine carrs (shrub-dominated wetlands) or subalpine forests at elevations of 2620m to 3110m, and montane forests below 2620m. Modern plant-distribution patterns and fossil records suggest that riparian areas, which typically have cooler, wetter microclimates, may serve as refugia of Pleistocene and older flora. Plant distributions in the Southern Rocky Mountains of the western USA, for example, indicate that the contemporary mountain flora once extended considerably downslope and eastward, and that the eastern woodland flora extended westward, probably along the major watercourses. Today the mountain flora has retreated to the higher elevations, leaving relicts at scattered points on the Great Plains (Weber, 1965; Axelrod and Raven, 1985) where shaded canyons or north-facing slopes have microclimates reminiscent of colder, wetter regional climate. Along many mountain rivers, climate may thus influence longitudinal, basin-length patterns of riparian vegetation. Acker et al. (1999) found a downstream increase in the complexity of riparian forest stands from upland to low-order to mid-order streamside forests in the western Cascade Range of Oregon. At the scale of the channel reach, vegetation may be primarily governed by the magnitude and frequency of disturbance by debris flows and floods (White, 1979; Harris, 1987; Baker, 1988b; Malanson and Butler, 1991; Walford and Baker, 1995), as filtered through channel and valley morphology, and as expressed in inundation, mechanical disturbances, substrate characteristics, and water availability.

The dynamic equilibrium model of riparian vegetation conceptualizes the roles of disturbance and productivity in controlling the diversity of riparian vegetation (Solbrig, 1992). Where potential productivity is low, and the rate of competitive exclusion is low, an increase in disturbance will decrease species richness. Where potential productivity is high, and the rate of competitive exclusion is high, an increase in disturbance will increase species richness (DéCamps and Tabacchi, 1994). In between these productivity extremes, an increase in disturbance will increase species richness to a maximum at some equilibrium level, and then cause a decrease in species richness (DéCamps and Tabacchi, 1994).

There are several levels of interaction among riparian vegetation and channel processes. Among the most well documented are the progression from a freshly deposited or scoured, unvegetated surface, to a stable, vegetated surface. Channel change and sedimentation may create habitat favorable to germination and growth of riparian vegetation (Everitt, 1980). Seed dispersal of cottonwood species, for example, typically coincides with declining river flows following spring snowmelt and storms, increasing the chance that seeds will be deposited on favorable sites along the channel (Braatne et al., 1996). The conditions necessary for seedling recruitment occur irregularly at intervals of 5-10 years or longer (Baker, 1990; Stromberg et al., 1991, 1993; Scott et al., 1996a,b). High flows during the dispersal phase may prevent exposure of recruitment sites until after the seeds have been dispersed or lost their viability (Braatne et al., 1996). High flows after the dispersal phase may bury or scour newly germinated seedlings. Along mountain rivers that are stable over periods of decades, channel reaches that are wider, shallower and more disturbed (such as tributary junctions, or sites of mass movement or large woody debris jams) may provide sites for establishment of seedlings, which then propagate clonally to more stable sites (Roberts et al., 1998). Once the riparian vegetation becomes established it may increase soil cohesion (Coppin and Richards, 1990), bank resistance and hydraulic roughness, and may facilitate further sediment deposition and channel change (Graf, 1978; Nadler and Schumm, 1981). As the elevation of the vegetation surface increases through sediment deposition, and flood inundation and scouring become less frequent, the vegetation influences soil development. Different plant communities develop over time (Walker and Chapin, 1986; Kalliola and Puhakka, 1988; Malanson and Butler, 1990; Binkley et al., 1994).

Riparian vegetation may also influence water quantity and quality in the river. In arid and semiarid regions, evapotranspiration by phreatophytic vegetation may be a source of significant water transfer between the subsurface and the atmosphere (Young et al., 1984); measured evapotranspiration rates for riparian vegetation in the western US range from 1 to 279 cm/yr (Graf, 1988).

The influence of riparian vegetation on soil and water chemistry has been documented in several studies. A study of soil development on terraces along the Tanana River, Alaska (USA) indicated that younger (< 5 years), lower alluvial surfaces had soils high in calcium carbonate and sulfate (Van Cleve et al., 1993). Establishment of riparian vegetation between 5-10 years created evapotranspiration that controlled soil water potential. Newly-formed surface litter layers further helped eliminate evaporation and concentration of salts. Soil properties changed markedly as continued sedimentation and channel movement reduced inundation frequency and subsurface saturation in the alluvial surface, as vegetation continued to deposit organic matter, and as alder fixed nitrogen in the soil (Van Cleve et al., 1993).

An example of the effect of riparian vegetation on stream chemistry comes from a study at an upland site in Wales (Fiebig et al., 1990). Dissolved organic carbon (DOC) concentrations were consistently higher in riparian soil waters than in the stream, suggesting an average carbon input of 2500 g C m^{-2} per year to the stream, and an important influence on stream productivity. Fiebig et al. (1990) interpreted observed patterns to indicate that: (1) soil water DOC reaching the channel via saturated throughflow of the streambank and bed was mobilized within the hyporheic zone, prior to its discharge into the channel; (2) during higher flows, DOC entering via the unsaturated zone of the streambank could directly influence the stream; and (3) DOC in soil water further back from the channel could also directly influence the stream, reaching the channel by macropore flow.

The Hyporheic Zone

The hyporheic zone is the portion of unconfined, near-stream aquifers where stream water is present. Exchanges between groundwater and stream water associated with this zone may substantially impact stream water chemistry, temperature, and the availability of nutrients. Along rivers with broad, gravel floodplains, the hyporheic zone may extend up to 2 km laterally from the active channel (Stanford and Ward, 1988). Along mountain channels more closely constrained by bedrock, the hyporheic zone may extend less than 30 m into the floodplain (Wondzell and Swanson, 1999), or even less than 1 m (Wroblicky et al., 1998).

Water exchange between the stream channel and adjacent aquifer is governed by vertical and horizontal hydraulic gradients. Local sites of upwelling and downwelling are determined by geomorphic features such as streambed topography (Harvey and Bencala, 1993) and associated variation in channel-bed grain-size distribution and depth to bedrock. Along a third-order gravel-bed river in the Rocky Mountains of Colorado, recharge to the hyporheic zone occurred where stream water slope increased, at the transition from pools to steeper channel segments. Return flow to the stream occurred where stream water slope decreased, at the transition from steeper channel segments to pools. Hyporheic flow paths recharged by stream water were generally short (1-10 m) (Harvey and Bencala, 1993). Large-scale hyporheic exchange processes are controlled mainly by catchment geology (Brunke and Gonser, 1997). Comparing headwater streams in New Mexico, USA, for example, Morrice et al. (1997) found that a sandstone-siltstone catchment with a fine-grained alluvium of low hydraulic conductivity had much more limited groundwater-surface water exchange than volcanic catchments with alluvium of intermediate grain size and hydraulic conductivity, or a granite/gneiss catchment of coarse, poorly sorted alluvium with high hydraulic conductivity.

The characteristics of the hyporheic zone tend to vary widely in space and time. Temporal variations may be a function of discharge. Wroblicky et al. (1998) found that the size of the hyporheic zone lateral to two mountain streams in New Mexico decreased by approximately 50% during high flows. Although Wondzell and Swanson (1996a) found that the overall pattern of hyporheic flow changed little over the course of an average year along fourth- and fifth-order mountain channels in Oregon, they found that floods with recurrence intervals of 50 to 100 years dramatically changed the hyporheic zones (Wondzell and Swanson, 1999). In some unconstrained reaches, channel incision and lowering of the water table during these floods decreased the extent of the hyporheic zone. In other reaches, the extent of the hyporheic zone increased where channel incision steepened head gradients, or shifted in location where lateral channel jumps altered exchange flow paths. In constrained reaches with less depth and area of sediment available to be reworked by the flood, less change occurred in the hyporheic zone.

The characteristics of the hyporheic zone may also vary as a function of channel type. A gorge stream flowing in a single straight channel along a deep valley may have high transport capacity, unstable bed sediments, and limited alluvial fill, so that lateral and vertical exchange processes are of minor importance (Brunke and Gonser, 1997). A braided channel with rapid lateral migration across coarse alluvium may maximize lateral and vertical exchange, whereas the finer sediment loads of meandering channels may reduce such exchange (Brunke and Gonser, 1997).

The ecological importance of the hyporheic zone results from the use of interstitial habitat by fluvial organisms such as invertebrates (Stanford and Ward, 1988, 1993), and from its influence on water chemistry. Water temperature, dissolved oxygen, carbon dioxide, pH, nitrate, and ammonium are all influenced by groundwater-stream water exchanges. Physicochemical gradients in the hyporheic zone result from the different properties of surface and groundwaters, and from biogeochemical reactions associated with retention in areas of low hydraulic conductivity (Findlay, 1995; Brunke and Gonser, 1997). The hyporheic zone may act as a source or sink for dissolved organic matter, depending on the volume and direction of flow, dissolved organic carbon concentrations, and biotic activity (Brunke and Gonser, 1997). Primary productivity in mountain streams may be nitrogen limited (Gregory, 1980), so that the hyporheic transport of dissolved nitrogen, and hyporheic biogeochemical processes, may be especially important in these streams. Wondzell and Swanson (1996b) found that the hyporheic zone along McRae Creek, a fourth-order mountain river in Oregon, was a net source of nitrogen to the stream under all discharge conditions.

Despite the biochemical importance of hyporheic-stream water exchanges, hyporheic flow appears to constitute a very small portion of stream discharge in mountain rivers; 0.02% during winter baseflow discharge, 0.8% of discharge during summer low flow, and less than 0.1% of storm discharge along McRae Creek (Wondzell and Swanson, 1996a). Along larger, lowland alluvial rivers with deeper and broader valley fill, such as the Willamette River of Oregon, hyporheic discharge may constitute 15% of surface discharge (Laenen and Risley, 1997).

Although invertebrates use hyporheic habitat, its importance as a refuge during hydrological disturbance varies. Studying invertebrate response to floods of varying magnitude along a low-gradient (0.0015 m/m) sand-bed channel in Virginia, Palmer et al. (1992) found that faunal migration into the hyporheic zone prevented dislodgement of only a small fraction of the fauna. However, they noted that the hyporheic zone may be more important as a refuge along channels with more complex beds that are less susceptible to scour and fill during a flood.

Engineering modifications which involve straightening channels, eliminating secondary channels, reducing channel-floodplain connectivity, removing LWD, altering flow regime, or changing channel grain-size distribution may have substantial impacts on hyporheic zones (Brunke and Grosner, 1997; Wondzell and Swanson, 1999).

Conceptual Models

The river continuum concept is an important conceptual model of river ecosystems that emphasizes downstream gradients, and is thus very applicable to mountain rivers. The river continuum concept (Vannote et al., 1980) was developed from stable, unperturbed rivers in northern temperate, forested watersheds, but has been applied with at least partial success to rivers around the world (Johnson et al., 1995). Channels are differentiated on the basis of stream order (Strahler, 1957), with first- to third-order being small streams, fourth- to sixth-order being medium-sized rivers, and channels greater than sixth-order considered large rivers (Vannote et al, 1980). The relative importance of the three primary sources of energy for biological production (allochthonous, autochthonous, and transport of organic matter from upstream) varies along the river, with autochthonous sources and transport becoming increasingly important downstream. The proportions of benthic invertebrates in each of the four feeding groups also vary longitudinally as a result of changes in the physical channel characteristics and organic matter sources. Shredders and collectors dominate the small streams, and grazers and collectors the medium-sized rivers, whereas collectors are most important in large rivers. Mid-sized rivers are predicted to have the highest biological diversity because they have the widest range of temperature and hydraulic conditions and energy sources (especially benthic algae), although the highest fish diversity occurs in the downstream reaches of large basins (Vannote et al., 1980; Stanford et al., 1996). At least one study has documented that riparian species richness per site is higher along the main channel than along the tributaries, reaching a maximum at intermediate altitudes (Nilsson et al., 1994). This pattern has been attributed to characteristics of mean annual discharge and variety of substrates.

Mountain rivers in tropical regions may differ from the temperate rivers described in the river continuum concept in that first- and second-order tropical streams receive a continuous (rather than seasonal) supply of forest-produced leaf litter; daily discharge is unpredictable over annual time scales; extremely variable frequencies and magnitudes of rainfall-generated floods remove leaf detritus and scour the channel bed, thereby disrupting life history patterns and predator-prey dynamics; and freshwater vertebrates are low in abundance relative to decapods (Covich and McDowell, 1996). Although regional patterns of community structure are apparent in temperate-zone streams, no such patterns are clearly evident in stream communities across latitude (Covich, 1988).

Related to the river continuum concept is the idea that resources are stored periodically in biological reservoirs such as organisms or detritus, rather than flowing continuously downstream (Elwood et al., 1983). Nutrient cycling describes the passage of an atom or element from a phase in which it is a dissolved available nutrient, through its incorporation into living tissue and passage through various links in the food chain, to its eventual release by excretion and decomposition into a form in which it is once again a dissolved available nutrient (Allan, 1995). In terrestrial ecosystems this cycling may occur largely in place, but in rivers transport becomes an important component because the element may be transported downstream as a solute, then incorporated into the biota, and eventually returned to the water column as a solute. Hence, in rivers the phrase "nutrient spiraling" is used to describe the passage of nutrients through the river ecosystem (Webster and Patten, 1979). Small

streams tend to conserve or store resources because of the high organic matter retention behind debris dams, whereas large rivers tend to export relatively more organic
matter (Minshall et al., 1983) unless there is substantial storage on the floodplain.

Dams along the river (Ward and Stanford, 1983) and the local effects of a tributary junction (Bruns et al., 1984; Osborne and Wiley, 1992) may disrupt the longitudinal continuity of physical and biological features predicted by the river continuum
concept. Rivers in arid or semiarid regions that have sparse riparian vegetation (Wiley
et al., 1990; Davies et al., 1994), or large rivers with extensive floodplains (Sedell et
al., 1989; Welcomme et al., 1989; Bayley and Li, 1992) also may not be adequately
described by the river continuum concept. In general, the concept seems to best
describe large rivers confined to their channels, but not large floodplain rivers
(Johnson et al., 1995).

Much attention has been given in recent years to large rivers because these rivers
are perceived as being the most substantially altered by human activities (Johnson et
al., 1995). One outcome of this attention has been the development of a model known
as the flood-pulse concept, which includes some of the processes of lateral exchange
not accounted for in the river continuum concept. The flood-pulse concept is based
on the recognition that floods which inundate at least a portion of the floodplain are
critical as a mechanism for providing clear, shallow water in overbank areas for
autochthonous production; for fish nursery habitat and feeding; and for exchanging
nutrients and organic matter between the channel and floodplain (Junk et al., 1989;
Bayley, 1991). The floodplain is an aquatic-terrestrial transition zone that has a gradient of plant species adapted to seasonal gradients of inundation, nutrients, and light
(Junk et al., 1989). As a flood spreads out from the channel across the floodplain, it
creates a moving littoral, where the littoral consists of the inshore zone from the
water's edge to a few meters depth (Bayley, 1995). The moving littoral traverses a
floodplain that may be much larger than the area of permanent moving or standing
water associated with the channel. As a result, high primary production rates occur
during the rising limb of the flood, with high decomposition rates during the flood
peak, and nutrient runoff and concentration during the descending limb (Bayley,
1995). As Mertes (1997) documents, some rivers may inundate dry floodplains with
water from the main channel, other rivers may inundate fully saturated floodplains
that have contributions from local water (groundwater, and waters from the hyporheic zone, from tributary channels and from precipitation). Waters from each source will
have different sediment loads, chemistry and nutrients, and the perirheic zone that is
created by the mixing of river and local water may form an ecotone (Mertes, 1997).

Under the flood-pulse concept (Junk et al., 1989), biotic communities should
exhibit a dynamic equilibrium with physical features of the flood pulse, such as timing, duration, and rate of rise and fall in water level (Bayley, 1995). Rivers in both
tropical and temperate regions have a higher multispecies fish yield per unit mean
water area when a natural, predictable flood pulse occurs along the river because the
flood pulse creates floodplain lakes that are connected to the main channel (Bayley,
1991). And a regular flooding regime and associated floodplain sedimentation help

maintain high biotic diversity in riparian forests (Salo et al., 1986; DéCamps et al., 1988). The flood-pulse concept is most relevant for lowland rivers with broad flood-plains.

Some of the habitats and processes associated with floodplains may also occur in the slower, shallower flows of secondary channels (Amoros, 1991), or in areas of flow separation along a single, confined channel. Working on a braided, gravel-bed river in Quebec, Canada, Payne and Lapointe (1997) found that a stream reach with secondary channels offered up to five times more potential habitat for juvenile fish than did single channel reaches. Backwater habitats associated with eddies along con-fined rivers also provide low-velocity, seasonally warm refuges for juvenile fish, and groundwater enriched in ammonium and dissolved organic carbon that is utilized by riparian plants (Kaplinski et al., 1998).

In addition to lateral and longitudinal variability, geomorphic and ecological characteristics of a river vary temporally in response to disturbance patterns such as floods and droughts (White, 1979; Bender et al., 1984; Forman and Godron, 1986; Resh et al., 1988; Wissmar and Swanson, 1990; Johnson et al., 1998). Frissell et al. (1986) differentiate recovery time and sensitivity to disturbance on the basis of spa-tial scale: microhabitats (e.g. gravel patches) are very sensitive to disturbance but recover quickly, whereas a watershed has a low sensitivity and long recovery time. A microhabitat (10^{-1} m), for example, could be disturbed by scour during a small flood, but would likely recover within a few months or a year. A channel reach (10^1 m) might be disturbed by a debris flow, and require 10^1-10^2 years to recover. A water-shed (10^3 m) disturbed by a climatic change might require 10^2-10^4 years to recover (Naiman et al., 1992). Biotic recovery is likely to occur more rapidly in rivers with a history of episodic disturbance because of selection for species within the communi-ty that can rapidly recolonize following displacement (Poff and Ward, 1990; Milner, 1994). Larger rivers may also be likely to recover more rapidly from a natural dis-turbance such as a flood because of a greater upstream source of colonizers and a greater availability of different types of food resources (Gore and Milner, 1990). A human-induced disturbance (chemical spill, or dam), however, may affect a large river with stable communities more than a smaller river that has disturbance-tolerant species.

Fisher et al. (1998a) have conceptualized the influence of disturbances on nutri-ent processing in rivers in the form of a telescoping ecosystem model. The process-ing length, or linear distance required to biogeochemically transform organic materi-als in transport, is specific to each subsystem (surface stream, hyporheic zone, ripar-ian zone, etc.) within the river ecosystem. A disturbance causes the processing length to increase. In this model, the river ecosystem is composed of several connected sub-systems which increase and decrease in processing length as a function of time since disturbance, analogous to the cylinders of a telescope.

One of the challenges to integrating our understanding of physical and biologi-cal processes in rivers has been determining which physical factors best describe, or correlate with, biotic communities (Heede and Rinne, 1990; Milner et al., 1991;

Naiman et al., 1992; Poff, 1997). Studying four streams in Europe, the United Kingdom, and the USA, Statzner and Borchardt (1994) found that longitudinal patterns of hydraulic shear stress explained far more than 50% of the variability in ecological responses by fish and invertebrates. Flow regime (magnitude, frequency, duration, timing, rate of change) has also been identified as a key variable that governs water quality, energy sources, physical habitat, and biotic interactions and, ultimately, the distribution and abundance of riverine species (Resh et al., 1988; Karr, 1991; Power et al., 1995; Poff et al., 1997). High and low flows that constitute disturbances may be particularly ecologically relevant because they serve as "bottlenecks" that present critical stresses and opportunities for riverine species (Poff and Ward, 1989).

Poff (1996) categorized streams in the USA using ten ecologically-relevant hydrological characteristics (Table 5.1). Cluster analysis using these 10 characteristics from 806 sites identified ten distinctive stream types that Poff (1996) hypothesized would share ecological features. An analogous study indicated that hydrological data for 34 sites in the north-central U.S. could clearly separate two ecologically defined groups of fish assemblages (Poff and Allan, 1995).

Frissell et al. (1986) identified spatially nested levels of resolution (Figure 5.1) at which to characterize form and process, and Cupp (1989) adapted this concept to an actual classification system at the stream segment level for use in the state of Washington, USA. Poff (1997) used a similar spatial hierarchy to describe multi-scale filters, or habitat selective forces, that govern distribution and abundance of species. For example, the watershed-scale filter *seasonality of flow* influences which fish life history strategies succeed, whereas the microhabitat-scale filter *hydraulic stress* influences which fish body morphologies will predominate.

Additional research is needed to understand how habitat features at different scales are functionally linked; which habitat filters most strongly constrain potential keystone species; and how species traits respond to a particular filter (Poff, 1997). Most of the proposed approaches to the problem incorporate the assumptions that (1) physical structure can be related to biotic and physical functions in the channel, and (2) characteristics of the riparian forest reflect in-channel dynamics (Naiman et al., 1992). Figure 5.2 illustrates two tropical streams in which differences in habitat features result in different biotic communities.

Biological Stream Classifications

Closely linked to the correlation of physical and biological characteristics are biological classifications for rivers. As with the geomorphic classifications reviewed in chapter 4, biological river classifications are designed to facilitate comparison and generalization. A key aspect of any river classification scheme is whether it emphasizes a downstream zonation of river attributes such that fairly distinct changes may be identified, or a downstream continuum in which attributes change gradually and continuously.

Table 5.1. Stream classification using ecologically relevant hydrological characteristics (after Poff, 1996). Mountain rivers may be any one of the nine stream types, but are particularly likely to be snow and rain, snowmelt, perennial flashy, or intermittent flashy.

Hydrological characteristics

1) *coefficient of variation of daily flows*: average across all years of record of the standard deviation of the daily flows divided by the annual mean daily flow, multiplied by 100
2) *predictability of daily flows*: index ranging from 0 to 100, composed of constancy (a measure of temporal invariance) and contingency (a measure of periodicity)
3) *flood frequency*: the average number of discrete floods per year with a magnitude equal or greater than the 1.67-year flood
4) *flood duration*: average number of days that flow remains above the flood threshold for a site
5) *seasonal predictability of flooding*: the maximum proportion of all floods over the period of record that fall in any one of six 60-day "seasonal" windows
6) *seasonal predictability of non-flooding*: maximum proportion of year (number of days/365) during which no floods have ever occurred over the period of record
7) *baseflow index*: average annual ratio of lowest daily flow to mean daily flow
8) *extent of intermittence*: average annual number of days without measured discharge
9) *seasonal predictability of low flow*: proportion of low flows ≥ 5 yr magnitude falling in a 60-day seasonal window
10) *seasonal predictability of non-low flow*: maximum proportion of year during which no 5-year low flows have ever occurred over the entire period of record

Stream types

Perennial
  perennial runoff: low flood seasonality, high seasonality of low flow, variable daily flow
  stable groundwater: low variability of daily flow, aseasonal flooding
  superstable groundwater: extremely stable daily flow, very high base flow stability
  snow and rain: intermediate seasonality of flooding, very high seasonality of low flow
  snowmelt: high seasonality of flooding; type 1 - lower elevations and earlier onset of flooding than type 2
  perennial flashy: high flow variability, high flood frequency, low seasonality for floods and low flows

Intermittent
  intermittent runoff: high intermittence
  intermittent flashy: very high coefficient of variation, high flood frequency, very low seasonal predictability of non-low flows, high intermittence
  harsh intermittent: very high intermittence

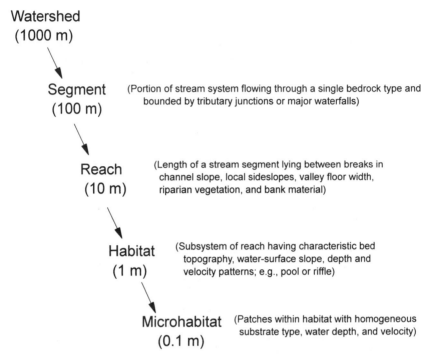

Figure 5.1. Spatially nested levels of resolution at which to characterize mountain river form and process (after Frissell et al., 1986).

Initial attemps at biological river classification were zonation schemes (Hawkes, 1975; Naiman et al., 1992) based on: (1) physical factors such as substrate (rocky, gravel, sand/silt), gradient, temperature, or channel geomorphic units (e.g. Pennak, 1971; Hawkins et al., 1993); (2) biotic assemblages such as the European scheme of trout-grayling-barbel-bream (Huet, 1954), or the biomass, numbers, or presence/absence of macroinvertebrates (Dodds and Hisaw, 1925; Carpenter, 1928); or (3) combined physical, chemical and biological factors (e.g. Ilies, 1961; Ilies and Botosaneanu, 1963). Hynes' (1975) paper "The stream and its valley" highlighted the importance of controls beyond the channel on biotic characteristics, and led river ecologists to give increased attention to geomorphic ideas of how flow energy dissipation affected downstream attributes. The River Continuum Concept grew out of this shift in perspective. Although this continuum-based classification is not very accurate at predicting differences between specific sites, it does accurately predict downstream trends and emphasizes that downstream patterns depend on upstream processes (Allan, 1995). The importance of subsurface hydrologic processes (Frissell, 1999), reach-based in-channel disturbance regime (Poff and Wohl, 1999), and hydrological response to watershed-scale disturbance (Goodman et al., 1999) are among other criteria which have been proposed as a basis for fluvial ecosystem classification.

Figure 5.2. Two high-gradient channels in the Luquillo Experimental Forest of Puerto Rico. Quebrada Prieta (a) is a second-order channel underlain by tuffaceous sandstone (Scatena, 1989) which weathers into large boulders. The channel in this upstream view is approximately 20 m wide. The Rio Icacos (b) is a second-order channel characterized by reaches of sandy substrate separated by bedrock knickpoints. The channel in this upstream view is approximately 10 m wide. Both of these channels have LWD, but Quebrada Prieta has higher LWD retention rates. The location of bedrock knickpoints (which limit the upstream migration of fish predators), the mobility of the channel substrate, and the complexity of available habitat control species richness and species distributions or dominance along these channels. The sandy Rio Icacos has greater substrate mobility, less biofilm, and less habitat complexity, and thus has lower species richness and distributions. Photographs courtesy of Alan P. Covich.

Managers attempting to evaluate or monitor fluvial aquatic ecosystems have used some form of instream habitat unit classification, such as that of Frissell et al. (1986) or Hawkins et al. (1993). However, this type of classification may be inappropriate for quantifying aquatic habitat or channel morphology when monitoring the response of individual rivers to human activities because (i) the subjectivity of the measure introduces observer bias, (ii) geomorphological and ecological changes may not be manifested as changes in habitat-unit frequency or characteristics, and (iii) classification data are nominal and thus of limited use for statistical analysis (Poole et al., 1997).

Mountain Rivers

In an excellent summary of mountain river ecology, Ward (1992) described the eco-logically-relevant characteristics of mountain rivers (Table 5.2). Added to these is the instability of some mountain rivers relative to lowland river systems. Mountain rivers may be subject to more frequent and diverse disturbances and usually have stronger

Table 5.2.   Mountain river ecological characteristics (after Ward, 1992).

Physical and chemical characteristics

*   high turbulence produces oxygen levels near saturation, and water that is chemi-
    cally and thermally homogeneous
*   hydraulic and habitat heterogeneity
*   high water clarity, but dense shading and low water temperatures and nutrient lev-
    els limit autotrophic production
*   total dissolved solids and water hardness increase downstream as groundwater
    input increases
*   organic matter is mostly allochthonous

Biological characteristics

*   organisms mostly benthic
*   primary attached macrophytes are bryophytes (mosses and lichens)
*   few floating or rooted angiosperms
*   zoobenthic community dominated by insects
*   most migratory fish species spend their time swimming in the water column;
    many resident fish species are primarily bottom-dwellers
*   dense riparian woodlands shade channels, and affect water temperature and
    allochthonous inputs
*   stand age structure of riparian vegetation determined by frequency and magnitude
    of disturbance
*   dominated by riparian species that are tolerant of, and may depend on, disturbance
    (e.g. Salix spp., Populus spp.)

landform controls (Wissmar and Swanson, 1990). Natural disturbances include forest
fire, slope failure, avalanches, floods, tree blowdown, glacial activity, and geomorphic
changes in stream channels. These disturbances occur at different timescales and have
different effects spatially, so that each level of Frissell et al.'s (1986) hierarchical classification may be influenced by different disturbances. Floods, for example, have been
shown to affect the distribution, successional stages, and size of riparian forest patches
in rivers of the Cascade Mountains in the northwestern U.S. (Wissmar and Swanson,
1990; Swanson et al., 1992) at the reach scale (Figure 5.1). Floods may destroy and subsequently exclude plants, create new areas for vegetation colonization, and form elevational gradients where plants show varying tolerances to flows and sediment movement
(Menges and Waller, 1983). Flood disturbances along mountain rivers are dominated by
mechanical damage to stream and riparian habitats. Flood peaks may be brief and high,
accompanied by hillslope debris flows and rapid movement of coarse sediment and
woody debris along the channel (Swanson et al., 1998). Although the flood peak moves
along the entire channel, disturbance patterns are very patchy because of local changes
in channel and valley geometry and boundary resistance.

Studies along a montane stream in the Luquillo Experimental Forest of Puerto Rico following Hurricane Hugo in 1989 characterize the effects of disturbance at the watershed to reach scales. Hugo was a moderate intensity storm that produced up to 200 mm of rain and 10-30 year recurrence-interval floods in eastern Puerto Rico (Scatena and Larsen, 1991). The storm produced blowdown of trees in the floodplain forest, greatly increasing the accumulation of LWD on the forest floor, and consequently the long-term reservoir of organic mass and nutrients available to floodplain organisms (Frangi and Lugo, 1991). One month after the hurricane, the densities of freshwater shrimp were reduced on average by 50% in the headwater reaches of the channel (apparently from washout), and increased by 80% in the middle reaches of the channel because of unusually abundant food resources in the form of decomposing leaves and algae (Covich et al., 1999). The combination of moderate flood discharges, wide and deep pools that served as flood refuges, rapid formation of debris dams that retain food resources, and a food web dominated by detrivores and herbivores, appears to have promoted recovery of the benthic community in this forested mountain river following disturbance (Covich et al., 1991). However, five years after the hurricane, carbon and nutrient fluxes in the watershed had not recovered to pre-disturbance levels (Vogt et al., 1996).

Landform controls on mountain rivers include narrow valley bottoms and smaller floodplains that reduce the development of riparian vegetation patches (Pinay et al., 1990), variable sequences of constrained (e.g. landslides and canyons) and unconstrained channel reaches that control erosional and depositional patterns and hence substrate and disturbance for aquatic and riparian communities (Harris, 1988; Mussetter et al., 1999), and slope steepness and soil moisture that govern fire occurrence and slope stability (Wissmar and Swanson, 1990). The downstream variability in hydraulics and channel morphology imposed by these landform controls creates downstream variability in habitats and in nutrient availability, and consequently in biotic assemblages.

As described previously, organisms inhabiting mountain rivers have specific morphological, behavioral, and physiological adaptations to the high-velocity and coarse substrate of these rivers (Ward, 1992). Most organisms have morphological adaptations to maintain position in fast water or to avoid the full force of the current, such as attachment to solid surfaces for benthic algae and insects. Aquatic and riparian biota may also have specific responses to the disturbances characteristic of mountain rivers. Species may be resistant to change during the disturbance, taking refuge in secondary channels or streambed interstices, for example, and they may be resilient, recovering quickly after the disturbance (Swanson et al., 1998). Post-disturbance biological responses depend on the distribution of disturbance patches and refuges, on species-habitat relations, on dispersal among patches, on biotic interactions such as competition, and on the availability of food resources (Swanson et al., 1998). As an example of the latter factor, Valett et al. (1994) found that algae at hyporheic upwelling zones recovered from a flash-flood disturbance along a desert channel significantly faster than algae at downwelling zones. Hyporheic zones of desert streams may also provide a refuge for microbiota during flash floods (Grimm et al., 1991).

A downstream progression along a river in the Colorado Front Range, USA illustrates the structure of mountain river ecosystems (Bestgen, 1992, pers. comm.; Ward, 1992). The biomass of attached flora is greatest in the headwaters (approx. 3500-2800 m elevation), where mosses and lichens are well developed, and at the base of the mountains (below approx. 1700 m elevation), where filamentous algae and angiosperms proliferate. Biomass levels are low at mid-elevation sites (2800-1700 m elevation), where a variety of epilithic microalgae are dominant. Zoobenthic fauna is dominated by insects, which constitute from 79 to 99% of all zoobenthic organisms. Zoobenthic abundance is lowest in the headwaters, increases to the mid-elevation sites (approx. 2100 m), levels off, and then increases markedly beyond the mountains until the channel substrate becomes relatively mobile sand, at which point abundance again decreases. Zoobenthic diversity is low in the headwaters, increases steeply downstream, and levels off at the mid-elevation sites (approx. 2000 m).

The fish assemblage is controlled primarily by water temperature. Cold-water species of trout and sculpin dominate the higher elevations. Coolwater species of suckers and minnows appear at the lower mid-elevation sites, and warmwater species dominate beyond the mountain front. No more than three and usually only one species exist in a relatively short stream reach (500 m) in the headwaters, whereas up to 15-20 species may be present along such a reach beyond the mountains. This increasing fish species diversity probably results from increasing stream size and habitat complexity, and from the relatively greater number of warmwater fish species.

Riparian vegetation also tends to become more abundant and diverse downstream because of increasing valley-bottom width and habitat complexity. Riparian communities at the higher elevations are dominated by dwarf birch and willow, which give way to alder, birch, larger willows, and narrowleaf cottonwood at intermediate elevations, and finally to box elder and cottonwood near the base of the mountains.

Disturbance regime also varies with elevation along the rivers of the Colorado Front Range. The highest elevation, steepest channels may be subject to relatively frequent disturbance from debris flows or localized movement of large woody debris. Proceeding downstream, average channel gradient decreases and debris flows along the channel may become less frequent. Snowmelt floods may create seasonally regular, moderate disturbances, so that these second- to fourth-order channels are actually quite stable. Below approximately 2300m in elevation, channels are subject to flashy, thunderstorm-driven floods that occur irregularly and substantially modify channel configuration. Riparian and aquatic communities may reflect these disturbance regimes, as well as elevation-related changes in climate.

A Case Study of Human Impacts: The Columbia River Basin

The impact of human actions on the aquatic and riparian biota of mountain rivers is of great concern in many mountainous areas. The various types of human impacts on mountain rivers will be discussed more thoroughly in the next chapter, but the decline of salmonid fish in the northwestern U.S. provides an example of how multiple human impacts within a watershed may affect the biotic communities of mountain rivers.

Salmonid refers to fish of the family Salmoniidae, which includes salmon, trout, and whitefishes. Many salmonid species in the northwestern U.S. live a portion of their adult life in the Pacific Ocean, returning to freshwater to spawn. The migration of these fish upstream along the steep rivers of the Cascade Mountains is an amazing feat. Once the fish reach the appropriate channel segment, they construct a redd (nest) in gravel substrates (Everest et al., 1987). Redds are typically located at the tails of pools where water movement through the gravel will be continuous (Burner, 1951). The female selects and excavates the redd site, which is buried by upstream excavations after spawning. Low flows, dams, and weirs may prevent access to upstream spawning sites (Baxter, 1977; Reiser and Bjornn, 1979; Goldsmith and Hildyard, 1984; Nakano et al., 1990; Stanford and Hauer, 1992), and high velocity during high flows may prevent the female from constructing a redd. The adult fish die after spawning, and the eggs incubate in the gravel for up to nine months. During this period the eggs are vulnerable to high flows that mobilize the bed gravel and destroy the eggs (Montgomery et al., 1996b), to low flows that expose the bed and dessicate or freeze the eggs, and to silt- and clay-size particles that infiltrate the gravel matrix, reducing the flow of water and oxygen past the eggs and suffocating the embryos.

After hatching, the sac fry (young fish) live in the gravel. They remain vulnerable to reduced concentrations of dissolved oxygen, desiccation, or freezing during low flows (McNeil, 1966), and to crushing by bedload movement during high flows (Reiser and Bjornn, 1979). When the young fish emerge from the gravel, they must continually swim against the current to avoid being swept downstream. Shallow stream margins, pool eddies, and other sites of low velocity and protective cover provide ideal sites for newly emerged fish (Everest and Chapman, 1972). The fish then move to summer rearing sites that provide adequate food and living space (Chapman, 1966). Individual fish will choose sites that minimize energy costs of defense against other fish and of maintaining position in a current, while maximizing energy gain and growth through feeding (Fausch, 1984). Juvenile salmonids tend to face into the current, waiting for food items to drift within sight (Wickham, 1967; Fausch, 1984). Cover, in the form of woody debris, overhanging vegetation near the water surface, boulders, undercut banks, or deep water, is important to provide protection from predators, competitors, and variations in streamflow (Platts et al., 1983). During the autumn, fish move to sites with more cover and refuge from high velocity flow for winter rearing, before moving out to sea (Sullivan et al., 1987).

During the mid-1800s, 16 million salmon annually returned to the Columbia River system (Dietrich, 1995). Eighty percent of the 2.5 million fish that return today are hatchery fish, and the numbers of both wild and hatchery fish continue to drop. This precipitous decline in salmonids has been attributed to several factors (Palmer, 1994). From the 1930s to the 1970s, fifty-nine major dams were constructed in the 648,000 km^2 Columbia River drainage basin (Figure 5.3), primarily for hydroelectric power generation. Although an estimated $500 million has been spent on hatcheries, and on fish ladders and other structures to improve fish passage across the dams (Dietrich, 1995), the dams remain a

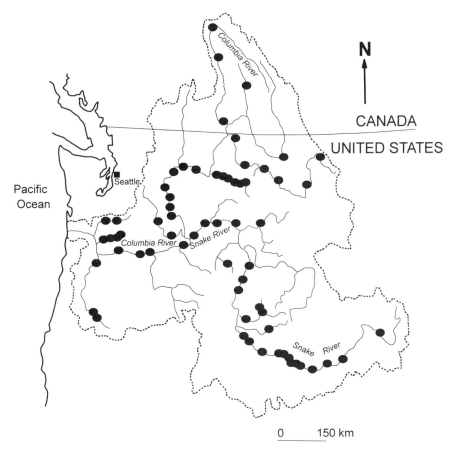

Figure 5.3. Map of the Columbia River basin in the northwestern USA and southwestern Canada. Dark circles represent dams. The majority of the river basin is mountainous.

substantial barrier to salmonid migration. The alteration of flow regime associated with dam operation has also impacted the salmonids, from flooding of spawning and rearing sites by reservoirs to exposure of redds by unnaturally low flows (Ligon et al., 1995).

Overfishing by commercial operators has also been implicated in salmonid decline. The commercial catch of chinook salmon peaked at 19.5 million kilograms in 1883, and then plunged from overfishing (Dietrich, 1995). Native American fishermen noted that the huge salmon runs had disappeared from Priest Rapids on the middle Columbia River by 1905 because of unregulated commercial fishing; this was more than 30 years before the first major dam on the river was completed (Dietrich, 1995).

A third major impact on the salmonids of the Columbia River basin has been the timber harvest in this region of humid climate, tectonic uplift, high relief, and naturally unstable slopes. Timber harvest exacerbates slope instability, leading to mass movements that greatly increase the sediment load of mountain rivers, causing siltation of spawning grav-els and infilling of pools (Slaney et al., 1977; Sullivan et al., 1987; Kasran, 1988; Platts et al., 1989; Overton et al., 1993). The removal of surrounding upland and riparian vegeta-tion reduces the supply of large woody debris to the channel and removes overhanging vegetation, leading to increased water temperatures, reduced nutrient input, and loss of cover (Heede, 1991b; Fausch and Northcote, 1992; Richmond and Fausch, 1995).

The cumulative impact of all of these human activities has been to substantially alter many of the stream channel reaches that provide habitat critical to salmonids. Channels that naturally had a diverse morphology and substrate, with pool-riffle sequences, sand-to boulder-size clasts, and large woody debris, have become more uniform runs or riffles with fewer low velocity areas, less cover and nutrients, and a flow regime that may bear little resemblance to natural precipitation cycles. Such complete alteration of mountain river systems is unfortunately common in developed nations, and is proceeding rapidly in developing countries. Recommended strategies for facilitating salmonid recovery include modification of human-imposed disturbance regimes to create and maintain a range of habitat conditions in space and time within and among watersheds containing salmon, and establishment of watershed reserves that contain the best existing habitats and include the most ecologically intact watersheds (Reeves et al., 1995).

Summary

The aquatic and riparian communities of mountain rivers have some distinctive char-acteristics relative to lowland rivers. Much of the primary production in mountain rivers is allochthonous, with biofilm assemblages and macroinvertebrate shredders and collec-tors processing the organic matter and then serving as prey for other organisms. Aquatic insects and fish have behavioral strategies and morphologies that facilitate survival in swift, turbulent flow. Aquatic and riparian species along mountain rivers tend to be those which can tolerate natural disturbances such as floods or debris flows. The disturbance regime of a mountain river is partly a function of the spatial scale being considered; microhabitats are subject to more frequent disturbances than are stream segments (Figure 5.1). Depending on the scale of the disturbances, river characteristics from hyporheic zone chemistry and nutrient availability (Valett et al., 1990; Fisher et al., 1998b) to reach-scale riparian vegetation (Swanson et al., 1998) may be affected. A critical component of under-standing and predicting the behavior of aquatic and riparian ecosystems is being able to elucidate the mechanisms, including disturbance, generating pattern at different spatial and temporal scales (Hildrew and Giller, 1994; Raffaelli et al., 1994). The downstream gradients described in the river continuum concept characterize many mountain rivers well, although these gradients and the processes which produce them are increasingly being disrupted by human activities.

6

MOUNTAIN RIVERS AND HUMANS

Humans inevitably modify any landscape that they occupy. As long as this modification is of low intensity or limited extent or duration, the processes operating along hillslopes or in river channels are unlikely to cross a substantial threshold as a result of human modification. Hunter-gatherer societies may start wildfires or cultivate small patches of land, but are unlikely to alter hillslope water and sediment yield enough to cause a change in channel morphology. The development of sustained, intensive agriculture (crops and grazing), however, has marked a turning point for many societies in terms of impact on the landscape. This development was followed by channel alluviation in regions as diverse as Mesolithic Britain (Limbrey, 1983), Neolithic Poland (Starkel, 1988), Neolithic China (Mei-e and Xianmo, 1994), the 18th century eastern United States (Chorley et al., 1984; Kearney and Stevenson, 1991), and contemporary Greece (Astaras, 1984). Although much of this alluviation occurred in the transport and depositional zones of the middle and lower portions of drainage basins (Hooke and Redmond, 1992), much of the sediment originated in the uplands and was transported along headwater channels. At the end of the 20th century, about 10% of the world's population lived in mountainous regions (Grötzbach and Stadel, 1997). As increasing world population and demand for food continue to bring formerly marginal, upland regions into cultivation, human impacts have spread throughout the world's mountainous regions, exacerbating changes that have already resulted from other human activities.

Types of Impact

Human impacts on rivers may be indirect if they involve changes in water and sediment yield to the channel as a result of changes in hillslope processes. The impacts may also be direct in that the discharge of water or sediment, or channel morphology, is modified by human activities within the channel (Knighton, 1984). The human activities that principally impact mountain rivers are listed in Table 6.1. An increase in natural hazards is closely associated in many mountainous regions with changes in hillslope and channel processes resulting from human activities. An activity such as timber harvest, for example, not only increases hillslope water and sediment yields, but may sufficiently destabilize the slopes that debris flow magnitude and frequency increase, leading to channel aggradation and an increase in out-of-bank flooding.

Table 6.1. Human impacts on mountain rivers.

Indirect

timber harvest and road building
grazing
crops
urbanization
lode mining
climate change

Direct

beaver trapping, removal of large woody debris, tie drives
dams and flow regulation
mining (placer, sand and gravel)

Indirect Impacts

(1) Timber harvest and road building. The cutting of trees and the associated road building may greatly increase hillslope sediment yield over the short term (approximately 1-10 years), and water yield over longer periods (approximately 1-30 years) until vegetation grows back (Bosch and Hewlett, 1982; Haigh et al., 1990; Roberts et al., 1994). Logging in the mountains of Peninsular Malaysia, for example, resulted in 70-90% increases in suspended sediment yield (Kasran, 1988) and a 470% increase in water yield (Nik, 1988) over a 4-6 year period. The magnitude of these changes will depend on climate, and on slope characteristics of substrate type, steepness, length and aspect, as well as on the methods used in timber harvest and the intensity and extent of forest removal and subsequent recovery.

Mineral soils exposed during timber harvest become more susceptible to surface erosion (Megahan and Kidd, 1972; Johnson and Beschta, 1980). Compaction reduces infiltration rates, and may increase overland flow and sheetwash or rilling. Reduction in interception and evapotranspiration may cause elevated soil moisture levels that increase the weight of the soil and decrease slope stability (Megahan and Bohn, 1989), as well as increasing soil pipeflow and subsurface pore pressures (Keppeler and Brown, 1998). As positive pore water pressures become more likely, landslides may increase (Swanston and Swanson, 1976). Removal of vegetation causes a decline in the tensile strength of root material (Gray and Megahan, 1981), leading to lower soil shear strength. Bank erosion and channel headward expansion in cut areas, and windthrow along streams for which a fringe of riparian trees has been left, can also increase sediment yield to the channel (Lewis, 1998).

Roads constructed in association with the timber harvest increase the slope angle at the cut and fill slope, redistribute the weight on hillslopes, alter the downslope flow of water (Swanston and Swanson, 1976), destabilize the slope and promote slope failure (Sah and Mazari, 1998), and contribute substantial fine sediment (Reid and Dunne, 1984; Froehlich, 1995) long after vegetative cover has regrown. Studies in the humid-tropical mountains of Puerto Rico indicate that landslide frequency within 85 m of a road was five times the frequency found at greater distances from a road (Larsen and Parks, 1997). In the nearby U.S. Virgin Islands, road erosion since 1950 has caused at least a fourfold increase in island-wide sediment yields (MacDonald et al., 1997). For the 44,000 km of roads constructed in the mountains of India during the previous 25 years, 40,000-80,000 m^3 of debris had to be moved for each kilometer of road, creating an average 550 m^3 of erosion material per kilometer of road (Valdiya, 1987). In the Upper Konto watershed of Indonesia, roads occupy only 3% of the total area, but contribute 15% of the sediment (Rijskijk and Bruijnzeel, 1991). Road construction in the mountainous drainage of North Halawa Valley, Hawaii produced 90% of the fluvial fine-sediment load during the period of construction (Hill et al., 1998). Sediment yields from roads may be greatly reduced if roadside vegetation is retained and roadside ditches are not cleaned (Luce and Black, 1999).

Several mechanisms may increase water yields following timber harvest. The removal of vegetation reduces evapotranspiration (Cline et al., 1977), and may increase snowmelt (Berris and Harr, 1987). Additional water stored in the soil may contribute to summer baseflow, and previously intermittent stream reaches and soil pipes may become perennial (Keppeler, 1998). Burning during site preparation may form temporarily hydrophobic soil layers that decrease infiltration (DeByle, 1973). Compaction along roads decreases infiltration and intercepts subsurface flow. Increased water yields may in turn enhance peak flows in the channel (Ziemer, 1981; Harr, 1986; Cheng, 1989). The combined increase in water and sediment yields following timber harvest commonly results in channel aggradation, bank erosion, loss of pool habitat and woody debris, and an increased potential for overbank flow and channel change during floods (Madsen, 1995).

Numerous studies describe the processes by which altered hillslope water and sediment yields cause change in mountain channel geometry. Heede (1991a) found a 62% increase in the peak discharge of the South Fork of Thomas Creek, Arizona (USA), a small mountain catchment, during an eight-year period after basal area of timber stand was reduced to 28%. This increase in peak discharge caused channel cross-sectional area to increase by 10%, and removed nearly half of the previously existing log and clast steps within the channel. During a 15-year study of the 10 km^2 Carnation Creek watershed in western Canada, bank erosion, channel width, and channel mobility increased within clearcut reaches, but not along uncut channel segments (Hartman and Scrivener, 1990). Forest clearing in the Ruahine Range of New Zealand caused the Tanaki River to increase in width from 5m to 10m in the early 1920s, to 54 m by 1942, and to 60 m by 1976 (Mosley, 1978). Timber harvest in the Caspar Creek watershed of California initially caused increased inputs of bed material, although this trend was expected to reverse as existing large woody debris decayed and LWD inputs from depleted riparian sources decreased (Lisle and Napolitano, 1998). Changes in channel morphology associated with the effects of timber harvest may persist more than a century after logging ceases (Napolitano, 1998).

In addition to altered channel morphology, the increase of hillslope water yield following timber harvest may cause increased flooding. Deforestation, combined with minor climatic variability, caused an increase in the number of damaging floods in Switzerland during the 19th century (Vischer, 1989).

Finally, timber harvest may affect stream chemistry. Forest-floor and soil organic matter decline, leading to a net loss of nitrogen from the soil and increased export of inorganic nitrogen in streams (e.g. Dahlgren, 1998), as demonstrated at the Hubbard Brook Experimental Forest in New Hampshire and at Coweeta, North Carolina, both in the USA (Bormann and Likens, 1979; Nihlgård et al., 1994; Waide et al., 1998). Increased availability and loss of NO_3^- also increased the loss of cations from the ecosystem (Likens et al., 1977). Solute fluxes of calcium and potassium required five years to return to pre-logging levels (Swank, 1986; Johnson et al., 1994). The magnitude of these responses is largely determined by soil type, site climate, and harvesting intensity (Reynolds et al., 1995b). Studies of logging in Malaysian rainforests have shown similar increases in solutes (Johnson et al., 1994). Removal of the forest canopy adjacent to streams increases solar heating of surface waters and thus increases maximum summer water temperatures (Swank and Johnson, 1994).

(2) Grazing. In upland regions of a drainage basin, heavy grazing compacts the soil, reduces infiltration, and increases runoff substantially enough that the runoff regime may be altered from variable source area to Hortonian overland flow (Trimble and Mendel, 1995). One study in the southeastern US demonstrated up to 80% decreases in infiltration rate as a result of upland grazing (Holtan and Kirkpatrick, 1950). One review noted that, worldwide, overgrazing characterizes mountain livestock husbandry, leading to land degradation (Hamilton and Bruijnzeel, 1997). Erosion and sediment yield increase (Bari et al., 1993) as vegetation cover is reduced (Hofmann and Ries, 1991), fertility and organic matter content decrease (Trimble and Mendel, 1995), and soil aggregate stability is reduced by trampling. An aerial study of soil erosion in Nepal found severe erosion associated with overgrazed land immediately above cultivated zones (Pereira, 1989). The effects of increased water and sediment yield on channel morphology, stability, and flooding are as described for timber harvest and road construction.

Grazing within the riparian zone decreases channel bank resistance by reducing vegetation (Platts, 1981; Marlow and Pogacnik, 1985; Myers and Swanson, 1996b) and exposing the substrate, and by trampling that directly erodes banks (Kauffman and Krueger, 1984; Trimble and Mendel, 1995). Grazing animals may create ramps along steep or wooded channel banks, and these bank irregularities enhance turbulence and bank erosion during high flows (Trimble, 1994). Trails along the floodplain may also channel flow and promote erosion during overbank flows (Cooke and Reeves, 1976). Enhanced bank and overbank erosion may lead to deposition of fine sediments on the channel bed, reducing pool volume and spawning habitat (Myers and Swanson, 1996a). Channels with banks of low cohesivity are most susceptible to these effects (Myers and Swanson, 1992) (Figure 6.1).

Figure 6.1. Photographs of portions of Sheep Creek, Colorado, USA. (a) View downstream of a channel reach protected from grazing by a fence. Channel has dense riparian vegetation (willows) and is approximately 4 m wide. (b) View across channel of reach immediately upstream from the reach shown in A. This channel reach is not excluded from grazing, and cattle have trampled the banks and removed the riparian vegetation. Channel is approximately 9 m wide here.

Both riverine and upland areas are commonly grazed simultaneously, so that channel erosion is enhanced by increased water yield and bank weakening (Trimble and Mendel, 1995). Channel erosion is most pronounced during flood flows. Associated flood hazards to aquatic communities include siltation along the channel bed (Myers and Swanson, 1991) and loss of bank cover by overhanging and riparian vegetation. Where riparian-zone grazing is limited by exclosures, channel recovery may still be inhibited by a lag time for vegetation re-establishment and sediment deposition, or by continued grazing in upland regions (Kondolf, 1993).

(3). Crops. The planting of crops alters the infiltration capacity of the soil, and thus the water and sediment yields from hillslopes (Dunne, 1979), analogous to the changes accompanying timber harvest and grazing. The magnitude of these alterations will vary with the spatial extent and type of crops. Klimek (1987) correlated enhanced sediment yields, increased flood peaks, and a change from meandering to braided channel pattern following the rapid development of "potato plantations" in the Polish Carpathian Mountains during the latter half of the 19th century. Rawat and Rawat (1994) found that agricultural land in the central Himalaya of India had an erosion rate of 0.18 mm/yr, as compared to rates of 0.02-0.04 mm/yr under natural forests. During the month of heaviest rainfall, suspended sediment yields were 7 to 26 times higher in the most disturbed agricultural land than in the forest. The timing of crop cycles may also be important. For example, the pre-monsoon rains in Nepal's Middle Mountains occur when the fields are not yet adequately vegetated. As a result, soil loss during this period can be greater than during the heavier monsoon rains (Carver and Nakarmi, 1995).

Much of the sediment yield increase resulting from mountain agriculture during the last 100, and particularly the last 50 years, has been associated with the migration of people from the lowlands to the mountains (Hamilton and Bruijnzeel, 1997). In contrast to long-term mountain residents who successfully practice soil and water conservation via techniques such as terracing (Pereira, 1989), people from the lowlands often apply inappropriate agricultural methods and then move on to clear new lands when the existing land becomes degraded (Wiesmann, 1992). Terracing has been found to reduce soil loss by 80% in the cultivated mountainous regions of the Philippines (Daño and Siapno, 1992).

(4) Urbanization. Although human population densities are generally not as high in mountainous regions as in adjacent lowland and piedmont areas, many mountain rivers do pass through large urbanized areas such as Kingston, Jamaica (Barker and McGregor, 1988), Quito, Ecuador, or Yogyakarta, Java. Increasing residential use of mountainous regions during the 21st century is likely to increase the impacts of smaller urban centers on mountain rivers.

The transition from natural or agricultural vegetation to buildings and roads dramatically effects water and sediment yield from a drainage basin. During the initial phase of construction, vegetation is largely removed, and the land surface is leveled or artificially contoured. This results in very high yields as the unconsolidated surface is exposed to rainbeat, sheet flow, and rilling (Goldman et al., 1986; Ruslan, 1995).

After the completion of construction, when ground surfaces are stabilized beneath roads, buildings, and lawns, sediment yield drops to a negligible value that is commonly lower than pre-urbanization values. Over the longer term, urbanization results in a substantial increase in water yield as impervious surface area in the basin is greatly increased. The increase in surface runoff may cause sheetflooding and damage to low-lying structures unless the runoff is quickly channelized and removed from the surface. The installation of storm sewers rapidly drains road surfaces, but also further decreases infiltration and time for water to move from hillslopes and into channels. This results in flood peaks of higher magnitude and shorter duration, which can trigger further channel instability.

The classic study of the effects of urbanization on sediment yield and channel response was conducted on channels in the Piedmont region of Maryland, USA (Wolman, 1967; Wolman and Schick, 1967). Increases in sediment yield following timber harvest in the early 1800s and the initial phase of construction in the early 1960s were documented from the sedimentary record, with channel aggradation accompanying the increased sediment yields. Subsequent reductions in sediment yield were associated with channel erosion. Numerous subsequent studies have supported these findings for a range of environments (Miller et al., 1971; Lvovich and Chernogaeva, 1977; Park, 1977; Morisawa and LaFlure, 1979; Nanson and Young, 1981; Harvey et al., 1983; Balamurugan, 1991; Urbonas and Benik, 1995).

Another important aspect of urbanization is the introduction of contaminants into stream channels via runoff and sediment. These contaminants include biodegradable organics which may reduce dissolved oxygen in the stream. Contaminants may also take the form of nutrients which may cause eutrophication, or solids that contribute to turbidity and toxicity. Bacteria which may pose a hazard to human health may be contaminants. Contaminants can also be metals and hydrocarbons that may be toxic to a variety of organisms (Ellis, 1987). The treatment or purification of urban runoff varies greatly among cities, from no treatment through primary treatment (an infiltration basin designed to remove primarily solids and bacterial contaminants) to tertiary treatment plants which remove solids, microbes, and hydrocarbons, and use flocculants such as alum to remove colloidal solids including metals. Contaminants reaching the stream channel may be transported in solution or as particulate matter in suspended or bedload. The contaminants may also be stored in bed, bank, and floodplain sediments. Benthic organisms, phytoplankton, fish and other aquatic organisms may accumulate contaminants from any of these reservoirs, with effects as described in the section on in-channel mining.

(5) Lode mining. Lode or hard-rock mining that occurs within a watershed may increase sediment yield to channels if the surface is extensively disturbed, as in the case of rock quarrying near the Sungai Relau (river) in Malaysia (Ismail and Rahaman, 1994). Nearly 30 m of weathered rock has to be removed to reach fresh rock in this humid tropical environment, and the disruption of slope vegetation and substrate produces suspended sediment concentrations 1200 times greater than those under natural forest cover. Tailings piles associated with the mining activities may

also contribute sediment directly or via hillslope erosion to stream channels (Vincent and Elliott, 1999). Tailings discharge into the OkTedi River in Papua New Guinea increased annual suspended sediment load in the river anywhere from 1.1 to 38 times pre-mining levels at different locations along the river (Markham and Day, 1994).

At sites where mine tailings have been chemically treated to extract ore minerals, the sediment and runoff from the tailings piles may be a source of toxic contaminants to the river (Meyer and Watt, 1999; Vincent and Elliott, 1999). Drainage from mine adits and tailings can be very acidic, and the bed of the receiving river can become coated with hydrated ferric oxide slimes (Davies, 1983). Acid oxidizing conditions may mobilize other metals from the mining waste, and these metals may be transported downstream in solution, or complexed and adsorbed onto suspended sediment (Merefield, 1995) (see also River chemistry, chapter 2). Metals in solution may continue to be transported from the drainage basin decades after mining has ceased (Grimshaw et al., 1976). In the Carson River valley of Nevada, for example, mercury used to process gold in the mid- to late-1800s is now associated with the fine-grained (< 63 μm) sediment fraction of the channel alluvium. The sediment and mercury are preferentially eroded, redeposited, and stored along channel reaches characterized by low gradients and wide valley floors, as occurred during a 1997 flood (Miller et al., 1999).

(6) Climate change. The final indirect form of human impact on mountain rivers is less understood and predictable than those described previously. Both systematic sampling of atmospheric gases during the past forty years and air bubbles trapped in polar ice sheets indicate that atmospheric concentrations of CO_2 and other compounds (CH_4, N_2O, chlorofluorocarbons) have increased since the start of the Industrial Revolution. These so-called greenhouse gases permit a given volume of air to absorb more infrared radiation, and are believed to contribute to global warming. Continued increases of CO_2 have been projected to cause a rise of 2-4 °C in average global temperature (U.S. National Academy of Sciences, 1983).

As discussed in chapter 3, the climates of mountain regions are especially complex because of their temporal and spatial variability, and are poorly recorded by existing systematic records. The General Circulation Models (GCMs) used to simulate potential global warming scenarios presently do not have sufficient resolution to adequately address mountain climates. As a result, two approaches have been adopted for projecting climate changes in mountains (Price and Barry, 1997). Statistical down-scaling has been used to relate local climate variables to large-scale meteorological predictors (Von Storch et al., 1993; Gyalistras et al., 1997). Alternatively, a more detailed regional model may be nested within a GCM (Giorgi et al., 1994; Marinucci et al., 1995).

Relating predicted climate change to hydrology is also problematic for mountain regions. In addition to uncertainty of model simulations for regional to local scales, processes of precipitation, soil moisture, and runoff may be difficult to model because of orographic modifications of cloud microphysics and mesoscale weather systems, and interrelated changes in snowpack, snow-line elevation, and the timing of accumulation and ablation seasons (Price and Barry, 1997). General predictions are that precipitation totals will increase in high latitudes, and in mid-latitudes during winter. The variability of precipitation and possibly the frequency of extreme precipitation events will increase in the tropics. Snow cover duration will decrease, and mid-latitude soil moisture may decrease in summer (Kattenberg et al., 1996).

These predicted changes will inevitably impact mountain rivers. As vegetation and soil-forming processes respond to changes in temperature and precipitation, infiltration capacity, water yield, stream chemistry, and slope stability will change. Because temperature or precipitation thresholds influence the magnitude and frequency of mass movements such as debris flows, climate change may substantially alter sediment yields to mountain rivers. Sediment transport patterns may change in response to changes in both sediment supply and flow characteristics. Changes in the magnitude, frequency, duration, temperature, and predictability of flow play an important role in regulating river ecological processes and patterns (Poff, 1992), and aquatic organisms will be affected by climate change. A study of Alaskan streams that assessed the impact of warming-induced increases in glacial runoff, for example, demonstrated that as flow regime, water temperature, and sediment discharge changed, corresponding changes occurred in channel substrate, bedforms, channel stability, leaf litter quantity and quality, and habitat complexity (Oswood et al., 1992). Changes in flood magnitude and frequency may trigger channel incision along arid-region rivers, removing the deep hyporheic sediments that support microbial communities, while changes in precipitation and runoff alter the availability of nitrogen, which is a limiting element in these rivers (Grimm and Fisher, 1992). Finally, by altering water availability to human communities, climate change may impact water management and use (Chang et al., 1992).

Numerous studies have assessed the potential impacts of climate change on water resources in mountain regions from the scale of small drainage basins to entire mountain ranges (Price and Barry, 1997). McCabe and Hay (1995), for example, assumed an increase of 4° C in mean annual temperature for the 775 km^2 East River basin of Colorado. This resulted in a 4-5% increase in annual precipitation and larger, earlier runoff peaks for this snowmelt-dominated basin. Analogous studies have been conducted in Australia (Whetton et al., 1996), Europe (Bultot et al., 1992), New Zealand (Garr and Fitzharris, 1994), the United States (Nash and Gleick, 1991), and Greece (Mimikou et al., 1991).

Direct Impacts

(7) Beaver trapping. Beavers are herbivorous rodents that build dams and canals along waterways in North America and Europe. Beaver density averages 2-3 colonies per kilometer along streams with suitable habitat of permanent and relatively constant water flow, valley widths of approximately 45 m, channel gradients less than 15%, and aspen or willow growing nearby (Allen, 1983; DeByle, 1985). Beaver (*Castor canadensis*) were present historically throughout much of North America. The beaver

population prior to the coming of Europeans is estimated at between 60 and 400 million animals, or a range of 6 to 40 animals per kilometer of stream (Naiman et al., 1986). The European beaver, *Castor fiber*, was historically found from Britain in the west across the whole Eurasian continent, and from the Mediterranean Sea in the south to the tundras in the north (Hartman, 1996).

Channels inhabited by beavers have a stepped appearance (Figure 6.2). Water ponds behind the dams of wood and sediment constructed by the beavers, creating reaches of low gradient that are punctuated by abrupt drops of 1-2 m over the dams. The ponds serve to decrease flow velocity, store sediment, reduce channel bed and bank erosion, promote more uniform stream flows during periods of high and low discharge, and diversify aquatic and riparian habitat (Naiman et al., 1988; Olson and Hubert, 1994). As sediment gradually fills the beaver pond, meadow grasses and riparian shrubs and trees take over the site, providing a broad, stable floodplain that continues to store sediment and slow the passage of floodwaters (Butler and Malanson, 1995).

Hunting and change of land use drove the European beaver close to extinction throughout its range by the 19th century (Hartman, 1996; Gurnell, 1998). Similarly, beaver trapping for the fur trade nearly eradicated beavers in North America. The eastern portions of the continent were trapped out as early as the 1600s, the interior and western regions by the 1830s (Sandoz, 1964). Beaver populations are presently 15-50% of those prior to trapping (Naiman et al., 1986). In the upper Mississippi River basin, 99% of the beaver ponds present in 1600 A.D. were gone by 1990. At a depth of 1 m, the original area ponded by beaver dams in this 21 million hectare region could have stored more than three floods the size of the destructive summer 1993 flood on the upper Mississippi River (Hey and Philippi, 1995).

The removal of beaver resulted in channel incision and bank erosion, increased channel gradient, and higher sediment discharge. Hydrographs became more peaked, and aquatic and riparian habitat became less diverse along the channels affected. Although many of these changes occurred prior to systematic study of river systems, recent re-introductions of beaver indicate the magnitude of change that can occur along rivers, as exemplified by Currant Creek, Wyoming (USA). Following beaver reestablishment along this channel, daily sediment transport decreased from 30,000 to 3,600 kg (Brayton, 1984; Parker, 1986).

(8) Removal of large woody debris, and tie drives. Large woody debris has been removed from river channels to reduce flooding, and to enhance river navigation and fish passage. Historic records indicate that rivers across a wide range of drainage basin sizes, channel gradients, and climatic regimes contained substantial woody debris. Some of the largest logjams were described for lowland rivers. Veatch (1906) wrote of more than 20 lakes formed by logjam impoundments along a 260-km reach of the Red River, Louisiana (USA). The entire structure was called the Great Raft, and constantly migrated upstream as new woody debris was added to the upper reaches and debris about 200 years older decayed and dispersed at the downstream end. These logs were cleared from the Red River in 1873, and the lakes began draining.

Figure 6.2. Looking upstream along a small channel that has a series of beaver dams, North Park, Colorado. The field of view is approximately 10 m wide, and the drop of the dam in the foreground is approximately 1.5 m.

Eight hundred thousand snags were removed along a 16-km stretch of the lower Mississippi River from 1870-1920 (Sedell et al., 1982), and similarly massive log-jams occurred on rivers in the northwestern U.S. (Sedell and Froggatt, 1984) and in Europe (Piégay and Gurnell, 1997). Personal observation in old-growth forest of the Colorado Rocky Mountains and the Cascade Range of the northwestern U.S. indicates that logjams spanning the channel may extend several channel widths upstream, and individual pieces of woody debris or smaller jams are ubiquitous (Figure 6.3).

The consequences of woody debris removal on rivers both large and small are similar to those described following the eradication of beaver. The channel initially becomes unstable, with more rapid passage of flood waves, enhanced bed and bank erosion, and

Figure 6.3. Upstream view of East St. Louis Creek, Colorado, showing abundant woody debris in channel. Channel is approximately 4 m wide. Photograph courtesy of Janet H. Curran.

higher sediment discharge. When the channel does stabilize, the earlier hydraulic and substrate diversity have been replaced by a more uniform run or riffle-type channel that provides much less habitat for aquatic and riparian organisms. The numerous functions of large woody debris in mountain rivers are described in chapter 3.

The use of river channels for navigation or transport of goods may have effects similar to those described from removing debris jams. The use of streams in the Rocky Mountains of Colorado and Wyoming (USA) for the transport of railroad cross-ties provides an example. During the 1870s and 1880s, timber cut in the mountains was sent downstream to lumbermills via the river channels. Many of the rivers did not carry a sufficient volume of water to float timber except during the annual spring snowmelt floods. The ties cut during fall and winter were stored beside the rivers and in the channels. The timing for releasing the ties at high water had to be carefully planned; insufficient water would prevent the ties from reaching their destination, but an unexpected flood could scatter broken ties along the valley (Wroten, 1956). In an attempt to control water flow, splash dams were built along many streams to store water that could then be released at appropriate times to ease the ties through difficult channel reaches. It was also common practice to facilitate the downstream movement of ties by altering irregularities along the rivers. Such alterations in the lower gradient or meandering rivers including blocking off sloughs, swamps, low meadows, and banks along wider sections with log cribbing (Schmal and Wesche, 1989). In higher-gradient reaches, large boulders, logs, debris, and encroaching riparian vegetation were cut or blasted to facilitate passage. The ties still became jammed along the rivers, in some cases creating jams 9-12 m high with water running over them in waterfalls (Wroten, 1956). The base of the jam then had to be blasted or broken up with long pikes. At some point downstream, usually where a railroad crossed the river, a boom was built to catch the ties. The distance from cutting area to boom varied from a few kilometers on short streams to more than 80 km on the main rivers. During the winter of 1868-69, more than 200,000 ties were cut and floated down the Poudre River, with a similar rate of operations maintained the next year (Wroten, 1956).

Subsequent research on mountain streams in the Medicine Bow National Forest of southern Wyoming has compared analogous streams that did and did not have tie drives. The streams that had drives tended to be 1 to 3.6 times wider, with minimal bank development, riparian or bank cover for fish, and habitat diversity (Schmal and Wesche, 1989). They had more riffles, less well-developed pools, less large organic debris, and fewer debris-related habitats for aquatic organisms (Young et al., 1990, 1994). The riparian zones of these streams were dominated by uniformly-aged lodgepole pine (*Pinus contorta*) dating to the time of the last drive, in contrast to the uneven-aged, old-growth vegetation of the streams without drives (Young et al., 1990).

(9) Dams and flow regulation. The construction of dams and the regulation of river flow by reservoirs and diversions have been undertaken for purposes of flood control, water supply, navigation, and hydroelectric power generation. Dams have been built since circa 2800 B.C. (Smith, 1971), but the construction of dams larger than 15 m tall has accelerated substantially since the 1950s (Goldsmith and Hildyard, 1984; Petts, 1984). Dams in the European Alps, for example, provide an important power supply because of the abundance of water and the high energy associated with steep channel gradients. In the winter of 1972-73 such dams supplied 24% of Switzerland's power consumption (Wilhelm, 1994). In some cases, such as the Grande Dixence hydropower scheme in southern Switzerland, which involves 35 glacier basins, meltwater intake structures divert virtually all of the meltwater from proglacial streams into tunnels to a large storage reservoir (Gurnell et al., 1990). As of 1970, 322 reservoirs were present in the Alps, with an effective volume of approximately 10.4 km^3 (Wilhelm, 1994). Austria alone has 30 major reservoirs, and these generate 23% of the country's electric power (Pircher, 1990). Large dams greater than 150 m high were being completed at a rate of one every 1.65 years in Europe as of 1989 (Petts, 1989), and these dams are increasingly being sited in mountainous regions.

The effect of a dam or flow regulation on a river will depend on the nature of the alterations in water and sediment discharge, and on the characteristics of the channel. Dam construction commonly reduces the mean and the coefficient of variation of annual peak flow; increases minimum flows; shifts the seasonal flow variability; and, in the case of hydroelectric dams, may greatly increase diurnal flow fluctuations. Average annual floods downstream from 29 dams in the central and western United States ranged from 3% to 90% of pre-dam values, with an average of 40% (Williams and Wolman, 1984). Many dams operate under minimum-release requirements that increase the magnitude of low flows occurring within a given recurrence interval. Annual seven-day low flows on the Columbia River in southwestern Canada nearly doubled following construction of a reservoir (Hirsch et al., 1990). The high flows released during peak production times (approximately 6 hours per day, 5 days per week) from hydroelectric dams may be nearly as large as the mean annual flood that occurred in pre-dam conditions (Hirsch et al., 1990). During evening and weekend low production, flow release may drop precipitously.

The channel downstream from a dam commonly adjusts its morphology to the altered flow regime and sediment supply caused by the sediment-trapping properties of the dam. Along channels with high suspended sediment concentrations, the change in sediment transport may be substantial. Three major dams were finished between 1952 and 1955 on the Missouri River in the USA. The post-dam annual suspended sediment load 8 km downstream from the lowest dam was less than 1% of the pre-dam load, and the load was only 30% of pre-dam levels 1200 km downstream (Williams and Wolman, 1985). Construction of the Mosul Dam on the Tigris River in Iraq reduced suspended sediment load 60 km downstream from the dam by more than 95%, causing channel incision and coarsening of the bed sediment (Al-Taiee, 1990).

Channel adjustment may take the form of incision that occurs during the first few years after dam construction, and may extend hundreds of kilometers downstream from the dam (Galay, 1983; Weiss, 1994; Jiongxin, 1996). The reduction in peak flows below the dam may also reduce sediment transport capacity to the point that tributary inputs cause channel aggradation or narrowing (Petts, 1977; Allen et al., 1989). The reduction in flood scouring may enhance the establishment of riparian vegetation, so that bars, islands, and channel banks are stabilized and the channel is narrowed. Channel adjustment varies with distance downstream from the dam (Lagasse, 1981; Andrews, 1986).

Dams not only interfere with the movement of water and sediment, but also with the migration of fish, with water temperature regime and chemistry, and with the movement of nutrients and the coarse woody debris that enhances pool formation and the diversity of aquatic habitat (Baxter, 1977; Brooker, 1981; Ligon et al., 1995; Stanford et al., 1996). Fish may also be severely impacted by the loss of floodplain spawning and nursery habitat when reduced peak flows limit overbank flooding (Jubb, 1972; Chikova, 1974; Lake, 1975; Whitley and Campbell, 1974), or by reductions in minimum flow that prevent spawning (Bundi et al., 1990).

The impact of flow regulation on aquatic biota is illustrated by the Colorado squawfish (*Ptychocheilus lucius*). The squawfish is an endangered species inhabiting the Colorado River basin. The squawfish spawns at a limited number of gravel bars during the recessional limb of the annual snowmelt hydrograph. Sediment deposition and bar formation along a channel reach studied by Harvey et al. (1993) occur at discharges greater than 280 m^3/s. Spawning habitat is formed by bar dissection and erosion of sand and finer sediments at flows of 10-140 m^3/s. The squawfish cannot successfully spawn if the historical May-June peak flow is prolonged too late into the season by dam releases because prolonged sand deposition restricts adult fish access to spawning gravel and may smother developing embryos. This has been a problem since the construction of a dam upstream from the study reach in 1962, and has contributed to the endangered status of the squawfish.

Another example of the impacts of dam-related flow regulation on aquatic ecosystems comes from the Flathead River basin of Montana, USA, which includes both unregulated channel reaches and three dams operated for flood control and hydroelectric power generation. Wetting and subsequent drying of the channel edges and floodplain (the varial zone) occur once a year during spring snowmelt floods along the unregulated channels. Along regulated channels, the varial zone is unpredictably flooded and dried so that aquatic and riparian biota have little chance of naturally colonizing new areas as the stage rises, or emigrating when the stage falls. As a result, aquatic biodiversity is drastically reduced along the regulated reaches (Stanford and Hauer, 1992).

The changes in hydrology and channel morphology associated with dams may impact riparian vegetation in various manners (Pearlstine et al., 1985; Merritt, 1999; see also chapter 5, this volume). Altered channel morphology may reduce or eliminate the freshly-scoured surfaces necessary for riparian seedling establishment. Seedlings may be killed by prolonged submersion because of increased base flows. Low flows occurring at the wrong time of year may not adequately transport riparian seeds downstream. Changing grain-size distribution along the banks and bars of the channel may inhibit seedling establishment. Changes in the water table beneath the floodplain as a result of changed flow regime may cause soil salinization that kills riparian vegetation in arid and semiarid regions (Jolly, 1996). Numerous studies document lower species-richness and percentage cover of riparian vegetation along regulated rivers than along unregulated rivers (Nilsson et al., 1991; Dynesius and Nilsson, 1994).

As dams continue to be constructed at an accelerating pace along mountain rivers in developing countries, other countries are attempting to mitigate the negative impacts of dams by operating the dams so as to mimic a more natural flow regime, or by removing the dam. At least 121 dams were removed between 1930 and 1999 in the United States, with the majority of these removals occurring in the 1990s (Draft Report, 1999). Removal of the Grangeville Dam on the South Fork of the Clearwater River (drainage area 27,000 km^2) in Idaho provides an example. The 17 m tall, 134 m wide arched concrete structure was built in 1903 for hydroelectric power. After the dam's fish ladder failed in 1949, migration of salmon along the river ended. By 1963 the reservoir behind the dam was filled with silt, and the dam was removed. Reservoir sediment was flushed downstream within a few weeks, and 70 km of main channel habitat and more than 170 km of tributaries were opened to migratory fish, revitalizing local fish stocks (Draft Report, 1999).

Flow regulation via diversions has many of the same effects on water and sediment discharge and on channel morphology as do dams and reservoirs. Diversion for irrigation or for flood control commonly reduces both base flows and flood peaks (Schleusener et al., 1962; Richards and Wood, 1977), and thus impacts both channel morphology (Bray and Kellerhals, 1979) and riparian and aquatic communities (Johnson, 1978).

(10) *In-channel mining*. In-channel mining for sand and gravel used in construction

and for placer deposits of precious metals has been occurring for millenia in some regions of the world. This may be particularly common in mountain rivers because of the coarser bed-material and the proximity to in situ ore deposits. Systematic studies of the effects of these activities on rivers were not undertaken until the early 20th century, starting with Gilbert's (1917) work on mountain river channels impacted by placer gold mining in the Sierra Nevada of California (USA). It is now widely recognized that mining disrupts discharge and sediment transport, causing various channel adjustments in response. Large, localized excavations in the channel may initiate a knickpoint that migrates upstream from the excavation, and both bed and bank erosion may be accelerated downstream from the excavation as sediment transport is disrupted. A 50-year flood along Tujunga Wash, California triggered knickpoint migration from a 300m x 460m x 15-23m deep gravel pit (Bull and Scott, 1974). The knickpoint caused the failure of three major highway bridges, and lateral scour downstream from the pit destroyed 7 homes and a long section of a major highway. The upper 100 km of the Arno River incised 1-3 m between 1945 and 1960 as a result of gravel mining and the construction of two dams (Rinaldi and Simon, 1998).

Placer mining that disrupts a coarse, stable channel bed-surface may increase sediment mobility and preferential transport of fine sediments, leading to downstream aggradation and bank instability associated with braiding. The banks of many mountain rivers are resistant to erosion because either the bank is composed of very coarse, tightly-packed sediment, or the bank is capped by a layer of silt and clay held in place by dense tussock grasses or willow and alder roots. If the erosional resistance of the channel banks is lowered through the disruption associated with mining, the channel often becomes laterally unstable, repeatedly shifting back and forth across the valley bottom in a braided pattern. The rapid lateral movement of braided channels discourages thick accumulations of fine-grained overbank sediment, making it difficult for riparian vegetation to become established. The continual shifting also increases the amount of sediment introduced to the river, causing further increases in suspended load. In addition, the instability of the channel substrate is likely to affect aquatic macroinvertebrates, by mimicking the effect of frequent large, erosive floods. The erosion and deposition of bed sediments during periods of high discharge (or channel change) can destroy sessile, stone-surface communities, and cause the downstream displacement of bottom-dwelling animals, which need refuges such as backwaters in order to survive disruptive events. In general, streams which flood or are disrupted frequently may show a marked succession of stream flora and fauna with time, in contrast to those that are not continually disturbed (Winterbourn and Townsend, 1991).

The Middle Fork of the South Platte River in the Colorado Rocky Mountains provides an example of channel instability associated with mining (Hilmes and Wohl, 1995). Historical documents and photographs of the Middle Fork prior to mining, and analogous, unmined rivers nearby (such as the South Fork of the South Platte) provide information about pre-mining channel configuration. The Middle Fork was a relatively deep, narrow stream that meandered through broad meadows of willows and grasses. The channel bed was gravel to cobble size material, and the banks had an upper layer of fine sediment held in place by dense vegetation. Today, reaches of the river that were mined are less sinuous, in many cases having changed from meandering to braided. Mined reaches have been more mobile, as observed in comparisons of aerial photographs from 1938 to 1990, and have coarser bed sediments than unmined reaches, although it has been 65 to 80 years since mining occurred in some of these reaches (Hilmes, 1993).

The mined portions of the Middle Fork flow through the broad intermontane valley of South Park. In contrast, where mined channels are closely constrained by bedrock valley walls, as in many mountain canyons, the channel may respond to increased sediment primarily through changes in bed configuration and slope, rather than planimetric form (Graf, 1979). Other examples of channel instability include the American River of California, which aggraded anywhere from 1.5 m to 9 m during the primary hydraulic mining period (1861-1884), causing channel avulsions (James, 1994) and overbank flooding and deposition (Fischer and Harvey, 1991). The river later degraded as sediment input decreased (Gilbert, 1917). More than 5 m of aggradation, increases of up to 300% in channel width, and enhanced braiding resulted from placer tin mining along the Ringarooma River, Tasmania, and bridges had to be frequently replaced following floods (Knighton, 1989). Heavy sedimentation of tailings and waste rock along the Ok Tedi River system in Papua New Guinea has resulted in aggradation of the channel bed, flooding problems, and the loss of a substantial area of riparian forest (Higgins et al., 1987; Parker et al., 1997).

The adverse impact of mining on aquatic organisms is illustrated by studies of sediment increases associated with placer mining along Alaskan streams. These studies have indicated that mining-related increases in turbidity, total residue concentration, and settleable solids reduced gross primary productivity to undetectable levels, primarily by eliminating algal production (Van Nieuwenhuyse and LaPerriere, 1986). Similarly, the suspended sediment decreased the density and biomass of invertebrates (Wagener and LaPerriere, 1985). Increased suspended sediment also affected fish by impairing feeding activity, reducing growth rates, and causing downstream displacement, color changes, decreased resistance to toxins and, in extreme cases, death (McLeay et al., 1987).

Placer mining may also indirectly cause diminution or augmentation of river discharge as water is diverted to work the placer deposits. Diminution of flow would result in decreased ability to transport sediment, which could lead to channel aggradation as sediment coming from the hillslopes accumulates in the channel. Diminution of flow also could stress aquatic organisms through decreased oxygen and nutrients, and increased temperatures. In the extreme cases where flow is completely diverted so that the former channel bed can be thoroughly worked over by the miners, it seems appropriate to consider the river as ceasing to exist for a time.

In contrast, augmented channel flow would increase the river's sediment transport capability. This might be offset by increased sediment introduction, or it might cause erosion of the channel bed and banks. Prolonged high levels of flow during seasons other than the traditional high flow period could also stress aquatic biota by affecting water temperature and clarity, and the necessity to expend energy. Some fish, for example, do not efficiently process the lactic acid produced by activity. If they are forced to be active (e.g., to maintain a position in a strong current) for too long they will die from exhaustion. Most aquatic organisms have adapted to the flow regime of the specific river they inhabit. Numerous studies have documented that indigenous organisms are stressed or extirpated in rivers where the flow regime abruptly changes as a result of flow regulation (Stanford and Hauer, 1992).

The final direct effect of mining comes from the introduction of toxic materials used in mining. Toxins such as heavy metals may enter the channel in solution or adsorbed to sediment. Metals in solution may come from abandoned tailings piles, which have been found to contain substantial concentrations of heavy metals that may enter the ground and water surface by leaching of precipitation through the pile material (Ralston and Morilla, 1974).

Toxic materials have a deleterious effect on stream biota, interfering with the respiratory, growth, and reproductive functions of members of the entire food chain. The toxic materials act as a time bomb, for they have an impact at many spatial and temporal levels. There is the initial introduction, followed by processes of bioaccumulation and biomagnification over a period of years. In biomagnification, some toxic materials are not expelled by organisms, but accumulate in fatty tissues (Burton, 1992). Any predator thus ingests all of the toxins accumulated by each of its prey organisms, so that concentrations of toxins increase with distance up the food chain, culminating in raptors or humans. Longer-lived organisms may also continually ingest more of the toxin without expelling it, leading to bioaccumulation (Burton, 1992). In addition, the toxins may be adsorbed onto clay or silt particles, lie buried in a sedimentary deposit, and then be remobilized at some later date by channel-bed erosion or lateral channel shifting during a flood (Lewin et al., 1977).

The most general effects of any pollutant are to reduce community diversity within a channel (Mackenthun and Ingram, 1966; Haslam, 1990), and to reduce biomass and cover provided by rooted aquatic plants (Haslam, 1990). Pollutants may be excess organic matter (such as that introduced by human wastes), excess sediment, or heavy metals. Degradable organic matter reduces dissolved oxygen and light penetration, while increasing nitrite, nitrate, ammonia, and turbidity (Haslam, 1990; Ward and Kondratieff, 1992). The aquatic insects in many mountain rivers, which may constitute the great majority of the bottom-dwelling fauna, are adapted to the cold, clear waters high in dissolved oxygen that normally characterize these streams (Ward and Kondratieff, 1992). Excess sediment can smother aquatic plants, abrade or clog respiratory surfaces and collect on the feeding parts of macroinvertebrates (Haslam, 1990), and smother fish eggs and larvae.

The toxicity of any substance varies with the species under consideration, as well as with the organic matter, oxygen, temperature, and combination of pollutants present in the river (Haslam, 1990). Acute toxicity kills organisms outright, whereas chronic toxicity is caused by long-continued exposure to sublethal levels of a toxin. The most toxic heavy metals are mercury, copper, cadmium, and zinc (Haslam, 1990). Creatures from unicellular to higher organisms absorb heavy metals from their food or directly from the water. Some organisms can excrete the toxins, and are generally more tolerant of polluted environments, but other organisms absorb them permanently (Bryan, 1976). Among the organisms that most efficiently concentrate metals are molluscs, followed by many types of aquatic plants (Haslam, 1990). Molluscs tend to store metals in their tissues and digestive glands; crustaceans in their exoskeleton and hepatopancreas; fish in liver and muscle; and mammals in bone, kidneys, and liver (Bryan, 1976). The metals can be enzyme inhibitors (Bryan, 1976), and they may damage the gill surfaces of fish and interfere with respiration (Hughes, 1976).

Heavy metal pollution (manganese, iron, copper, zinc, lead, molybdenum, and cadmium) associated with historic mining along the Arkansas River of the Colorado Rocky Mountains provides an example of toxic contamination. The U.S. Environmental Protection Agency has designated California Gulch, a mining area within the Arkansas River basin, as a Superfund site. Concentrations of metals in the Arkansas River are highly dependent on flow and tend to increase during high spring runoff. This suggests that these metals are abundant in the fine sediments that are carried as suspended load during high flows (Roline and Boehmke, 1981). Much of the historic mining activity within the basin occurred along tributary streams. Today, the diversity and total abundance of aquatic macroinvertebrates are lower downstream from the junction of the contaminated tributary streams, and higher below the junction of clean tributaries. The bottom-dwelling invertebrate communities below the contaminated tributaries are shifted toward more metal-tolerant species (Rees, 1994), whereas the fish population is reduced or absent (Roline and Boehmke, 1981). The invertebrates at polluted sites also have higher concentrations of zinc, cadmium, and copper than those upstream, as do the gut and gill tissue of trout (Rees, 1994). Gills and gut are the primary route for uptake of heavy metals by fish, and the brown trout at the study sites rarely reached the age of four years or greater. The condition of trout in all age classes was judged generally poor (Rees, 1994). Brown trout along the length of the channel downstream from polluted tributaries showed bioaccumulation of copper and zinc in their livers, and chronically high concentrations of these metals are present in the water (Roline and Boehmke, 1981).

In-channel alterations such as channelization, the construction of levees, the introduction of exotic vegetation, and channel stabilization may affect portions of some mountain rivers, but these activities commonly focus on channels in the middle and lower portions of drainage basins. Where channelization has been carried out for debris flow or flood control, as in the Austrian Alps or the Polish Carpathian Mountains, channel incision has also occurred (Habersack and Nachtnebel, 1994), leading to flashier flood peak discharges and increased flood hazards (Wyzga, 1996). Worldwide, it is difficult to estimate which, if any, single type of activity has had the greatest impact on mountain rivers. In-channel mining has dramatically affected the Sierra Nevada Mountains of the western United States, for example, and beaver trapping has substantially altered many rivers in the Rocky Mountains. Overall, deforestation has probably had the single greatest effect on mountain rivers, although the rapid and continuing construction of dams in the world's mountainous regions is also creating significant impacts.

Hazards

The occurrence of hazards along mountain rivers is inextricably tied to human impacts on these systems. In some cases, increased hazards result from attempts to mitigate naturally-occurring hazards, as when a flash flood in the Arás drainage basin of Spain destroyed more than 30 check dams full of sediment, flushing a huge amount of debris downstream to an alluvial fan inhabited by people (Benito et al., 1998; Gutiérrez et al., 1998; Batalla et al., 1999). The combined effect of a high-energy environment and human land use is that a disproportionate number of the world's natural disasters occur in mountain lands (Hewitt, 1997). Of mountain disasters, 60% are associated with earthquakes and floods (including debris flows), with a high percentage occurring in southern and southwestern Asia and in south-central America (OFDA, 1988).

Hazards associated with mountain rivers occur principally in the form of floods and debris flows. Lahars may also be significant hazards in volcanically active areas (Fairchild, 1987), and other forms of slope instability (e.g. landslides, rockfalls, avalanches, sturzstroms) may or may not be associated with river channels. Worldwide, these types of mass movements kill hundreds to thousands of people and cause extensive property damage each year (e.g. Ericksen et al., 1970; Williams and Guy, 1971; Cooley et al., 1977; Alexander, 1983; Zicheng and Jing, 1987; Benitez, 1989; Willi, 1991). The floods and debris flows may occur during fairly predictable, seasonally-driven periods, or they may be unpredictable, aperiodic events. Much of the research devoted to hazards along mountain rivers focuses on (1) recognizing hazardous locations; (2) understanding the controls on the occurrence of hazardous processes; (3) predicting magnitude and frequency of hazardous processes; and (4) mitigating the unwanted effects of these processes.

A key first step in mitigating hazards involves recognizing the potential for hazardous processes at a given location. Many people appear to regard the landscape as a static entity. They do not recognize that substantial landscape change, in the form of forest fire or flood, is likely to occur during their tenure at a specific location. Consequently, these people take no precautions to protect themselves or their property from natural hazards. One of the first responsibilities of natural scientists and engineers is therefore to increase public and governmental awareness of potential hazards.

Various criteria may be used to identify the past occurrence of debris flows, and debris flows are conservative in the sense that they tend to recur in the same locations. Historical records may include both the location, approximate magnitude, and date of occurrence of past debris flows (Eisbacher and Clague, 1984; Clark, 1987b). Debris flow stratigraphy along channels and on debris fans, when constrained by various chronologic techniques, may be used to estimate debris flow frequency in a drainage basin (Kochel, 1987; Osterkamp and Hupp, 1987; Shlemon et al., 1987; Wohl and Pearthree, 1991). The presence of debris flow scars and levees (Eisbacher and Clague, 1984) and specific landscape characteristics, such as alluvial fan gradient, surface morphology, or drainage basin ruggedness number (Jackson et al., 1987; Whipple, 1993), may indicate areas prone to mass movements. Topographic maps, surficial geologic maps, aerial photographs, and field evaluations may be used to locate past debris flows or potentially unstable terrain (Chatwin et al., 1991; Wieczorek et al., 1997). The physical characteristics that govern debris flow occurrence (e.g. climate and vegetation, lithology, aspect, slope angle, etc) can be compared with past debris flow magnitude and frequency using Geographic Information Systems technology (Gupta and Joshi, 1990; Mejia-Navarro and Wohl, 1994; Mejia-Navarro et al., 1994; Rowbotham and Dudycha, 1998) or digital elevation models (Dietrich and Montgomery, 1992; Mark, 1992) to develop a hazards map for a region (Akojima, 1996).

In addition to the use of past debris flow indicators, regional trends may be used to delineate hazard areas at the basin scale. A study of Japanese mountain rivers, for example, demonstrated that rivers flowing through areas of high relief have longitudinal profiles that can be described by power or linear functions. Sediment is transported by debris flows and floods all the way to the lower portions of these drainages. In contrast, rivers flowing through areas of lower relief have longitudinal profiles that can be approximated by exponential functions, and these basins are likely to have substantial sediment deposition in their middle reaches (Ohmori and Shimazu, 1994). As another example, recently de-glaciated valleys may be particularly prone to mass movements because glacial erosion has created u-shaped valleys with steep flanks, and glacial deposition has left moraine sediments perched along the valley walls (Kuhle et al., 1998), or temporarily impounding meltwater (Shroder et al., 1998).

Once the past, or probable future, occurrence of debris flows has been recognized, it becomes important to define the thresholds governing that occurrence. These thresholds may be governed by precipitation intensity and duration (Campbell, 1975; Caine, 1980; Kobashi and Suzuki, 1987; Cannon, 1988; Wilson et al., 1992; Larsen and Simon, 1993), or by snowmelt (Wieczorek et al., 1989). Thresholds may be dependent on the volume of colluvium accumulated in hollows (Johnson and Sitar, 1990; Dengler and Montgomery, 1989; Montgomery et al., 1991), on the combination of precipitation and sediment accumulation (Church and Miles, 1987; Neary and Swift, 1987; Wieczorek, 1987; Thornes and Alcántara-Ayala, 1998), or on the rate of regolith development and subsurface water accumulation (Roesli and Schindler, 1990; Chatwin et al., 1991). Forest fires may trigger debris flows in some regions (Parrett, 1987; Wells, 1987; Garcia-Ruiz et al., 1988; Wohl and Pearthree, 1991).

Predicting the magnitude and frequency of hazardous debris flow processes depends in part on the ability of models to simulate debris flow velocity, hydrograph, flow depth, and depositional areas. One- and two-dimensional mathematical models (Gallino and Pierson, 1985; Chen, 1987; Mizuyama et al., 1987; Takahashi et al., 1987; Rickenmann, 1990; Takahashi, 1991a; O'Brien, 1993; Rickenmann and Koch, 1997), flume experiments (Melosh, 1987; O'Brien and Julien, 1988; Takahashi, 1991a; Costa, 1992; Iversen and LaHusen, 1992), and empirical relations between peak discharge and flow volume or sediment concentration (Parrett, 1987; Webb et al., 1988; Gavrilovic and Matovic, 1991; Mizuyama et al., 1992) have each been used to study the mechanical processes of debris flows.

Figure 6.4. Two examples of types of slope stabilization, here both in Japan. This view shows a concrete lattice fastened to the underlying substrate with rock bolts. View on the next page is of a metal net hung along the slope face and covered with concrete.

Methods of debris flow hazard mitigation include (1) passive measures of hazard mapping and zoning, building codes, and warning inhabitants once a debris flow starts, and (2) active measures that focus either on preventing a debris flow from occurring, or on containing the debris flow and keeping it separate from areas of human occupation (Eisbacher and Clague, 1984; Hungr et al., 1987; Wieczorek, 1993). Warning and evacuation systems may rely on indirect methods such that a warning is issued when rainfall enters a critical magnitude-intensity domain defined by the rainfall which has triggered debris flows in the past. Direct warning systems use either wires installed across debris flow channels that are cut when a debris flow occurs, or vibration sensors that are activated by the movement of a debris flow.

Figure 6.4 (continued)

These direct methods allow only a few minutes to evacuate potentially hazardous areas (Mizuyama, 1993).

Active debris flow mitigation measures may focus on debris flow source, transport, or depositional zones. Hillslope hollows that accumulate debris may be artificially drained to prevent the build-up of pore-water pressure that can trigger slope failure (Reneau and Dietrich, 1987; Montgomery et al., 1991), or debris can be artificially removed on a controlled basis (Baldwin et al., 1987; Chatwin et al., 1991). Reforestation measures can be used to stabilize cut or burned slopes, and timber harvest and road construction can be controlled (Croft, 1967; Eisbacher, 1982; Hungr et al., 1987; Swanson et al., 1987; Chatwin et al., 1991). Hillslope reinforcement with rock riprap, retaining walls, hanging metal nets, fences, rock bolts, or concrete lattices is also used (Baldwin et al., 1987; Chatwin et al., 1991) (Figure 6.4). The channel bed and side slopes can be stabilized with channel linings or check dams in source areas (Liu, 1992). In the transportation zone of the debris flow channel, the passage of the debris flow can be trained by chutes, artificial channels, deflecting walls, or dikes, and transportation routes across the channel can use bypass tunnels or bridges sited well above the likely maximum debris flow height (Hungr et al., 1987; Willi, 1991). Free-standing baffles of timber, steel, or concrete can reduce debris flow velocity and promote deposition at sites accessible to maintenance equipment (Baldwin et al., 1987). Deposition basins, retention barriers, and tunnels or sheds over transportation routes can be used in the debris flow deposition zone (Hungr et al., 1987).

In many societies, the traditional belief has been that gods or other supernatural forces govern the occurrence of floods and debris flows (Eisbacher, 1982; Bjonness, 1986). However, active structural measures such as check dams have been extensively used for centuries in the European Alps (Jaeggi and Zarn, 1999) and in Japan. A Japanese imperial decree of 806 AD prohibited cutting of trees along riverbanks in an effort to control channel erosion, simultaneous with the construction of the first sabo dams, or sediment-retention structures (Japanese Ministry of Construction, 1993). George Perkins Marsh's 1864 book *Man and Nature* highlighted the importance of watershed protection and forest preservation using examples from the State of New York, but the U.S. government did not take national steps to preserve watershed characteristics until the 1935 establishment of the U.S. Soil Conservation Service. Governments in the European Alps were more proactive. The French government began afforestation programs along Alpine rivers in the 1890s (Clark, 1987a). The Austro-Hungarian Empire established in 1884 a state service for debris flow control (Armanini et al., 1991). Austria publishes a journal devoted entirely to the control of mountain torrents and snow avalanches (*Wildbach und Lawinenverbau*), and several national geological surveys (e.g. France, the Czech Republic, Canada, Italy, USA, Japan) have devoted considerable effort to mapping potentially unstable terrain and debris sources (Eisbacher, 1982). Journals such as Mountain Research and Development, Arctic, Antarctic, and Alpine Research, the Bulletin of the Association of Engineering Geologists (USA), Zeitschrift für Geomorphologie, and various national geological surveys regularly publish research on mountain-channel hazards. In 1994 the journal Mountain Research and Development devoted a special issue to mountain hazard geomorphology, dealing mainly with the Alps. Countries with moutainous regions are increasingly developing research programs focused on debris-flow hazards. China, for example, has hosted 3 national and 7 local symposia on debris flows since 1980, and has approximately 20 research teams actively investigating debris flows (Wang and Han, 1993).

The Japanese have been especially active in developing methods of mitigating the hazards from debris flows. Following extensive deforestation during World War II, Japan's Erosion-Control Engineering Society was established in 1947. As of 1995, the Society had 3,830 members. The activities of the Disaster Prevention Research Institute at Kyoto University, which has numerous field stations throughout the Japanese islands, illustrate Japan's approach to debris flow hazard mitigation. At the Institute's Hodaka Sedimentation Observatory in central Honshu, for example, an elaborate network of rain gages, sediment samplers, discharge gages, tv cameras, and radar velocity meters are connected in a telemeterized observation system that continuously records channel conditions and the passage of floods and debris flows in the 7.2 km² Ashiaraidani Creek drainage basin (Figure 6.5). These types of process studies help to identify thresholds of slope instability, and magnitude and frequency of mass movements.

The Institute is also actively investigating the effectiveness of various types of sabo dams and debris flow training structures. The combination in Japan of a wet climate, active tectonic uplift, volcanism, and high relief on the one hand, and a high population density and healthy economy on the other hand, has led to Japanese mountain rivers being among the most intensively engineered in the world (Figure 6.6). The Japanese typically design integrated debris flow control structures in mountainous drainage basins, with structures placed in appropriate locations to control, capture, disperse, channelize, and deflect debris flows (Figure 6.7). The volcanic mountain Sakurajima serves as an example. Sakurajima is an 80 km² stratovolcano in southern Kyushu that has had 4800 minor eruptions since 1965 (Ohsumi Works Office, 1995). An average of 70 debris

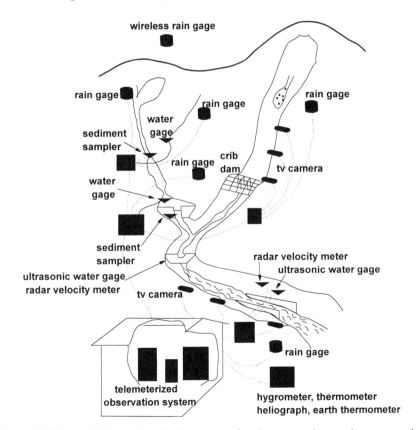

Figure 6.5. Schematic illustration of various types of equipment used to monitor water and sediment movement at Ashiaraidani Creek, Japan.

Figure 6.6. Upstream view of a highly stabilized channel in the Japan Alps. Channel is in an area formerly mined for copper, which has had extensive deforestation. Channel is approximately 15 m wide.

flows occur each year on Sakurajima, and the Japanese Ministry of Construction has
implemented extensive monitoring and control facilities. Sabo dams were first constructed on the mountain by the local government in 1943. Sabo dams may be open
structures of concrete with slits or steel-pipe grids (Figure 6.8). These are designed to
temporarily trap sediment which can then be gradually transported by subsequent water
flows with less hazard (Armanini et al., 1991; Mizuyama, 1993). The open-type sabo
dams have the advantage over closed sabo dams (gravity dams of massive concrete) of
not being filled by sediment from normal water discharges or by a single debris flow.

In 1965 the implementation at Sakurajima of wire-triggered on-site automatic
recording of debris flows using video cameras began, and this was expanded to 11 sites
by 1971 (Ohsumi Works Office, 1995). As of 1995, the system included 21 rain gages,

23 gages for volcanic ash, 16 cameras, 8 debris flow detector lines, 8 discharge gages and current meters, and more than 200 sabo dams and other control structures (Ohsumi Works Office, 1995) (Figures 6.9 and 6.10). The intensity of this monitoring program is representative of similar efforts in many mountainous regions of Japan.

Although either debris flows or floods may occur throughout mountainous drainage basins, the prevalent geologic hazard is likely to change from debris flows to floods in the lower parts of a drainage basin. Ohmori and Shimazu (1994) found that this transition commonly occurs at channel gradients between 0.08 and 0.001 in Japan. Misidentifying debris flows as water floods may lead to over-estimation of discharge and to inappropriate design of mitigation structures (Costa and Jarrett, 1981).

Many of the issues already discussed for debris flows also apply to floods along mountain rivers. Both active and passive hazard mitigation procedures may be employed to reduce flood hazards. Flood hazards commonly take the form of changes in channel configuration, and changes in sediment transport. Both types of changes may occur very rapidly during a single flood, or they may occur over a period of years to decades as progressive, small alterations resulting from a shift in the magnitude, frequency, and sediment transport of floods. The rate and magnitude of channel change during a flood will be a function of flood hydrology and hydraulics, particularly as these compare to more frequent, sustained flows. Channel change will also be governed by channel boundary resistance as this determines the flow energy necessary to

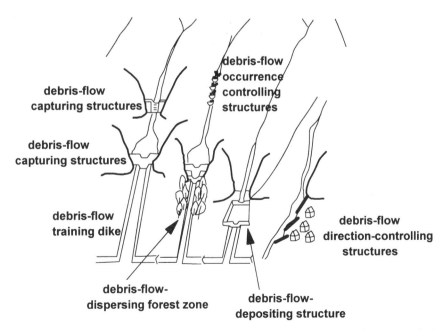

Figure 6.7. Representative examples of debris-flow control structures used in Japan and other countries. (After Mizuyama, 1993, Figure 1).

Figure 6.8. Two types of sabo dams commonly used in Japan for debris-flow control. (a) View of the downstream side of an open sabo dam at the Hodaka Sediment Station, Japan Alps. View is approximately 20 m wide. (b) A series of closed sabo dams, now filled with sediment, at Mt. Unzen. Mt. Unzen last erupted in 1993, and the channels draining the volcano have abundant pyroclastic, debris-flow, and flood sediments. View is approximately 50 m wide.

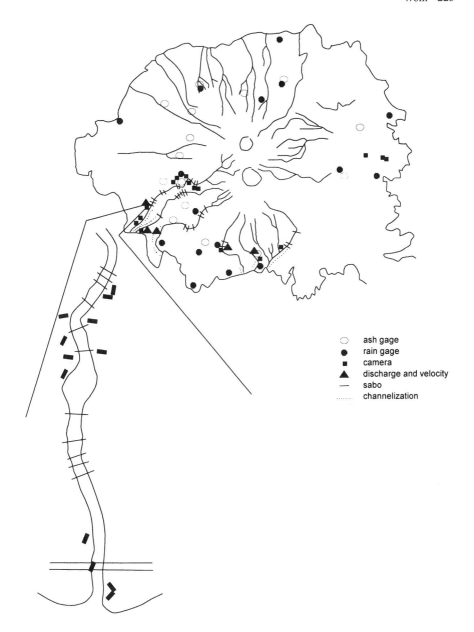

Figure 6.9. Schematic map of hazard-mitigation and monitoring equipment at Sakurajima, Japan. Enlargement shows details of a single channel reach. (After Ohsumi Works Office, 1995, Figures 1-8, 3-4 and 5-7).

Figure 6.10. Examples of debris-flow hazard mitigation measures at Mt. Unzen, Japan. (a) Aerial view downstream along channel on flanks of volcano, showing debris-flow training structures, channelization, and grade-control structures. (b) Control room with video monitors displaying scenes continuously photographed by video cameras placed around Mt. Unzen.

modify channel boundaries and the form of boundary change (e.g. cavitation of bedrock or slumping of unconsolidated banks). Sediment supply, as it influences the erosive forces exerted on the channel boundaries during a flood, will influence channel change. Finally, channel change will relate to the sequence of flows preceding a flood as these govern how much adjustment is required for the channel to convey the flood flow (Wohl, 2000). Flood hazards may result from sediment deposition, erosion, lateral channel movement and planform change, or overbank flow of water.

Transport of wash load, suspended load, and bedload each generally increases during a flood. For example, studies of a small high-relief catchment in Hong Kong indicated that 85% of the bedload transported during a five-year period moved during two storms (Peart et al., 1994). Deposition resulting from this type of increased sediment transport may take the form of aggradation or in-channel deposition that raises the level of the channel bed (Lisle, 1982; Nolan and Marron, 1985; Vuichard and Zimmermann, 1987). Deposition may also occur as the growth of bars or islands within a channel (Scott and Gravlee, 1968), or as lateral boulder berms beside the low-flow channel (Scott and Gravlee, 1968; Carling and Glaister, 1987; Cenderelli and Cluer, 1998; Cenderelli and Wohl, 1998). Flood deposition may occur via the formation of an alluvial fan where a steep, confined channel joins a broader valley (Williams and Guy, 1973; Jarrett and Costa, 1986; Schick and Lekach, 1987). Deposition may also occur via lateral accretion of the floodplain through the construction of point bars as a meander bend migrates, and vertical accretion of the floodplain as sediment settles from suspension in overbank flows (see also chapter 3). The in-channel forms of deposition are particularly prevalent along mountain rivers.

Erosion is more likely to occur along particularly steep or confined portions of a channel (Shroba et al., 1979). The alluvial veneer may be partially or wholly stripped from the channel (Vuichard and Zimmermann, 1987; Church, 1988) and the bedrock substrate may be quarried (Tinkler, 1993), eroded via cavitation (Eckley and Hinchcliff, 1986), or abraded. Bed scour at the base of obstacles such as bridge piers is particularly hazardous (Williams and Guy, 1973; Landers et al., 1994). During a 1982 flood in the upper Segre Valley of the southern Pyrenees, for example, more than half of the bridges were destroyed because of scouring more than 4m deep at bridge pier foundations, and damming by debris (Corominas and Alonso, 1990). Channel banks may be eroded by the collapse of blocks of sediment (Warburton, 1994; Russell et al., 1995) or by the continuous removal of individual clasts or small aggregates. Areas of overbank flow may also be eroded via longitudinal grooves (Smith and Zawada, 1988; Miller and Parkinson, 1993), widespread stripping of alluvium (Inbar, 1987), or solution in carbonate terrains (Hyatt and Jacobs, 1996). Within-channel deposition- and erosion-related flood hazards are likely to be most severe along mountain rivers, as these rivers are less likely to overflow their banks during floods than are lowland rivers.

Lateral channel movement may occur as predictable but rapid change, such as meander migration, or may occur as less predictable meander cutoff or avulsion along any type of channel (Scott and Gravlee, 1968). Mountain rivers are unlikely to be freely meandering for more than short segments, and the valley confinement common along mountain rivers will likely limit avulsion. Planform change commonly takes the form of (1) a single channel becoming braided, which may be particularly widespread downstream from glaciers (Fahnestock, 1963; Desloges and Church, 1992; Warburton, 1994) or in other regions of high sediment supply and low bank resistance, or (2) meander cutoff and channel straightening (Corominas and Alonso, 1990).

Rainfall, snowmelt, and rain-on-snow may cause flooding in mountainous regions. As reviewed in chapter 3, the magnitude of precipitation-related flooding in relation to normal flows varies as a function of regional climate (Pitlick, 1994b) and elevation (Jarrett, 1989). The largest floods ever measured (in terms of discharge versus drainage area) in temperate latitudes have occurred in semiarid to arid drainages (Costa, 1985).

In addition to precipitation-related causes of flooding, damburst floods are particularly important along mountain rivers because of the more widespread occurrence of natural dams. Natural dams may be glacial ice or moraine dams, or landslide/debris flow dams. (Catastrophic drainage of caldera lakes (Waythomas et al., 1996) may produce similar results.) Ice- or moraine-dammed lakes are widespread in Iceland, the Alps, Scandinavia, the Himalayas, and the coastal ranges of Alaska, British Columbia, and the Pacific Northwest of the United States. The failure of these dams may be a periodic phenomenon related to the increase in pressure behind the dam, as in ice-jam jökulhlaups (Young, 1980; Driedger and Fountain, 1989). The dam failure may also be a one-time occurrence resulting from gradual erosion of the dam sediments, or overtopping by a wave generated from an icefall or landslide into the lake, or seismic activity (Blown and Church, 1985; Vuichard and Zimmermann, 1987).

Landslide-dammed lakes may occur in any mountainous region with sufficiently large mass movements (e.g. Russell, 1972; Ouchi and Mizuyama, 1989; Reneau and Dethier, 1996). Costa and Schuster (1988) subdivided landslide dams into six types based on their distance of movement from the source area, morphology, and complexity (i.e., single or multiple dams from the same source). Of 73 documented landslide-dam failures, 27% occurred less than one day after formation, and approximately 50% failed within ten days. Overtopping was by far the most common cause of failure (Costa and Schuster, 1988).

The peak discharge produced by an outburst flood commonly exceeds by at least an order of magnitude the "normal" snowmelt- or rain-induced flood peak for a particular drainage basin. These floods are also particularly hazardous in that dam failure may be unpredictable and produces a very steep rising limb (Young, 1980; Ives, 1986). The mode of dam failure significantly controls rate of discharge rise and peak discharge magnitude; ice-marginal drainage or mechanical failure of part of the ice dam, for example, produces a significantly higher peak discharge than tunnel-drainage at the base of the ice (Walder and Costa, 1996). If a dammed lake is located, flood hazard can be reduced by monitoring lake level and dam condition (Braun and Fiener, 1995), artificially draining the lake, or stabilizing the dam (Eisbacher, 1982). Other flood hazard mitigation strategies are similar to those described for debris flows; passive measures of mapping, zoning, and warning, and active measures of prevention and containment. Examples of recent hazardous outburst floods in mountainous terrain caused by the failure of artificial dams include the Johnstown, Pennsylvania (USA) flood in 1874 (2200 deaths), the Vaiont, Italy dam failure in 1963 (2600 deaths), and the Sempor, Indonesia dam failure in 1967 (>2000 deaths) (Hewitt, 1997).

River Management

The implementation of active hazard mitigation measures can substantially alter the form and function of mountain rivers. Channelized and dammed streams lose riparian vegetation, allochthonous nutrient input, and large woody debris. Water temperature increases as a result of lack of shade and increased surface area. Pool-riffle sequences and other bedforms may be destroyed, reducing substrate and habitat diversity (Stanford et al., 1996), and providing fish no protection from high velocities during high flows (Barclay, 1978; Nunnally, 1978; Beschta and Platts, 1986). Fish passage and the flow of nutrients along the channel may be blocked (Nakano et al., 1990).

As humans increasingly recognize the value and crucial importance of naturally functioning river ecosystems, concern has grown over our alteration of these ecosystems. There are more efforts being made to restore or rehabilitate river channels using bioengineering (e.g. riparian vegetation to stabilize channel banks) (Coppin and Richards, 1990), environmentally sensitive structures (e.g. fish passages on dams, or log grade-control structures) (U.S. Dept. of Transportation, 1979), controlled floods (e.g. the 1996 Grand Canyon of the Colorado River flood; Collier et al., 1997), or a return to more natural hydrographs that include seasonally fluctuating flows (Kattelman, 1996; Stanford et al., 1996; Poff et al., 1997). Ultimately, these activities are designed to restore healthy riparian systems, which may be defined as those performing their ecological functions of protecting river banks against erosion, filtering diffuse pollution, and maintaining high levels of aquatic and terrestrial biodiversity (DéCamps and DéCamps, 1999). Restoration is defined as a return to a close approximation of the river condition prior to disturbance; rehabilitation refers to improvements of a visual nature, or "putting the channel back into good condition" (National Academy, 1992). Too often, attempts to restore or rehabilitate a river channel are site-specific measures that do not give sufficient consideration to upstream-downstream or channel-hillslope interactions, or to the impacts of the rehabilitation measures on all aspects of the river ecosystem (Montgomery et al., 1995). It seems appropriate to approach all attempts at channel manipulation within the framework used by physicians; first, do no harm (K. Prestegaard, 1998, pers. comm.). It is also appropriate to use a series of questions to guide restoration efforts: What are you restoring to? How have the controlling factors of water and sediment yield to the channel changed? What are the goals of restoration—channel stability, flood conveyance, habitat enhancement? How will the proposed restoration measures likely affect other aspects of river function beyond those explicit in the restoration design? How will the restoration design likely perform over time? No river channel exists isolated in time or space. The channel has a history of interactions between process and form that is at least partially recorded in local stratigraphy, and this record may provide critical insights into how channel form results from process, and may respond to future changes in process (J. Pizzuto, 1998, pers. comm.). If the channel is incised, for example, the bankfull discharge may be meaningless, and it becomes important to understand the recurrence interval and shear stress exerted by floods of varying magnitude in order to predict channel-stability. Ultimately, river management is not really restoration or rehabilitation, but another form of channel design.

River restoration, rehabilitation, and environmental assessment have received increasing attention since the 1970s (egs. Orsborn and Anderson, 1986; Brookes, 1988, 1990; National Academy, 1992). Although much of this attention has been directed toward the lowland rivers that have been most altered by human activities, mountain rivers have also been the focus of studies (e.g. Jaeggi and Zarn, 1999). The headwater reaches of many river basins control not only downstream water and sediment movement, but also the biological integrity of the whole river ecosystem, as in the case of salmonid fish in western North America (Salo and Cundy, 1987). At the same time, the growing world-wide pressure on land and its renewable resources is forcing people into geomorphically unstable mountainous regions, and thus increasing human exposure to natural hazards and the consequent need to mitigate those hazards (Eisbacher, 1982; Davies, 1991). The 6100 km^2 Province of Trent, Italy, for example, has more than 10,000 check dams on 4,000 km of mountain river channels, and an annual budget of more than $15 million for debris flow control (Armanini et al., 1991). Attempts to rehabilitate these intensely engineered channels may be complicated by remaining structures that can be damaged by the associated increase in sediment movement (e.g. Bechteler et al., 1994), or by a lack of attention to potential upstream and downstream influences on the rehabilitation measures (Newson and Leeks, 1987).

In the United States, attempts to manage mountain rivers must balance historical land-use activities and environmental impacts. As public pressure is brought to bear on the government agencies that manage large tracts of public land, the agencies have developed standardized procedures for assessing and monitoring channel condition on these lands (e.g. Ziemer, 1998). The U.S. Bureau of Land Management, for example, manages 110 million hectares of public lands, 9% of which is riparian-wetland areas. The BLM has developed a field-based checklist that is used to rank river channels as being in (1) proper functioning condition, (2) functional but at risk, or (3) nonfunctional, with respect to ecological status based on characteristics of hydrology, vegetation, and erosion/deposition (USDI, 1993). This approach is also used by the U.S. Forest Service, which relies on Rosgen's (1994) stream classification (see chapter 4) for inventorying rivers and for predicting likely channel response to land use activities. One of the great challenges for these agencies is to develop a field-based classification system that can be applied by technicians with minimal training, but that is based on geomorphically meaningful categories (Miller and Ritter, 1996).

Once a portion of a river is perceived as being nonfunctional or at risk, river

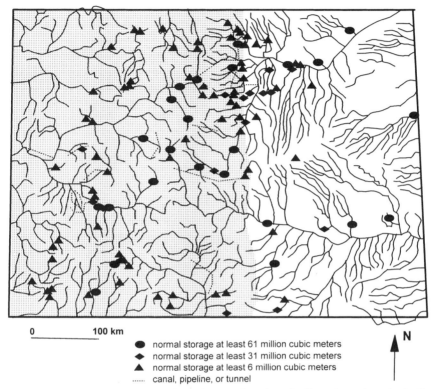

Figure 6.11. Map of primary reservoirs and water-diversion pipelines along rivers in the State of Colorado, USA. The western two thirds of the state are mountainous (shaded area). (After, Surface-water and related-land resources development in the United States and Puerto Rico, 1982, U.S. Geological Survey map, scale 1: 3,168,000).

restoration may be implemented. Passive restoration may involve removing structures within the channel or altering hillslope conditions within the drainage basin so as to control water and sediment yield to the channel. Active restoration involves introducing structures into the channel or artificially re-shaping the channel to a desired configuration. Active restoration may implement traditional engineering materials such as concrete, or may implement "soft" or "bio" engineering methods in which natural materials such as large woody debris are used (Newbury and Gaboury, 1993; Abbe et al., 1998; Bolton et al., 1998; Drury et al., 1998; Pess et al., 1998). As noted by Wilcock (1997), active re-shaping of channels is unlikely to succeed if the new channel configuration is based on water and sediment yield estimates pre-watershed disturbance, or on measurements from a nearby, undisturbed channel. The artificially restored channel must be allowed to equilibrate with contemporary water and sediment yield.

Many channel restoration projects have not had the desired effect, or been able to withstand larger than normal flood flows. The small mountain watershed of

Tenmile Creek, west of Denver, Colorado, provides an example (Babcock, 1986). During the 1880s two narrow-gauge railroads changed the creek's location. In the course of the 20th century a gas pipeline, several power distribution systems, and a buried telephone cable, all with associated roads and construction, further disturbed the creek. Upstream mining introduced toxic drainage and mill tailings into the creek, and during the 1970s five kilometers of channel were relocated for Interstate Highway 70. Following this relocation, half a million dollars were spent on channel rehabilitation, which included log and rock check dams and deflectors, and habitat rocks (large boulders). The rehabilitated channel remained stable for approximately one and a half years, until a large flood removed most of the check dams, and returned the channel to its pre-rehabilitation configuration (Babcock, 1986). It is worthwhile to remember our inability to re-create naturally functioning river ecosystems as we continue to alter mountain drainage basins and river channels.

The world's mountains are very diverse. They provide more than half of the world's fresh water, much of its timber, mineral, and grazing resources, and a spiritual refuge for humans (Ives et al., 1997). Many of the world's industrialized nations recognized more than a century ago that to protect the natural processes and organisms of mountain regions was also to protect the lives and livelihoods of humans living in the surrounding lowlands. However, one can easily argue that the industrialized nations have not yet sufficiently protected their mountain drainage basins, even as the developing nations rush to exploit the natural resources in their own mountainous regions. And once people have come to depend on a resource, protection of that resource from alteration becomes much more difficult. Norway, Switzerland and Canada each generate a substantial portion of their electricity from dams on mountain rivers, for example (Bandyopadhyay et al., 1997). The State of Colorado (USA) obtains the majority of its water via dams and diversions on rivers in the Rocky Mountains (Figure 6.11). Although the citizens and governments of these regions are now well aware of the ecological and geomorphic disruptions along dammed rivers, only limited attempts are being made to alter flow regime from dams, and few dams are being removed.

At the most basic level, human communities in each mountain watershed and each nation will have to decide what balance they find acceptable between resource protection and resource use. In the worst case scenario, such decisions will not be consciously made, but will instead simply result from accidents of development, the increasing pressure of human population, and the relative strengths of contending factions. In the best case, contemporary scientific understanding of mountain rivers and watersheds will be systematically used to achieve the desired balance. In either case, the professional responsibility of river scientists extends to both understanding how mountain rivers operate, and to disseminating that understanding to the wider public so as to facilitate informed decisions. Let us hope and work for the best case scenario.

7

FIELD DATA, PLEASE

The diversity of conditions present among mountain rivers makes it difficult to create a single, grand synthesis. Differences in lithology, tectonic regime, and climate create characteristics that vary systematically by region, as well as unique conditions for individual drainage basins. Whatever coherent picture we may be able to develop is just beginning to emerge as a result of recent advances in both historical and process studies. Thanks to geochronologic techniques developed during the last two decades of the 20th century, we are now beginning to understand rates and styles of Quaternary tectonism, and to explore the implications of tectonics for landscape development from steady-state mountain belts to drainage network evolution, bedrock channel incision, and longitudinal profile development. Simultaneously, we are beginning to understand the mechanics of flow and sediment movement in mountain rivers, and the response times and styles of these channels. Ultimately, we will need to effectively integrate the knowledge resulting from these historical and process studies.

What we do know about mountain rivers is that there is likely to be a strong structural influence on drainage development. Tectonic regime may influence the arrangement of channels in the drainage network, sediment supply to the channel and the rate of channel incision, and the longitudinal profile of the channel. Bedrock is more likely to be present along mountain than along lowland rivers, and mountain rivers have relatively high rates of bedrock channel incision. These rates are spatially variable because of different erosional-process domains.

Mountain rivers are likely to have straight or convex longitudinal profiles with knickpoints. Downstream changes in lithology, climate, tectonic regime, or Quaternary history tend to create downstream changes in channel morphology and process, so that mountain rivers are most appropriately characterized at the reach scale. For a reach with a given gradient, discharge regime, and sediment supply, channel morphology and process domain are fairly predictable.

In general, mountain rivers have non-logarithmic velocity distributions and highly turbulent flow which is more commonly close to critical conditions than flow in lowland rivers. Mountain channels are coarse grained, with high boundary resistance to erosion and high flow resistance coefficients. The system is often supply-limited with low suspended sediment loads and episodic bedload discharge, although high sediment yields may occur following a disturbance such as a volcanic eruption or forest fire. Tectonic, climatic, and lithologic changes are more likely to influence water and sediment yields in mountain rivers in the absence of filtering mechanisms associated with thick, stable regolith. Drainage area-discharge relations are not linear because of downstream variations in runoff-generating mechanisms, which tend to be strongly seasonal and spatially variable.

Some mountain rivers are strongly influenced by the history of Quaternary climate change or Pleistocene glaciation. Pleistocene or contemporary glaciation may control discharge, river chemistry, sediment supply, and valley morphology. The history of high magnitude floods, such as landslide-dam or glacier-lake outburst floods, may also dominate channel and valley morphology. Debris flows and floods tend to exert a stronger influence on mountain river morphology and process than they do on lowland rivers because only these extreme events can overcome the high boundary resistance of mountain channels. Large woody debris may also be locally important along mountain rivers.

What do we *not* know about mountain rivers that we would like to know? With respect to physical processes, there remain at least four fundamental topics for which our understanding is very limited.

(1*) Hydraulics*. The distribution of velocity and shear stress, the sources of flow resistance, the forms of turbulence, and the interactions between turbulent flow and the channel boundaries all represent processes for which we have fairly few field data. There is a need for direct measurements of these processes and variables within the range of channel types that occur at high gradients. Although two decades of work on gravel-bed channels have demonstrated that hydraulics in these systems differ in important ways from low-gradient, sand-bed channels, we cannot yet empirically or theoretically describe the hydraulics of step-pool channels, for example. More extensive field data will allow both the development of empirical equations for the hydraulics of high-gradient channels, and the development of theoretical, predictive models. These equations and models could in turn be applied to the following three topics.

(2) *Sediment transport*. Three aspects of sediment transport along mountain rivers remain particularly difficult to measure and predict: particle entrainment under highly spatially and temporally variable conditions; the impact of limitations in sediment supply on entrainment and transport; and the stability or persistence of the coarse bed-surface layer and of bedforms. As with channel hydraulics, we need more field measurements from a range of channel types in order to improve our understanding of these processes. Even a cursory review of the literature on sediment transport along gravel-bed channels reveals the surprising dependence of many sediment transport equations on only a very few field datasets, such as the dataset from Oak Creek, Oregon (Milhous, 1973). It will probably be necessary to develop numerous sets of equations for roughness coefficient, velocity, and sediment transport, with each set applying to a specific channel type (eg. step-pool vs. pool-riffle).

(3) *Bedforms and channel morphology*. A few investigators have recently proposed that flow energy and sediment supply interact along a continuum of channel-bed gradient to produce predictable trends in channel bedforms and channel morphology (e.g. Montgomery and Buffington, 1997; Chin, 1998). These conceptual

models are limited by a lack of field-based data on how channel morphology varies as a function of potential controls. As of 2000, fewer than two dozen papers had been published in English on step-pool channels, for example, and these papers are unlikely to cover the full range of conditions under which step-pool channels occur. As we increase our understanding of hydraulics and sediment transport along high-gradient channels, it also becomes more feasible to develop theoretical models of the distribution of various channel morphologies.

(4) *Longitudinal profile development.* What governs the spatial distribution and relative importance of such processes of incision as debris flows, knickpoint retreat, and fluvial abrasion? How do rates of incision vary with respect to tectonic regime, climate, drainage area, and channel substrate? How do baselevel, channel gradient, and hillslope configuration interact in various settings? How are bedrock and alluvial channel reaches integrated downstream? What conceptual model best describes longitudinal profile development along mountain rivers; equilibrium, quasi-equilibrium, a stream-power erosion law, or something else? In the absence of detailed, extensive field measurements of hillslope and channel processes in mountain regions, our attempts to understand longitudinal profile development over geologic timescales are likely to remain black-box models in the sense that an observed profile development may be correlated with potential controls, without really understanding the mechanisms by which those controls act.

The common theme to the four topics outlined above is a lack of field data. Although exciting progress was made in field-based studies of mountain rivers during the closing decades of the 20th century, our ability to understand and predict channel processes in mountain environments, and thus to effectively manage river systems, will remain limited until government agencies and individual scientists undertake the type of extensive, prolonged data collection programs that have provided the foundation for our understanding of low-gradient, alluvial rivers. This is particularly critical as growing human populations continue to expand into mountain environments. For example, hydrological data on water levels, discharge, sediment and water quality are indispensable for water engineering works such as dams, and for water quality protection, water resources management, zoning, insurance, standards, legislation, and flood forecasting, yet these data are lacking for mountain regions because of difficult access, high spatial variability, sparse settlement with limited services, and a harsh physical environment (Kundzewicz, 1997). It seems appropriate to have some understanding of how mountain rivers operate as integrated physical-biological systems *before* we completely disrupt the river ecosystem. We might thereby avoid some of the costly mistakes that we have made along lowland rivers, and better equip ourselves for the increasingly intensive river management that is likely to characterize the 21st century.

REFERENCES

Abbe, T.B. and D.R. Montgomery, Large woody debris jams, channel hydraulics and habitat formation in large rivers, *Regulated Rivers: Research and Management,* 12, 201-221, 1996.

Abbe, T.B., D.R. Montgomery, G.R. Pess, T. Drury, and C. Petroff, Emulating organized chaos: engineered log jams as a tool for rehabilitating fluvial environments, *EOS, Transactions, Am. Geophysical Union,* 79, F345, 1998.

Abrahams, A.D., G. Li, and J.F. Atkinson, Step-pool streams: adjustment to maximum flow resistance, *Water Resources Research,* 31, 2593-2602, 1995.

Abrahams, A.D. and A.J. Parsons, Relation between sediment yield and gradient on debris-covered hillslopes, Walnut Gulch, Arizona, *Geological Society of America Bulletin,* 103, 1109-1113, 1991.

Acker, S.A., S.L. Johnson, F.J. Swanson, and G.S. Kennedy, Interactions of riparian vegetation and geomorphology from the stand to watershed scale in the western Cascade Range of Oregon , *Ecological Society of America, 1999 Annual Meeting Abstracts,* p. 5, 1999.

Ackroyd, P. and R.J. Blakely, En masse debris transport in a mountain stream, *Earth Surface Processes and Landforms,* 9, 307-320, 1984.

Adams, C.C., Base-leveling and its faunal significance, *American Naturalist,* 5, 839-852, 1901.

Adams, J., Sediment loads of North Island rivers, New Zealand - a reconnaissance, *Journal of Hydrology (New Zealand),* 18, 36-48, 1979.

Adams, K.D., W.W. Locke, and R. Rossi, Obsidian-hydration dating of fluvially reworked sediments in the West Yellowstone region, Montana, *Quaternary Research,* 38, 180-195, 1992.

Adenlof, K.A. and E.E. Wohl, Controls on bedload movement in a subalpine stream of the Colorado Rocky Mountains, USA, *Arctic and Alpine Research,* 26, 77-85, 1994.

Agata, Y., Change in runoff characteristics of a mountain river caused by a gigantic failure and debris flow, *Proceedings, International Symposium on Forest Hydrology,* pp. 359-366, Tokyo, Japan, 1994.

Aizen, V., E. Aizen and J. Melack, Characteristics of runoff formation at the Kirgizskiy Alatoo, Tien Shan, in *Biogeochemistry of seasonally snow-covered catchments,* edited by K.A. Tonnessen, M.W. Williams, and M. Tranter, pp. 413-430, IAHS Publ. no. 228, 1995.

Akojima, I., Designs of medium scale hazard maps of mountain slopes in Japan, *GeoJournal,* 38, 365-372, 1996.

Alexander, D., 'God's handy-worke in wonders' - landslide dynamics and natural hazard implications of a sixteenth century disaster, *Professional Geographer,* 35, 314-323, 1983.

Allan, J.D., *Stream ecology: structure and function of running waters,* Chapman and Hall, London, 388 pp., 1995.

Allen, A.W., *Habitat suitability index models: beaver,* U.S. Fish and Wildlife Service, Ft. Collins, Colorado, 20 pp., 1983.

Allen, P.M., R. Hobbs, and N.D. Maier, Downstream impacts of a dam on a bedrock fluvial system, Brazos River, central Texas, *Bulletin of the Association of Engineering Geologists,* 26, 165-189, 1989.

Al-Taiee, T.M., The influence of a dam on the downstream degradation of a riverbed: case study of the Tigris River in, *Hydrology in mountainous regions II. Artificial reservoirs, water and slopes,* edited by R.O. Sinniger and M. Monbaron, pp. 3-10, IAHS Publication no. 194, Wallingford, UK, 1990.

Amoros, C., Changes in side-arm connectivity and implications for river system management, *Rivers*, 2, 105-112, 1991.

Andrews, E.D., Scour and fill in a stream channel, East Fork River, western Wyoming, *U.S. Geological Survey Professional Paper 1117*, 49 pp., 1979.

Andrews, E.D., Entrainment of gravel from naturally sorted riverbed material, *Geological Society of America Bulletin*, 94, 1225-1231, 1983.

Andrews, E.D., Bed-material entrainment and hydraulic geometry of gravel-bed rivers in Colorado, *Geological Society of America Bulletin*, 95, 371-378, 1984.

Andrews, E.D., Downstream effects of Flaming Gorge Reservoir on the Green River, Colorado and Utah, *Geological Society of America Bulletin*, 97, 1012-1023, 1986.

Andrews, E.D. and D.C. Erman, D.C. , Persistence in the size distribution of surficial bed material during an extreme snowmelt flood, *Water Resources Research*, 22, 191-197, 1986.

Andrews, E.D. and J.M. Nelson, Topographic response of a bar in the Green River, Utah to variation in discharge, in *River meandering*, edited by S. Ikeda and G. Parker, pp. 463-484, AGU, Water Resources Monograph 12, 1989.

Andrews, E.D. and J.D. Smith, A theoretical model for calculating marginal bedload transport rates of gravel, in *Dynamics of gravel-bed rivers*, edited by P. Billi, R.D. Hey, C.R. Thorne and P. Tacconi, pp. 41-52, John Wiley and Sons, Chichester, 1992.

Arcement, G.J., Jr. and V.R. Schneider, Guide for selecting Manning's roughness coefficients for natural channels and flood plains, *U.S.Geological Survey Water-Supply Paper 2339*, 38 pp., 1989.

Armanini, A., Variation of bed and sediment load mean diameters due to erosion and deposition processes, in *Dynamics of gravel-bed rivers*, edited by P. Billi, R.D. Hey, C.R. Thorne and P. Tacconi, pp. 351-359, John Wiley and Sons, Chichester, 1992.

Armanini, A., F. Dellagiacoma, and L. Ferrari, From the check dam to the development of functional check dams, in *Fluvial hydraulics of mountain regions*, edited by A. Armanini and G. Di Silvio, pp. 331-344, Springer-Verlag, Braunschweig, 1991.

Armanini, A. and G. Di Silvio, (eds.), *Fluvial hydraulics of mountain regions*, Springer-Verlag, Berlin, 468 pp., 1991.

ASCE Task Committee on sediment transport and aquatic habitats, Sedimentation Committee, Sediment and aquatic habitat in river systems. *Journal of Hydraulic Engineering*, 118, 669-687, 1992.

Arnett, R.R., Slope form and geomorphological process: an Australian example, in *Slopes: form and process*, Special Publication 3, Institute British Geographers, 81-92, 1971.

Ashida, K., S. Egashira, and N. Ando, Generation and geometric features of step-pool bed forms. *Disaster Prevention Research Institute, Kyoto University, Japan, Ann.* 27, sect. B-2, 341-353, 1984.

Ashida, K., T. Takahashi, and T. Sawada, Sediment yield and transport on a mountain small watershed, *Bulletin of the Disaster Prevention Research Institute, Kyoto University, Japan*, 26, 119-144, 1976.

Ashmore, P.E., Lab modelling of gravel braided stream morphology, *Earth Surface Processes and Landforms*, 7, 201-225, 1982.

Ashmore, P.E., Bed load transport in braided gravel-bed stream models, *Earth Surface Processes and Landforms*, 13, 677-695, 1988.

Ashworth, P.J., Mid-channel bar growth and its relationship to local flow strength and direction, *Earth Surface Processes and Landforms*, 21, 103-123, 1996.

Ashworth, P.J. and R.I. Ferguson, Size-selective entrainment of bedload in gravel bed streams, *Water Resources Research*, 25, 627-634, 1989.

Ashworth, P.J., R.I. Ferguson, and D.M. Powell, Bedload transport and sorting in braided channels, in *Dynamics of gravel-bed rivers*, edited by P. Billi, R.D. Hey, C.R. Thorne and P. Tacconi, pp. 497-513, Wiley, Chichester, 1992.

Astaras, T., Drainage basins as process-response systems: an example from central Macedonia,

North Greece, *Earth Surface Processes and Landforms*, 9, 333-341, 1984.

Auble, G.T., J.M. Friedman and M.L. Scott, Relating riparian vegetation to present and future streamflows, *Ecological Applications*, 4, 544-554, 1994.

Aulenbach, B.T., R.P. Hooper, and O.P. Bricker, Trends in the chemistry of precipitation and surface water in a national network of small watersheds, *Hydrological Processes*, 10, 151-181, 1996.

Axelrod, D.I. and P.H. Raven, Origins of the Cordilleran flora, *Journal of Biogeography*, 12, 21-47, 1985.

Axtmann, E.V. and R.F. Stallard, Chemical weathering in the South Cascade glacier basin, comparison of subglacial and extra-glacial weathering, in *Biogeochemistry of seasonally snow-covered catchments*, edited by K.A. Tonnessen, M.W. Williams, and M. Tranter, pp. 431-439, IAHS Publ. no. 228, 1995.

Babcock, W.H., Tenmile Creek: a study of stream relocation, *Water Resources Bulletin*, 22, 405-415, 1986.

Bagnold, R.A., An approach to the sediment transport problem from general physics, *U.S. Geological Survey Professional Paper 422*, 37 pp., 1966.

Bagnold, R.A., Bed load transport by natural rivers, *Water Resources Research*, 13, 303-312, 1977.

Bagnold, R.A., An empirical correlation of bedload transport rates in flumes and natural rivers. *Proceed., Royal Society (London)*, 372A, 453-473, 1980.

Baker, J.P. and C.L. Schofield, Aluminum toxicity to fish in acid waters, *Water Air and Soil Pollution*, 18, 289-309, 1982.

Baker, V.R., Erosional forms and processes for the catastrophic Pleistocene Missoula floods in eastern Washington, in *Fluvial geomorphology*, edited by M. Morisawa, pp. 123-148, Publications in Geomorphology, State University of New York, Binghamton, 1973.

Baker, V.R., Paleohydraulic interpretation of Quaternary alluvium near Golden, Colorado, *Quaternary Research*, 4, 94-112, 1974.

Baker, V.R., Stream-channel response to floods with examples from central Texas, *Geological Society of America Bulletin*, 88, 1057-1071, 1977.

Baker, V.R., Paleoflood hydrologic techniques for the extension of streamflow records, in Improving estimates from flood studies, *Transportation Research Record No. 922*, pp. 18-23, Transportation Research Board, National Research Council, 1983.

Baker, V.R., Paleoflood hydrology and extraordinary flood events, *Journal of Hydrology*, 96, 79-99, 1987.

Baker, V.R., Flood erosion, in *Flood geomorphology*, edited by V.R. Baker, R.C. Kochel, and P.C. Patton, pp. 81-95, John Wiley and Sons, New York, 1988a.

Baker, V.R., L.L Ely, J. E. O'Connor, and J.B. Partridge, Paleoflood hydrology and design applications, in *Regional flood frequency analysis*, edited by V.P. Singh, pp. 339-353, D. Reidel, Boston, 1987.

Baker, V.R. and R.C. Kochel, Flood sedimentation in bedrock fluvial systems, in *Flood geomorphology*, edited by V.R. Baker, R.C. Kochel and P.C. Patton, pp. 123-137, John Wiley and Sons, New York, 1988.

Baker, V.R. and G. Pickup, Flood geomorphology of the Katherine Gorge, Northern Territory, Australia, *Geological Society of America Bulletin*, 98, 635-646, 1987.

Baker, V.R. and D.F. Ritter, Competence of rivers to transport coarse bedload material, *Geological Society of America Bulletin*, 86, 975-978, 1975.

Baker, W.L., Size-class structure of contiguous riparian woodlands along a Rocky Mountain river, *Physical Geography*, 9, 1-14, 1988b.

Baker, W.L., Classification of the riparian vegetation of the montane and subalpine zones in western Colorado, *Great Basin Naturalist*, 49, 214-228, 1989.

Baker, W.L., Climatic and hydrologic effects on the regeneration of *Populus angustifolia* along the Animas River, Colorado, *Journal of Biogeography*, 17, 59-73, 1990.

Baker, W.L. and G.M. Walford, Multiple stable states and models of riparian vegetation succession on the Animas River, Colorado, *Annals Assoc. Am. Geographers*, 85, 320-338, 1995.

Balamurugan, G., Some characteristics of sediment transport in the Sungai Kelang Basin, Malaysia, *Journal of the Institution of Engineers, Malaysia*, 48, 31-52, 1991.

Baldwin, J.E., H.F. Donley, and T.R. Howard, On debris flow/avalanche mitigation and control, San Francisco Bay area, California, in *Debris flows/avalanches: process, recognition, and mitigation*, edited by J.E. Costa and G.F. Wieczorek, pp. 223-236, Geological Society of America, Boulder, Colorado, 1987.

Ball, J. and S. Trudgill, Overview of solute modelling, in *Solute modelling in catchment systems*, edited by S.T. Trudgill, pp. 3-56, John Wiley and Sons, Chichester, 1995.

Banasik, K. and D. Bley, An attempt at modelling suspended sediment concentration after storm events in an Alpine torrent, in *Dynamics and geomorphology of mountain rivers*, edited by P. Ergenzinger and K.-H. Schmidt, pp. 161-170, Springer-Verlag, Berlin, 1994.

Bandyopadhyay, J., J.C. Rodda, R. Kattelmann, Z.W. Kundzewicz, and D. Kraemer, Highland waters - a resource of global significance, in *Mountains of the world: a global priority*, edited by B. Messerli and J.D. Ives, pp. 131-155, The Parthenon Publishing Group, London, 1997.

Bänzinger, R. and H. Burch, Acoustic sensors (hydrophones) as indicators for bed load transport in a mountain torrent, in *Hydrology in mountainous regions I. Hydrological measurements; the water cycle*, edited by H. Lang and A. Musy, pp. 207-214, IAHS Publication no. 193, Wallingford, UK, 1990.

Barclay, J.S., The effects of channelization on riparian vegetation and wildlife in south central Oklahoma, in *Strategies for protection and management of floodplain wetlands and other riparian ecosystems*, pp. 129-138, USDA Forest Service General Technical Report WO-12, 1978.

Bari, F., M.K. Wood, and L. Murray, Livestock grazing impacts on infiltration rates in a temperate range of Pakistan, *Journal of Range Management*, 46, 367-372, 1993.

Barker, D. and D.F.M. McGregor, Land degradation in the Yallahs basin, Jamaica: historical notes and contemporary observations, *Geography*, 73(2), 116-124, 1988.

Barnes, H.H., Jr., Roughness characteristics of natural channels, *U.S.G.S. Water Supply Paper 1849*, 213 pp., 1967.

Baron, J., ed., *Biogeochemistry of a subalpine ecosystem: Loch Vale watershed*, Springer-Verlag, New York, chp. 8, pp. 142-186, 1992.

Baron, J.S., E.J. Allstott and B.K. Newkirk, Analysis of long term sulfate and nitrate budgets in a Rocky Mountain basin, in *Biogeochemistry of seasonally snow-covered catchments*, edited by K.A. Tonnessen, M.W. Williams and M. Tranter, pp. 255-261, IAHS Publ. no. 228, 1995.

Barry, R.G., Mountain climatology and past and potential future climatic changes in mountain regions: a review, *Mountain Research and Development*, 12, 71-86, 1992.

Barry, R.G. and R.J. Chorley, *Atmosphere, weather, and climate*, 5th ed., Methuen, New York, 460 pp., 1987.

Barsch, D. (ed.)., *High mountain research, Special issue of Mountain Research and Development*, 4, 286-374, 1984.

Barsch, D., M. Gude, R. Mäusbacher, G. Schukraft, and A. Schulte, Sediment transport and discharge in a high arctic catchment (Liefdefjorden, NW Spitsbergen), in *Dynamics and geomorphology of mountain rivers*, edited by P. Ergenzinger and K.-H. Schmidt, pp. 225-237, Springer-Verlag, Berlin, 1994a.

Barsch, D., H. Happoldt, R. Mäusbacher, L. Schrott, and G. Schukraft, Discharge and fluvial sediment transport in a semi-arid high mountain catchment, Agua Negra, San Juan, Argentina, in *Dynamics and geomorphology of mountain rivers*, edited by P. Ergenzinger and K.-H. Schmidt, pp. 213-224, Springer-Verlag, Berlin, 1994b.

Barta, A.F., P.R. Wilcock, and C.C.C. Shea, The transport of gravels in boulder-bed streams, *Hydraulic engineering '94*, edited by G.V. Cotroneo and R.R. Rumer, pp. 780-784, Proceed. of the 1994 Conf, Hydraul Div, ASCE, New York, 1994.

Bartholomew, M.J. and H.H. Mills, Old courses of the New River: its late Cenozoic migration and bedrock control inferred from high-level stream gravels, southwestern Virginia, *Geological Society of America Bulletin*, 103, 73-81, 1991.

Bartnik, W. and A. Michalik, Fluvial hydraulics of streams and mountain rivers with mobile bed,in *Hydrdaulic engineering '94*, edited by G.V. Cotroneo and R.R. Rumer, pp. 767-771, Proceed. of the 1994 Conf., Hydraul Div, ASCE, New York, 1994.

Batalla, R.J., C. De Jong, P. Ergenzinger, and M. Sala, Field observations on hyperconcentrated flows in mountain torrents, *Earth Surface Processes and Landforms*, 24, 247-253, 1999.

Bathurst, J.C., Flow resistance estimation in mountain rivers, *ASCE Journal of Hydraulic Engineering*, 111, 625-641, 1985.

Bathurst, J.C., Critical conditions for bed material movement in steep, boulder-bed streams, in *Erosion and sedimentation in the Pacific Rim*, edited by R.L. Beschta, T. Blinn, G.E. Grant, G.G. Ice, and F.J. Swanson, pp. 309-318, Proceedings of the Corvallis Symposium, Aug. 1987, IAHS Publ. no. 165, 1987a.

Bathurst, J.C., Measuring and modelling bedload transport in channels with coarse bed materials, in *River channels: environment and process*, edited by K.S. Richards, pp. 272-294, Basil Blackwell, Oxford, 1987b.

Bathurst, J.C., Velocity profile in high-gradient, boulder-bed channels, *Proceed. International Assoc. Hydraul Res. International Conf. on Fluvial Hydraulics '88*, pp. 29-34,Budapest, Hungary, 1988.

Bathurst, J.C., Tests of three discharge gauging techniques in mountain rivers, in *Hydrology of mountainous areas*, edited by L. Molnar, pp. 93-100, IAHS Publication no. 190, Wallingford, UK, 1990.

Bathurst, J.C., Flow resistance through the channel network, in *Channel network hydrology*, edited by K. Beven and M.J. Kirkby, pp. 69-98, John Wiley and Sons, Chichester, 1993.

Bathurst, J.C., At-a-site mountain river flow resistance variation, in *Hydraulic engineering '94*, edited by G.V. Cotroneo and R.R. Rumer, pp. 682-686, Proceed. of the 1994 Conf., Hydraul Div, ASCE, New York, 1994.

Bathurst, J.C. and M. Ashiq, Dambreak flood impact on mountain stream bedload transport after 13 years, *Earth Surface Processes and Landforms*, 23, 643-649, 1998.

Bathurst, J.C., W.H. Graf, and H.H. Cao, Bed load discharge equations for steep mountain streams, in *Sediment transport in gravel-bed rivers*, edited by C.R. Thorne, J.C. Bathurst, and R.D. Hey, pp. 453-477, John Wiley and Sons, Chichester, 1987.

Bathurst, J.C., L. Hubbard, G.J.L. Leeks, M.D. Newson, and C.R. Thorne, Sediment yield in the aftermath of a dambreak flood in a mountain stream, in *Hydrology in mountainous regions II. Artificial reservoirs, water and slopes*, edited by R.O. Sinniger and M. Monbaron, pp. 287-294, IAHS Publication no. 194, Wallingford, UK, 1990.

Baumgart-Kotarba, M., Formation of coarse gravel bars and alluvial channels, braided Bialka River, Carpathians, Poland, in *International geomorphology 1986, Part I*, edited by V. Gardiner, pp. 633-648, John Wiley and Sons, Chichester, 1986.

Baxter, R.M., Environmental effects of dams and impoundments, *Annual Reviews of Ecological Systems*, 8, 255-283, 1977.

Bayley, P.B., The flood-pulse advantage and the restoration of river-floodplain systems, *Regulated Rivers: Research and Management*, 6, 75-86, 1991.

Bayley, P.B., Understanding large river-floodplain ecosystems, *BioScience*, 45, 153-158, 1995.

Bayley, P.B. and H.W. Li, Riverine fishes, in *The rivers handbook*, edited by P. Calow and G.E. Petts, pp. 251-281, Blackwell Scientific Publications, Oxford, UK, 1992.

Beaty, C.B., Great big boulders I have known, *Geology*, 17, 349-352, 1989.

Beaty, C.B., Anatomy of a White Mountain debris-flow — the making of an alluvial fan, in *Alluvial fans: a field approach*, edited by A.H. Rachocki and M. Church, pp. 69-89, John Wiley and Sons, New York, 1990.

Beaumont, C. and G. Quinlan, A geodynamic framework for interpreting crustal-scale seismic reflectivity patterns in compressional orogens, *International Journal of Geophysics*, 116, 754-783, 1994.

Bechteler, W., H.-J. Vollmers, and S. Wieprecht, Model investigations into the influence of renaturalization on sediment transport, in *Dynamics and geomorphology of mountain rivers*, edited by P. Ergenzinger and K.-H. Schmidt, pp. 37-52, Springer-Verlag, Berlin, 1994.

Begin, Z.B. and M. Inbar, Relationship between flows and sediment size in some gravel streams of the arid Negev, Israel, in *Sedimentology of gravels and conglomerates*, edited by E.H. Koster and R.J. Steel, pp. 69-75, Canadian Society of Petroleum Geologists, Memoir 10, 1984.

Benda, L., The influence of debris flows on channels and valley floors in the Oregon Coast Range, USA, *Earth Surface Processes and Landforms*, 15, 457-466, 1990.

Benda, L.E. and T.W. Cundy, Predicting deposition of debris flows in mountain channels, *Canadian Geotechnical Journal*, 27, 409-417, 1990.

Benda, L. and T. Dunne, Sediment routing by debris flow, in *Erosion and sedimentation in the Pacific Rim*, edited by R.L. Beschta, T. Blinn, G.E. Grant, G.G. Ice and F.J. Swanson, pp. 213-223, IAHS Publ. no. 165, 1987.

Benda, L. and T. Dunne, Stochastic forcing of sediment routing and storage in channel networks, *Water Resources Research*, 33, 2865-2880, 1997a.

Benda, L. and T. Dunne, Stochastic forcing of sediment supply to channel networks from landsliding and debris flow, *Water Resources Research*, 33, 2849-2863, 1997b.

Bender, E.A., T.J. Case, and M.E. Gilpin, Perturbation experiments in community ecology: theory and practice, *Ecology*, 65, 1-13, 1984.

Benischke, R. and T. Harum, Determination of discharge rates in turbulent streams by salt tracer dilution applying a microcomputer system. Comparison with current meter measurements, in *Hydrology in mountainous regions I. Hydrological measurements; the water cycle*, edited by H. Lang and A. Musy, pp. 215-221, IAHS Publication no. 193, Wallingford, UK, , 1990.

Benitez, S., Landslides: extent and economic significance in Ecuador, in *Landslides: extent and economic significance*, edited by Brabb and Harrod, pp. 123-126, Balkema, Rotterdam, 1989.

Benito, G., T. Grodek, and Y. Enzel, The geomorphic and hydrologic impacts of the catastrophic failure of flood-control-dams during the 1996-Biescas flood (Central Pyrenees, Spain), *Zeitschrift für Geomorphologie*, 42, 417-437, 1998.

Benito, G., M.J. Machado, and A. Perez-Gonzalez, *Climate change and flood sensitivity in Spain, in Global continental changes: the context of palaeohydrology*, edited by J. Branson, A.G. Brown, and K.J. Gregory, pp. 85-98, Geological Society Special Publ. no. 115, 1996.

Benson, M.A., Use of historical data in flood-frequency analysis, *Transactions, Am Geophys Union*, 31, 419-424, 1950.

Berg, N., A. Carlson, and D. Azuma, Function and dynamics of woody debris in stream reaches in the central Sierra Nevada, California, *Canadian Journal of Fisheries and Aquatic Sciences*, 55, 1807-1820, 1998.

Berger, R.C. and R.L. Stockstill, Finite-element model for high-velocity channels, *Journal of Hydraulic Engineering*, 121, 710-716, 1995.

Bergeron, N.E., An analysis of flow velocity profiles, stream bed roughness, and resistance to flow in natural gravel bed streams, in *Hydraulic Engineering '94*, edited by G.V. Cotroneo and R.R. Rumer, pp. 692-696, Proceed of the 1994 Conf, Hydraul Div, ASCE, New York, p. 692-696, 1994.

Berner, E.K. and R.A. Berner, *The global water cycle: geochemistry and environment*, Prentice-Hall, Englewood Cliffs, New Jersey, 397 pp., 1987.

Berris, S. and R.D. Harr, Comparative snow accumulation and melt during rainfall in forested and clearcut plots in the western Cascades of Oregon, *Water Resources Research*, 23, 135-142, 1987.

Berry, J.W., The climate of Colorado, in *Climates of the states*, v. 2, pp. 595-613, Water Information Center, Inc., Port Washington, NY, 1974.

Berti, M., R. Genevois, A. Simoni, and P. Rosella Tecca, Field observations of a debris flow event in the Dolomites, *Geomorphology*, 29, 265-274, 1999.

Beschta, R.L., The effects of large organic debris upon channel morphology: a flume study, in *Symposium on erosion and sedimentation*, edited by D.B. Simons, pp. 8-63 to 8-78, Simons,

Li, and Associates, Ft. Collins, Colorado, 1983.

Beschta, R.L., Conceptual models of sediment transport in streams, in *Sediment transport in gravel-bed rivers*, edited by C.R. Thorne, J.C. Bathurst, and R.D. Hey, pp. 387-419, John Wiley and Sons, Chichester, 1987.

Beschta, R.L., T. Blinn, G.E. Grant, G.G. Ice, and F.J. Swanson, (eds.), *Erosion and sedimentation in the Pacific Rim*, IAHS Publication no. 165, 1987.

Beschta, R.L. and W.L. Jackson, The intrusion of fine sediment into a stable gravel bed, *Journal of the Fisheries Research Board of Canada*, 36, 202-210, 1979.

Beschta, R.L. and W.S. Platts, Morphological features of small streams: significance and function, *Water Resources Bulletin*, 22, 369-379, 1986.

Best, J., On the entrainment of sediment and initiation of bed defects: insights from recent developments within turbulent boundary layer research, *Sedimentology*, 39, 797-811, 1992.

Best, J.L., On the interactions between turbulent flow structure, sediment transport and bedform development: some considerations from recent experimental research, in *Turbulence: perspectives on flow and sediment transport*, edited by N.J. Clifford, J.R. French, and J. Hardisty, pp. 61-92, John Wiley and Sons, Chichester, 1993.

Bestgen, K.R. pers. comm. 21 Oct. 1992. Larval Fish Laboratory, Colorado State University.

Beverage, J.P. and J.K. Culbertson, Hyperconcentrations of suspended sediment, *ASCE Journal of Hydraulics Division*, 90, 117-126, 1964.

Bezinge, A., Glacial meltwater streams, hydrology and sediment transport: the case of the Grande Dixence Hydroelectricity Scheme, in *International geomorphology 1986, Part I*, edited by V. Gardiner, pp. 473-498, John Wiley and Sons, Chichester, 1987.

Bhowmik, N.G. and M. Demissie, Bed material sorting in pools and riffles, *ASCE Journal of Hydraulic Engineering*, 108, 1227-1231, 1982.

Biedenharn, D.S., Knickpoint migration characteristics in the Loess Hills of northern Mississippi, USA, *US-China Sedimentation Symposium*, 8 pp., 1989.

Bilby, R.E., Influence of stream size on the function and characteristics of large organic debris, in *Proceedings, West Coast Meeting of National Council of Paper Industry for Air and Stream Improvement*, Portland, Oregon, 1985.

Bilby, R.E. and G.E. Likens, Importance of organic debris dams in the structure and function of stream ecosystems, *Ecology*, 61, 1107-1113, 1980.

Bilby, R.E. and J.W. Ward, Changes in characteristics and function of woody debris with increasing size of streams in western Washington, *Trans., Am Fisheries Society*, 118, 368-378, 1989.

Billi, P., Streambed dynamics and grain-size characteristics of two gravel rivers of the Northern Apennines, Italy, in *Dynamics and geomorphology of mountain rivers*, edited by P. Ergenzinger and K.-H. Schmidt, pp. 197-212, Springer-Verlag, Berlin, 1994.

Billi, P., R.D. Hey and C.R. Thorne, (eds.), *Dynamics of gravel-bed rivers*, John Wiley and Sons, Chichester, 1992.

Billi, P. and P. Tacconi, Bedload transport processes monitored at Virginio Creek measuring station, Italy, in *International geomorphology 1986, Part I*, edited by V. Gardiner, pp. 549-559, John Wiley and Sons, Chichester, 1987.

Binkley, D.R., F. Stottlemyer, F. Suarez, and J. Cortina, Soil nitrogen availability in some arctic ecosystems in northwestern Alaska: responses to temperature and moisture, *Ecoscience*, 1, 64-70, 1994.

Birkeland, P.W., Mean velocities and boulder transport during Tahoe-age floods of the Truckee River, California-Nevada, *Geological Society of America Bulletin*, 79, 137-142, 1968.

Birkeland, P.W., Subdivision of Holocene glacial deposits, Ben Oahu Range, New Zealand, using relative-dating methods, *Geological Society of America Bulletin*, 93, 433-449, 1982.

Bishop, P. and G. Goldrick, Morphology, processes and evolution of two waterfalls near Cowra, New South Wales, *Australian Geographer*, 23, 116-121, 1992.

Bisson, P.A., R.E. Bilby, M.D. Bryant, C.A. Dolloff, G.B. Grette, R.A. House, M.L. Murphy, K.V. Koski, and J.R. Sedell, Large woody debris in forested streams in the Pacific Northwest: past, present, and future, in *Streamside management: forestry and fishery implications*, edited by E.O. Salo and T.W. Cundy, pp. 143-190, University of Washington, Institute of Forest Resources, Contribution No. 57, 1987.

Bisson, P.A., J.L. Nielson, R.A. Palmason, and L.E. Grove, A system of naming habitat types in small streams, with examples of habitat utilization by salmonids during low streamflow, in *Acquisition and utilization of aquatic habitat inventory information*, edited by N.B. Armantrout, pp. 62-73, American Fisheries Society, Portland, Oregon, 1982.

Bjonness, I.-M., Mountain hazard perception and risk-avoiding strategies among the Sherpas of Khumbu Himal, Nepal, *Mountain Research and Development*, 6, 277-292, 1986.

Björnsson, H., Jökulhlaups in Iceland: prediction, characteristics and simulation, *Annals of Glaciology*, 16, 95-106, 1992.

Blackwelder, E., Mudflow as a geologic agent in semi-arid mountains, *Geological Society of America Bulletin*, 39, 465-484, 1928.

Blair, T.C., Sedimentary processes, vertical stratification sequences, and geomorphology of the Roaring River alluvial fan, Rocky Mountain National Park, Colorado, *Journal of Sedimentary Petrology*, 57, 1-18, 1987.

Blizard, C.R., *Hydraulic variables and bedload transport in East St. Louis Creek, Rocky Mountains, Colorado*, Unpublished MS thesis, Colorado State University, Ft. Collins, Colorado, 176 pp., 1994.

Blizard, C.R. and E.E. Wohl, Relationships between hydraulic variables and bedload transport in a subalpine channel, Colorado Rocky Mountains, USA, *Geomorphology*, 22, 359-371, 1998.

Bloom, A.L., *Geomorphology: a systematic analysis of late Cenozoic landforms*, Prentice Hall, New Jersey, 482 pp., 1998.

Blown, I. and M. Church, Catastrophic lake drainage within the Homathko River basin, British Columbia, *Canadian Geotechnical Journal*, 22, 551-563, 1985.

Blyth, K. and J.C. Rodda, A stream length study, *Water Resources Research*, 9, 1454-1461, 1973.

Bogen, J., The hysteresis effect of sediment transport systems, *Norsk Geogr. Tidsskrq.*, 34, 45-54, 1980.

Bogen, J., Sediment transport and deposition in mountain rivers, in *Sediment and water quality in river catchments*, edited by I. Foster, A. Gurnell, and B. Webb, pp. 437-451, John Wiley and Sons, Chichester, 1995.

Boll, J., T.J.M. Thewessen, E.L. Meijer, and S.B. Kroonenberg, A simulation of the development of river terraces, *Zeitschrift für Geomorphologie*, 32, 31-45, 1988.

Bolton, S., A. Watts, T. Sibley, and J. Dooley, A pilot study examining the effectiveness of engineered large woody debris (Elwd) as an interim solution to lack of LWD in streams, *EOS, Transactions, Am. Geophysical Union*, 79, F346, 1998.

Boon, P.J., The impact of river regulation on invertebrate communities in the U.K., *Regulated Rivers: Research and Management*, 2, 389-409, 1988.

Bordas, M.P. and J.H. Silvestrini, Threshold of sediment deposition in medium stream power flow, in *Erosion, debris flows and environment in mountain regions*, edited by D.E. Walling, T.R. Davies, and B. Hasholt, pp. 3-13, Proceedings, Chengdu Symposium, July 1992. IAHS Publ. no. 209, 1992.

Bormann, F.H. and G.E. Likens, *Pattern and process in a forested ecosystem*, Springer-Verlag, New York, 1979.

Bosch, J.M. and J.D. Hewlett, A review of catchment experiments to determine the effects of vegetation changes on water yield and evapotranspiration, *Journal of Hydrology*, 55, 3-23, 1982.

Boulton, A.J. and E.H. Stanley, Hyporheic processes during flooding and drying in a Sonoran Desert stream. II. Faunal dynamics, *Arch. Hydrobiol.*, 134, 27-52, 1995.

Bovis, M.J. and B.R. Dagg, Mechanisms of debris supply to steep channels along Howe Sound, southwestern British Columbia, in *Erosion and sedimentation in the Pacific Rim*, edited by R.L. Beschta, T. Blinn, G.E. Grant, G.G. Ice, and F.J. Swanson, pp. 191-200, IAHS Publ. no. 165, 1987.

Bowman, D., Stepped-bed morphology in arid gravelly channels, *Geological Society of America Bulletin*, 88, 291-298, 1977.

Boyce, R.C., Sediment routing with sediment delivery ratios, *Agricultural Research Service ARS-S-40*, pp. 61-65, 1975.

Boyer, E.W., G.M. Hornberger, K.E. Bencala and D.M. McKnight, Variation of dissolved organic carbon during snowmelt in soil and stream waters of two headwater catchments, Summit County, Colorado, in *Biogeochemistry of seasonally snow-covered catchments*, edited by K.A. Tonnessen, M.W. Williams and M. Tranter, pp. 303-312, IAHS Publ. no. 228, 1995.

Braatne, J.H., S.B. Rood and P.E. Heilman, Life history, ecology, and conservation of riparian cottonwoods in North America, in *Biology of Populus and its implications for management and conservation*, edited by R.F. Stettler, H.D. Bradshaw, P.E. Heilman and T.M. Hinckley, pp. 57-85, NRC Research Press, Ottawa, Canada, 1996.

Bradley, J.B. and McCutcheon, Influence of large suspended-sediment concentrations in rivers, in *Sediment transport in gravel-bed rivers*, edited by C.R. Thorne, J.C. Bathurst, and R.D. Hey, pp. 645-689, John Wiley and Sons, Chichester, 1987.

Bradley, J.B. and D.T. Williams, Sediment budgets in gravel bed streams, in *Hydraulic engineering '93*, edited by H.W. Shen, S.T. Su, and F. Wen, pp. 713-718, ASCE, New York, 1993.

Bradley, W.C. and A.I. Mears, Calculations of flow needed to transport coarse fraction of Boulder Creek alluvium at Boulder, Colorado: summary, *Geological Society of America Bulletin*, Part I, 91, 135-138, 1980.

Braudrick, C.A., G.E. Grant, Y. Ishikawa, and H. Ikeda, Dynamics of wood transport in streams: a flume experiment, *Earth Surface Processes and Landforms*, 22, 669-683, 1997.

Braun, M. and P. Fiener, *Report on the GLOF hazard mapping project in the Imja Khola/Dudh Kosi Valley, Nepal*, ICIMOD, Kathmandu, 30 pp., 1995.

Bray, D.I., Estimating average velocity in gravel-bed rivers, *Journal of Hydraulics Division, ASCE*, 105, 1103-1122, 1979.

Bray, D.I. and M. Church, Armored versus paved gravel beds, *Journal of Hydraulics Division, ASCE*, 106, 1937-1940, 1980.

Bray, D.I. and R. Kellerhalls, Some Canadian examples of the response of rivers to man-made changes, in *Adjustments of the fluvial system*, edited by D.D. Rhodes and G.P. Williams, pp. 351-372, George Allen and Unwin, London, 1979.

Brayshaw, A.C., Bed microtopography and entrainment thresholds in gravel-bed rivers, *Geological Society of America Bulletin*, 96, 218-223, 1985.

Brayshaw, A.C., L. F. Frostick, and I. Reid, The hydrodynamics of particle clusters and sediment entrainment on coarse alluvial channels, *Sedimentology*, 30, 137-143, 1983.

Brayton, S.D., The beaver and the stream, *Journal of Soil and Water Conservation*, 39, 108-109, 1984.

Brazier, V. and C.K. Ballantyne, Late Holocene debris cone evolution in Glen Feshie, western Cairngorm Mountains, Scotland, *Transactions, Royal Society of Edinburgh: Earth Sciences*, 80, 17-24, 1989.

Brazier, V., G. Whittington, and C.K. Ballantyne, Holocene debris cone evolution in Glen Etive, western Grampian Highlands, Scotland, *Earth Surface Processes and Landforms*, 13, 525-531, 1988.

Bridges, E.M., *World geomorphology*, Cambridge University Press, Cambridge, 260 pp., 1990.

Brierley, G.J. and E.J. Hickin, The downstream gradation of particle sizes in the Squamish River, British Columbia, *Earth Surface Processes and Landforms*, 10, 597-606, 1985.

Brooker, M.P., The impact of impoundments on the downstream fisheries and general ecology of rivers, in *Advances in applied biology*, edited by T.H. Coaker, v. 6, pp. 91-152, Academic Press, London, 1981.

Brookes, A., *Channelized rivers: perspectives for environmental management*, John Wiley and Sons, Chichester, 326 pp., 1988.

Brookes, A., Restoration and enhancement of engineered river channels: some European experiences, *Regulated Rivers: Research and Management*, 5, 45-56, 1990.

Brookfield, M.E., The evolution of the great river systems of southern Asia during the Cenozoic India-Asia collision: rivers draining southwards, *Geomorphology*, 22, 285-312, 1998.

Broscoe, A.J. and S. Thomson, Observations on an alpine mudflow, Steel Creek, Yukon, *Canadian Journal of Earth Sciences*, 6, 219-229, 1969.

Brown, C.B., Sediment transportation, in *Engineering hydraulics*, edited by H. Rouse, pp. 769-857, 1950.

Brown, D.J.A., The effect of pH and calcium on fish and fisheries, *Water Air Soil Pollution*, 18, 343-351, 1982.

Brunke, M. and T. Gonser, The ecological significance of exchange processes between rivers and groundwater, *Freshwater Biology*, 37, 1-33, 1997.

Bruns, D.A., G.W. Minshall, C.E. Cushing, K.W. Cummins, J.T. Brock, and R.L. Vannote, Tributaries as modifiers of the river-continuum concept: analysis by polar ordination and regression models, *Arch. Hydrobiol.*, 99, 208-220, 1984.

Brunsden, D., Barriers to geomorphological change, in *Landscape sensitivity*, edited by D.S.G. Thomas and R.J. Allison, pp. 7-12, John Wiley and Sons, Chichester, 1993.

Brunsden, D. and D.K.C. Jones, The evolution of landslide deposits in Dorset, *Philosophical Transactions of the Royal Society of London*, A283, 605-631, 1976.

Brunsden, D. and J. B.Thornes, Landscape sensitivity and change, *Transactions, Institute of British Geographers New Series*, 4, 463-484, 1979.

Bryan, G.W., Some aspects of heavy metal tolerance in aquatic organisms, in *Effects of pollutants on aquatic organisms*, edited by A.P.M. Lockwood, pp. 7-34, Cambridge University Press, Cambridge, 1976.

Bryan, K., Gully gravure, a method of slope retreat, *Journal of Geomorphology*, 3, 89-106, 1940.

Büdel, J., *Climatic geomorphology*, Princeton University Press, Princeton, New Jersey, 443 pp., 1982.

Buffington, J.M. and D.R. Montgomery, A procedure for classifying textural facies in gravel-bed rivers, *Water Resources Research*, 35, 1903-1914, 1999a.

Buffington, J.M. and D.R. Montgomery, Effects of hydraulic roughness on surface textures of gravel-bed rivers, *Water Resources Research*, 35, 3507-3521, 1999b.

Buffington, J.M. and D.R. Montgomery, Effects of sediment supply on surface textures of gravel-bed rivers, *Water Resources Research*, 35, 3523-3530, 1999c.

Bugosh, N. and S.G. Custer, The effect of a log-jam burst on bedload transport and channel characteristics in a headwaters stream, in *Headwaters hydrology*, pp. 203-211, American Water Resources Association, 1989.

Bull, W.B., Geomorphology of segmented alluvial fans in western Fresno County, California, U.S. *Geological Survey Professional Paper 352-E*, p. 89-129, 1964.

Bull, W.B., The alluvial fan environment, *Progress in Physical Geography*, 1, 222-270, 1977.

Bull, W.B. Threshold of critical power in streams, *Geological Society of America Bulletin*, 90, 453-464, 1979.

Bull, W.B., Floods; degradation and aggradation, in *Flood geomorphology*, edited by V.R. Baker, R.C. Kochel, and P.C. Patton, pp. 157-165, John Wiley and Sons, New York, 1988.

Bull, W.B., *Geomorphic responses to climatic change*, Oxford University Press, New York, 326 pp., 1991.

Bull, W.B. and P.L.K. Knuepfer, Adjustments by the Charwell River, New Zealand, to uplift and climatic changes, *Geomorphology*, 1, 15-32, 1987.

Bull, W.B. and K.M. Scott, Impact of mining gravel from urban stream beds in the southwestern US, *Geology*, 2, 171-174, 1974.

Bultot, F., D. Gellens, M. Spreafico, and B. Schädler, Repercussions of a CO_2 doubling on the water balance - a case study in Switzerland, *Journal of Hydrology*, 137, 199-208, 1992.

Bundi, U., E. Eichenberger, and A. Peter, Water flow regime as the driving force for the formation of habitats and biological communities in Alpine rivers, in *Hydrology in mountainous regions II. Artificial reservoirs, water and slopes*, edited by R.O. Sinniger and M. Monbaron, pp. 197-

204, IAHS Publ. no. 194, Wallingford, UK, 1990.

Bunte, K., Experiences and results from using a big-frame bed load sampler for coarse material bed load, in *Hydrology in mountainous regions I. Hydrological measurements; the water cycle,* edited by H. Lang and A. Musy, pp. 223-230, IAHS Publication no. 193, Wallingford, UK, 1990.

Bunte, K., Particle number grain-size composition of bedload in a mountain stream, in *Dynamics of gravel-bed rivers,* edited by P. Billi, R.D. Hey, C.R. Thorne and P. Tacconi, pp. 55-72, John Wiley and Sons, Chichester, 1992.

Bunte, K., Analyses of the temporal variation of coarse bedload transport and its grain size distribution: Squaw Creek, Montana, USA, *USDA Forest Service, General Technical Report RM-GTR-288,* 123 pp., 1996.

Burbank, D.W., J. Leland, E. Fielding, R.S. Anderson, N. Brozovic, M.R. Reid, and C. Duncan, Bedrock incision, rock uplift and threshold hillslopes in the northwestern Himalayas, *Nature,* 379, 505-510, 1996.

Burner, C.J., Characteristics of spawning nests of Columbia River salmon, *U.S. Fish and Wildlife Service Bulletin,* 61, 97-110, 1951.

Burton, A., T.J. Arkell, and J.C. Bathurst, Field variability of landslide model parameters, *Environmental Geology,* 35, 100-114, 1998.

Burton, A. and J.C. Bathurst, Physically based modelling of shallow landslide sediment yield at a catchment scale, *Environmental Geology,* 35, 89-99, 1998.

Burton, G.A., Jr. (ed.), *Sediment toxicity assessment,* Lewis Publishers, Boca Raton, Florida, 1992.

Busskamp, R., The influence of channel steps on coarse bed load transport in mountain torrents: case study using the radio tracer technique 'PETSY', in *Dynamics and geomorphology of mountain rivers,* edited by P. Ergenzinger and K.-H. Schmidt, pp. 129-139, Springer-Verlag, Berlin, 1994.

Butler, D.R. and G.P. Malanson, Sedimentation rates and patterns in beaver ponds in a mountain environment, *Geomorphology,* 13, 255-269, 1995.

Byrd, T.C., *Dynamical analysis of nonlogarithmic velocity profiles in steep, rough channels,* Unpublished MS thesis, Florida State University, Tallahassee, Florida, 74 pp., 1997.

Caine, N., The geomorphic processes of the alpine environment, in *Arctic and alpine environments,* edited by J.D. Ives and R.G. Barry, pp. 721-748, Methuen, London, 1974.

Caine, N., Summer rainstorms in an alpine environment and their influence on soil erosion, San Juan Mountains, Arizona, *Arctic and Alpine Research,* 8, 183-196, 1976.

Caine, N., The rainfall intensity-duration control of shallow landslides and debris flows, *Geografiska Annaler,* 62A, 23-27, 1980.

Caine, N. and P.K. Mool, P.K., Channel geometry and flow estimates for two small mountain streams in the Middle Hills, Nepal, *Mountain Research and Development,* 1, 231-243, 1981.

Campbell, A.J. and R.C. Sidle, Bedload transport in a pool-riffle sequence of a coastal Alaska stream, *Water Resources Bulletin,* 21, 579-590, 1985.

Campbell, D.H., D.W. Clow, G.P. Ingersoll, M.A. Mast, N.E. Spahr, and J.T. Turk, Nitrogen deposition and release in alpine watersheds, Loch Vale, Colorado, USA, in *Biogeochemistry of seasonally snow-covered catchments,* edited by K.A. Tonnessen, M.W. Williams and M. Tranter, pp. 243-253, IAHS Publ. no. 228, 1995a.

Campbell, D.H., D.W. Clow, G.P. Ingersoll, M.A. Mast, N.E. Spahr, and J.T. Turk, Processes controlling the chemistry of two snowmelt-dominated streams in the Rocky Mountains, *Water Resources Research,* 31, 2811-2821, 1995b.

Campbell, R.H., Soil slips, debris flows, and rainstorms in the Santa Monica Mountains and vicinity, southern California, *U.S. Geological Survey Professional Paper 851,* 51 pp., 1975.

Cannon, S.H., Regional rainfall-threshold conditions for abundant debris-flow activity, in Landslides, floods, and marine effects of the storm of January 3-5, 1982, in the San Francisco bay region, California, edited by S.D. Ellen and G.F. Wieczorek, pp. 35-42, *U.S. Geological Survey Professional Paper 1434,* 1988.

Carling, P.A., Threshold of coarse sediment transport in broad and narrow natural streams, *Earth Surface Processes and Landforms*, 8, 1-18, 1983.

Carling, P.A., Comparison of suspended sediment rating curves obtained using two sampling methods, in *Channel processes - water, sediment, catchment controls*, edited by A.P. Schick, pp. 43-49, Catena Supplement 5, 1984a.

Carling, P.A., Deposition of fine and coarse sand in an open-work gravel, *Canadian Journal of Fisheries and Aquatic Sciences*, 41, 263-270, 1984b.

Carling, P.A., Bedload transport in two gravel-bedded streams, *Earth Surface Processes and Landforms*, 14, 27-39, 1989a.

Carling, P.A., Hydrodynamic models of boulder berm deposition, *Geomorphology*, 2, 319-340, 1989b.

Carling, P.A., Particle over-passing on depth-limited gravel bars, *Sedimentology*, 37, 345-355, 1990.

Carling, P.A., An appraisal of the velocity-reversal hypothesis for stable pool-riffle sequences in the River Severn, England, *Earth Surface Processes and Landforms*, 16, 19-31, 1991.

Carling, P.A., Palaeohydraulic reconstruction of floods in upland UK bedrock streams: progress, problems and prospects, in *Hydraulic engineering '94*, edited by G.V. Cotroneo and R.R. Rumer, pp. 860-864, Proceed of the 1994 Conf, Hydraul Div, ASCE, New York, 1994a.

Carling, P.A., Particle dynamics and bed level adjustments in a mountain stream, in *Hydraulic engineering '94*, edited by G.V. Cotroneo and R.R. Rumer, pp. 839-843, Proceed of the 1994 Conf, Hydraul Div, ASCE, New York, 1994b.

Carling, P.A., Flow-separation berms downstream of a hydraulic jump in a bedrock channel, *Geomorphology*, 11, 245-253, 1995.

Carling, P.A. and M.S. Glaister, Rapid deposition of sand and gravel mixtures downstream of a negative step: the role of matrix-infilling and particle-overpassing in the process of bar-front accretion, *Journal of the Geological Society, London*, 144, 543-551, 1987.

Carling, P.A. and T. Grodek, Indirect estimation of ungauged peak discharges in a bedrock channel with reference to design discharge selection, *Hydrological Processes*, 8, 497-511, 1994.

Carling, P.A. and M.A. Hurley, A time-varying stochastic model of the frequency and magnitude of bed load transport events in two small trout streams, in *Sediment transport in gravel-bed rivers,* edited by C.R. Thorne, J.C. Bathurst, and R.D. Hey, pp. 897-920, John Wiley and Sons, Chichester, 1987.

Carling, P.A., A. Kelsey, and M.S. Glaister, Effect of bed roughness, particle shape and orientation on initial motion criteria, in *Dynamics of gravel-bed rivers*, edited by P. Billi, R.D. Hey, C.R. Thorne and P. Tacconi, pp. 23-39, John Wiley and Sons, Chichester, 1992.

Carling, P.A., H.G. Orr and M.S. Glaister, Preliminary observations and significance of dead zone flow structures for solute and fine particle dynamics, in *Mixing and transport in the environment,* edited by K.J. Beven, P.C. Chatwin, and J.H. Millbank, pp. 139-157, John Wiley and Sons, 1994.

Carling, P.A. and N.A. Reader, Structure, composition and bulk properties of upland stream gravels, *Earth Surface Processes and Landforms*, 7, 349-365, 1982.

Carling, P.A. and K. Tinkler, Conditions for the entrainment of cuboid boulders in bedrock streams: an historical review of literature with respect to recent investigations, in *Rivers over rock: fluvial processes in bedrock channels*, edited by K.J. Tinkler and E.E. Wohl, pp. 19-34, Am. Geophys. Union Geophysical Monograph 107, 1998.

Carling, P.A. and N. Wood, Simulation of flow over pool-riffle topography: a consideration of the velocity reversal hypothesis, *Earth Surface Processes and Landforms*, 19, 319-332, 1994.

Carlson, J.Y., C.W. Andrus, and H.A. Froehlich, Woody debris, channel features, and macroinvertebrates of streams with logged and undisturbed riparian timber in northeastern Oregon, U.S.A., *Canadian Journal of Fisheries and Aquatic Sciences*, 47, 1103-1111, 1990.

Carpenter, K.E., *Life in inland waters*, Macmillan Company, New York, 267 pp., 1928.

Carson, M.A. and G.A. Griffiths, Bedload transport in gravel channels, *Journal of Hydrology (NZ)*, 26, 1-151, 1987.

Carson, M.A. and M.J. Kirkby, *Hillslope form and process*, Cambridge University Press, London, 1972.

Carver, M. and G. Nakarmi, The effect of surface conditions on soil erosion and stream suspended sediments, in *Challenges in mountain resource management in Nepal*, edited by H. Schreier, P.B. Shah, and S. Brown, pp. 155-162, ICIMOD, Kathmandu, 1995.

Cencetti, C., P. Tacconi, M. Del Prete, and M. Rinaldi, Variability of gravel movement on the Virginio gravel-bed stream (central Italy) during some floods, in *Variability in stream erosion and sediment transport*, edited by L.J. Olive, R.J. Loughran and J.A. Kesby, pp. 3-11, IAHS Publication no. 224, Wallingford, UK, 1994.

Cenderelli, D.A., *Glacial-lake outburst floods in the Mount Everest region of Nepal: flow processes, flow hydraulics, and geomorphic effects*, Unpublished PhD dissertation, Colorado State University, Ft. Collins, Colorado, 247 pp., 1998.

Cenderelli, D.A., Floods from natural and artificial dam failures, in *Inland flood hazards: human, riparian, and aquatic communities*, edited by E.E. Wohl, pp. 73-103, Cambridge University Press, Cambridge, 2000.

Cenderelli, D.A. and B.L. Cluer, Depositional processes and sediment supply in resistant-boundary channels: examples from two case studies, in *Rivers over rock: fluvial processes in bedrock channels*, edited by K.J. Tinkler and E.E. Wohl, pp. 105-131, Am. Geophys. Union Geophysical Monograph 107, 1998.

Cenderelli, D.A. and J.S. Kite, Erosion and deposition by debris flows in mountainous channels on North Fork Mountain, eastern West Virginia, *Hydraulic engineering '94*, edited by G.V. Cotroneo and R.R. Rumer, pp. 772-776, Proceed of the 1994 Conf, Hydraulic Div, ASCE, New York, 1994.

Cenderelli, D.A. and J.S. Kite, Geomorphic effects of large debris flows on channel morphology at North Fork Mountain, eastern West Virginia, USA, *Earth Surface Processes and Landforms*, 23, 1-19, 1998.

Cenderelli, D.A. and E.E. Wohl, Sedimentology and clast orientation of deposits produced by glacial-lake outburst floods in the Mount Everest region, Nepal, in *Geomorphological hazards in high mountain areas*, edited by J. Kalvoda and C.L. Rosenfeld, pp. 1-26, Kluwer Academic Publishers, The Netherlands, 1998.

Chacho, E.F., Jr., W.W. Emmett, and R.L. Burrows, Monitoring grain movement using radio transmitters, in *Hydraulic engineering '94*, edited by G.V. Cotroneo and R.R. Rumer, pp. 785-789, Proceed of the 1994 Conf, Hydraul Div, ASCE, New York, 1994.

Chang, L.H., C.T. Hunsaker, and J.D. Draves, Recent research on effects of climate change on water resources, *Water Resources Bulletin*, 28, 273-286, 1992.

Chanson, H., Hydraulics of nappe flow regime above stepped chutes and spillways, *Australian Civil Engineering Transactions*, CE 36, 69-76, 1994.

Chanson, H., *Hydraulic design of stepped cascades, channels, weirs and spillways*, Pergamon, Tarrytown, New Jersey, 292 pp., 1995.

Chanson, H., Comment on 'Step-pool streams: adjustment to maximum flow resistance' by A.D. Abrahams, G. Li and J.F. Atkinson, *Water Resources Research*, 32, 3401-3402, 1996.

Chapman, D.W., Food and space as regulators of salmonid populations in streams, *American Naturalist*, 100, 345-357, 1966.

Chapman, D.W., Critical review of variables used to define effects of fines in redds of large salmonids, *Transactions of the American Fisheries Society*, 117, 1-21, 1988.

Chase, K.J., Thresholds for gravel and cobble motion, in *Hydraulic engineering '94*, edited by G.V. Cotroneo and R.R. Rumer, pp. 79-794, Proceedings of the 1994 Conference, Hydraulics Division, ASCE, New York, 1994.

Chatwin, S.C., D.E. Howes, J.W. Schwab, and D.N. Swanston, A guide for management of landslide-prone terrain in the Pacific Northwest, *British Columbia Ministry of Forests, Land Management Handbook no. 18*, 212 pp., 1991.

Chen, C.-L. Comprehensive review of debris flow modeling concepts in Japan, in *Debris flows/ava-*

lanches: process, recognition, and mitigation, edited by J.E. Costa and G.F. Wieczorek, pp. 13-29, Geological Society of America, Reviews in Engineering Geology, v. 7, Boulder, Colorado, 1987.

Chen, C.W., S.A. Gherini, J.D. Dean, R.J.M. Hudson and R.A. Goldstein, Development and calibration of the Integrated Lake-Watershed Acidification study model, in *Modeling of total acid precipitation impacts*, edited by J. Schoor, pp. 175-203, Ann Arbor Science, Ann Arbor, Michigan, 1984.

Chen, J. and A. Ohmura, On the influence of Alpine glaciers on runoff, in *Hydrology in mountainous regions I. Hydrological measurements, the water cycle*, edited by H. Lang and A. Musy, pp. 117-125, IAHS Publication no. 193, Wallingford, UK, 1990.

Cheng, J.D., Streamflow changes after clearcut logging of a pine-beetle infested watershed in southern British Columbia, Canada, *Water Resources Research*, 25, 449-456, 1989.

Cherkauer, D.S. Minimization of power expenditure in a riffle-pool alluvial channel, *Water Resources Research*, 9, 1613-1628, 1973.

Cherry, J. and R.L. Beschta, Coarse woody debris and channel morphology: a flume study, *Water Resources Bulletin*, 25, 1031-1036, 1989.

Chikova, V.M., Species and age composition of fishes in the lower reach (downstream) of the V.I. Lenin Hydroelectric Station, in *Biological and hydrological factors of local movements of fish in reservoirs*, edited by B.S. Kuzin, pp. 185-192, Amerind Publishing Co., New Delhi, India, 1974.

Chin, A., Step pools in stream channels, *Progress in Physical Geography*, 13, 391-407, 1989.

Chin, A., On the stability of step-pool mountain streams, *Journal of Geology*, 106, 59-69, 1998.

Chin, A., On the origin of step-pool sequences in mountain streams, *Geophysical Research Letters*, 26, 231-234, 1999a.

Chin, A., The morphologic structure of step-pools in mountain streams, *Geomorphology*, 27, 191-204, 1999b.

Chorley, R.J., Geomorphology and the general systems theory, *U.S. Geological Survey Professional Paper 500-B*, 1962.

Chorley, R.J. and B.A. Kennedy, *Physical geography, a systems approach*, Prentice-Hall, London, 370 pp., 1971.

Chorley, R.J., S.A. Schumm, and D.E. Sugden, *Geomorphology*, Methuen, London, 1984.

Chow, V.T., *Open-channel hydraulics*, McGraw-Hill Book Company, New York, 679 pp., 1959.

Christophersen, N. and R.F. Wright, Sulfate budget and a model for sulfate concentrations in streamwater at Birkenes, a small forested catchment in southernmost Norway, *Water Resources Research*, 17, 377-389, 1981.

Church, M., Baffin Island Sandurs. A study of arctic fluvial processes, *Geological Survey of Canada Bulletin 216*, 208 pp., 1972.

Church, M., Palaeohydrological reconstructions from a Holocene valley fill, in *Fluvial sedimentology*, edited by A.D. Miall, pp. 743-772, Memoir 5, Can Soc Petrol Geologists, 1978.

Church, M., Floods in cold climates, in *Flood geomorphology*, edited by V.R. Baker, R.C. Kochel and P.C. Patton, pp. 205, 229, John Wiley and Sons, New York, 1988.

Church, M., M.A. Hassan, and J.F. Wolcott, Stabilizing self-organized structures in gravel-bed stream channels: field and experimental observations, *Water Resources Research*, 34, 3169-3179, 1998.

Church, M. and M.J. Miles, Meteorological antecedents to debris flow in southwestern British Columbia; some case studies, in *Debris flows/avalanches: process, recognition, and mitigation*, edited by J.E. Costa and G.F. Wieczorek, pp. 63-79, Geological Society of America, Reviews in Engineering Geology, v. 7, Boulder, Colorado, 1987.

Church, M., J.F. Wolcott, and W.K. Fletcher, A test of equal mobility in fluvial sediment transport: behavior of the sand fraction, *Water Resources Research*, 27, 2941-2951, 1991.

Church, M.A., D.G. McLean, and J.F. Wolcott, River bed gravels: sampling and analysis, in *Sediment transport in gravel-bed rivers*, edited by C.R. Thorne, J.C. Bathurst, and R.D. Hey, pp. 43-88, John Wiley and Sons, Chichester, 1987.

Clague, J.J. and S.G. Evans, The 1994 jökulhlaup at Farrow Creek, British Columbia, Canada, *Geomorphology*, 19, 77-87, 1997.

Clark, C., Deforestation and floods, *Environmental Conservation*, 14, 67-69, 1987a.

Clark, G.M., Debris slide and debris flow historical events in the Appalachians south of the glacial border, in *Debris flows/avalanches: process, recognition, and mitigation*, edited by J.E. Costa and G.F. Wieczorek, pp. 125-38, Geological Society of America, Reviews in Engineering Geology, v. 7, Boulder, Colorado, 1987b.

Clarke, G.K.C., Glacier outburst floods from 'Hazard Lake', Yukon Territory, and the problem of flood magnitude prediction, *Journal of Glaciology*, 28, 3-21, 1982.

Clemence, K.T., Influence of stratigraphy and structure on knickpoint erosion, *Bulletin of the Association of Engineering Geologists*, 25, 11-15, 1988.

Clifford, N.J., Differential bed sedimentology and the maintenance of riffle-pool sequences, *Catena*, 20, 447-468, 1993a.

Clifford, N.J., Formation of riffle-pool sequences: field evidence for an autogenetic process, *Sedimentary Geology*, 85, 39-51, 1993b.

Clifford, N.J., Morphology and stage-dependent flow structure in a gravel-bed river, in *Coherent flow structures in open channels*, edited by P.J. Ashworth, S.J. Bennett, J.L. Best and S.J. McLelland, pp. 545-566, John Wiley and Sons, Chichester, 1996.

Clifford, N.J. and J.R. French, Monitoring and analysis of turbulence in geophysical boundaries: some analytical and conceptual issues, in *Turbulence: perspectives on flow and sediment transport*, edited by N.J. Clifford, J.R. French, and J. Hardisty, pp. 93-120, John Wiley and Sons, Chichester, 1993a.

Clifford, N.J. and J.R. French, Monitoring and modelling turbulent flow: historical and contemporary perspectives, in *Turbulence: perspectives on flow and sediment transport*, edited by N.J. Clifford, J.R. French, and J. Hardisty, pp. 1-34, John Wiley and Sons, Chichester, 1993b.

Clifford, N.J., J. Hardisty, J.R. French, and S. Hart, Downstream variation in bed material characteristics in the braided River Swale: a turbulence-controlled form-process feedback mechanism, in *Braided rivers: form, process and economic applications*, edited by J.L. Best and C.S. Bristow, pp. 89-104, Geological Society Special Publication 75, London, Geological Society, 1993.

Clifford, N.J., A. Robert, and K.S. Richards, Estimation of flow resistance in gravel-bedded rivers: A physical explanation of the multiplier of roughness length, *Earth Surface Processes and Landforms*, 17, 111-126, 1992.

Cline, R.G., H. Haupt, and G. Campbell, Potential water yield response following clearcut harvesting on north and south slopes in northern Idaho, *USDA Forest Service Research Paper INT-191*, 1977.

Clow, D.W. and M.A. Mast, Composition of precipitation, bulk deposition, and runoff at a granitic bedrock catchment in the Loch Vale watershed, Colorado, USA, in *Biogeochemistry of seasonally snow-covered catchments*, edited by K.T. Tonnessen, M.W. Williams, and M. Tranter, pp. 235-242, IAHS Publ. no. 228, 1995.

Cluer, B.L., Cyclic fluvial processes and bias in environmental monitoring, Colorado River in Grand Canyon, *Journal of Geology*, 103, 411-421, 1995.

Code, J.A. and S. Sirhindi, Engineering implications of impoundment of the Indus River by an earthquake-induced landslide, in *Landslide dams: processes, risk, and mitigation*, edited by R.L. Schuster, pp. 97-110, American Society of Civil Engineers, New York, 1986.

Collier, M.P., R.H. Webb, and E.D. Andrews, Experimental flooding in Grand Canyon, *Scientific American*, 66-73, 1997.

Collins, D.N., Seasonal and annual variations of suspended sediment transport in meltwaters draining from an Alpine glacier, in *Hydrology in mountainous regions I. Hydrological measurements, the water cycle*, edited by H. Lang and A. Musy, pp. 439-446, IAHS Publication no. 193, Wallingford, UK, 1990.

Collins, D.N., Daily patterns of discharge, solute content and solute flux in meltwaters draining from two alpine glaciers, in *Biogeochemistry of seasonally snow-covered catchments*, edited by K.A. Tonnessen, M.W. Williams and M. Tranter, pp. 371-378, IAHS Publ. no. 228, 1995a.

Collins, D.N., Diurnal variations of flow-through velocity and transit time of meltwaters traversing moulin-conduit systems in an alpine glacier, in *Biogeochemistry of seasonally snow-covered catchments*, edited by K.A. Tonnessen, M.W. Williams and M. Tranter, pp. 363-369, IAHS Publ. no. 228, 1995b.

Collins, D.N. and D.P. Taylor, Variability of runoff from partially-glacierised Alpine basins, in *Hydrology in mountainous regions I. Hydrological measurements, the water cycle*, edited by H. Lang and A. Musy, pp. 365-372, IAHS Publication no. 193, Wallingford, UK, 1990.

Colman, S.M. and K.L. Pierce, Weathering rinds on andesitic and basaltic stones as a Quaternary age indicator, western United States, *U.S. Geological Survey Professional Paper 1210*, 56 pp., 1981.

Colwell, R., Balancing the biocomplexity of the planet's living systems: a twenty-first century task for science, *BioScience*, 48, 786-787, 1998.

Cooke, R.U. and R.W. Reeves, *Arroyos and environmental change in the American South-West*, Clarendon Press, Oxford, 1976.

Cooley, M.E., B.N. Aldridge, and R.C. Euler, Effects of the catastrophic flood of December 1966, North Rim area, eastern Grand Canyon, Arizona, *U.S. Geological Survey Professional Paper 980*, 43 pp., 1977.

Coon, W.F., Roughness coefficients for high-gradient channels in New York State, in *Hydraulic engineering '94*, edited by G.V. Cotroneo and R.R. Rumer, pp. 722-726, Proceed. of the 1994 Conf, Hydraul Div, ASCE, New York, 1994.

Coppin, N.J. and I.G. Richards, *Use of vegetation in civil engineering*, Butterworths, London, 292 pp., 1990.

Corbel, J., Vitesse de l' érosion, *Zeitschrift für Geomorphologie*, 3, 1-28, 1959.

Corn, P.S. and R.B. Bury, Logging in western Oregon: response of headwater habitats and stream amphibians, in *Forest ecology and management*, pp. 39-57, Elsevier, Amsterdam, 1989.

Corominas, J. and E.E. Alonso, Geomorphological effects of extreme floods (November 1982) in the southern Pyrenees, in *Hydrology in mountainous regions II. Artificial reservoirs, water and slopes*, edited by R.O. Sinniger and M. Monbaron, pp. 295-302, IAHS Publ. no. 194, Wallingford, UK, 1990.

Cortecci, G. and A. Longinelli, Isotopic composition of sulfate in rain water, Pisa, Italy, *Earth and Planetary Science Letters*, 8, 36-40, 1970.

Cosby, B.J., G.M. Hornberger, J.N. Galloway and R.F. Wright, Modeling the effects of acid deposition: assessment of a lumped parameter model of soil water and streamwater chemistry, *Water Resources Research*, 21, 51-63, 1985.

Costa, J.E., Holocene stratigraphy in flood frequency analysis, *Water Resources Research*, 14, 626-632, 1978.

Costa, J.E., Paleohydraulic reconstruction of flash-flood peaks from boulder deposits in the Colorado Front Range, *Geological Society of America Bulletin*, 94, 986-1004, 1983.

Costa, J.E., Physical geomorphology of debris flows, in *Developments and applications of geomorphology*, edited by J.E. Costa and P.J. Fleisher, pp. 268-317, Springer-Verlag, Berlin, 1984.

Costa, J.E., Interpretation of the largest rainfall-runoff floods measured by indirect methods on small drainage basins in the conterminous United States, *Proceedings, China-U.S. Bilateral Symposium on the Analysis of Extraordinary Flood Events*, 1985.

Costa, J.E., Hydraulics and basin morphometry of the largest flash floods in the conterminous United States, *Journal of Hydrology*, 93, 313-338, 1987.

Costa, J.E., Characteristics of a debris fan formed at the U.S. Geological Survey debris-flow flume, H.J. Andrews Experimental Forest, Blue River, Oregon, *EOS*, 73, 227, 1992.

Costa, J.E. and R.D. Jarrett, Debris flows in small mountain stream channels of Colorado and their hydrologic implications, *Association of Engineering Geologists Bulletin*, 18, 309-322, 1981.

Costa, J.E. and R.L. Schuster, The formation and failure of natural dams, *Geological Society of America Bulletin*, 100, 1054-1068, 1988.

Cotroneo, G.V. and R.R. Rumer, (eds.), *Hydraulic engineering '94*, pp. 634-880 and 1257-1300, Proceedings of the 1994 Conference, Hydraulics Division, ASCE, New York: Sessions MR-01 to MR-10 and TM-01 to TM-03, 1994.

Covich, A.P., Geographical and historical comparisons of neotropical streams: biotic diversity and detrital processing in highly variable habitats, *Journal of the North American Benthological Society*, 7, 361-386, 1988.

Covich, A.P. and T.A. Crowl, Effects of hurricane storm flow on transport of woody debris in a rain forest stream (Luquillo Experimental Forest, Puerto Rico), in *Tropical hydrology and Caribbean water resources*, edited by J. Hari Krishna, V. Quiñones-Aponte, F. Gómez, and G.L. Morris, pp. 197-205, American Water Resources Association, Bethesda, Maryland, 1990.

Covich, A.P., T.A. Crowl, S.L. Johnson, D. Varza and D.L. Certain, Post-Hurricane Hugo increases in atyid shrimp abundances in a Puerto Rican montane stream, *Biotropica*, 23, 448-454, 1991.

Covich, A.P. and W.H. McDowell, The stream community, in *The food web of a tropical rain forest*, edited by D. P. Reagan and R.B. Waide, pp. 433-459, The University of Chicago Press, Chicago, 1996.

Covich, A.P., M.A. Palmer and T.A. Crowl, The role of benthic invertebrate species in freshwater ecosystems, *BioScience*, 49, 119-127, 1999.

Cowan, W.L., Estimating hydraulic roughness coefficients, *Ag. Engin.*, 37, 473-475, 1956.

Crandell, D.R., Postglacial lahars from Mount Rainier Volcano, Washington, *U.S. Geological Survey Professional Paper 677*, 75 pp., 1971.

Crawford, N.H. and R.K. Lindsley, *The synthesis of continuous streamflow hydrographs on a digital computer*, Dept. of Civil Engineering, Stanford University, Technical Report No. 12, 1962.

Croft, A.R., *Rainstorm debris floods: a problem in public welfare*, University of Arizona, Agricultural Experiment Station, Tucson, 36 pp., 1967.

Cronin, S.J., V.E. Neall, J.A. Lecointre, and A.S. Palmer, Dynamic interactions between lahars and stream flow: a case study from Ruapehu volcano, New Zealand, *Geological Society of America Bulletin*, 111, 28-38, 1999.

Crowder, D. and P. Diplas, Some benefits of grid by number sampling, in *Hydraulic engineering '94*, edited by G.V. Cotroneo and R.R. Rumer, pp. 795-799, Proceed. of the 1994 Conf, Hydraulics Div., ASCE, New York, 1994.

Crowl, T.A. and A.P. Covich, Predator-induced life history shifts in a freshwater snail, *Science*, 247, 949-951, 1990.

Cudney, J.J., *The influence of variable width on flow structure in a steep mountain stream*, Unpublished MS thesis, Florida State University, Tallahassee, Florida, 103 pp., 1995.

Cuker, B.E., P.T. Gama, and J.M. Burkholder, Type of suspended clay influences lake productivity and phytoplankton community response to phosphorus loading, *Limnology and Oceanography*, 35, 830-839, 1990.

Cummins, K.W., Structure and function of stream ecosystems, *BioScience*, 24, 631-641, 1974.

Cummins, K.W., C.E. Cushing, and G.W. Minshall, Introduction: an overview of stream ecosystems, in *River and stream ecosystems*, edited by C.E. Cushing, K.W. Cummins and G.W. Minshall, pp. 1-8, Elsevier, Amsterdam, 1995.

Cupp, C.E., *Stream corridor classification for forested lands of Washington*, Washington Forest Protection Association, Olympia, Washington, 1989.

Curran, J.H., *Hydraulics of large woody debris in step-pool channels, Cascade Range, Washington*, Unpublished MS thesis, Colorado State University, Ft. Collins, Colorado, 197 pp., 1999.

Curry, R.R., Observation of alpine mudflows in the Tenmile Range, central Colorado, *Geological Society of America Bulletin*, 77, 771-776, 1966.

Dahlgren, R.A., Effects of forest harvest on stream-water quality and nitrogen cycling in the Caspar Creek watershed, in *Proceedings of the conference on coastal watersheds: the Caspar Creek story*, edited by R.R. Ziemer, pp. 45-53, Pacific Southwest Research Station, USDA, Albany, California, 1998.

Dalrymple, T. and M.A. Benson, Measurement of peak discharge by the slope-area method, *Techniques of water-resources investigations of the U.S. Geological Survey*, Book 3, chp. A2, pp. 1-12, 1967.

Daño, A.M. and F.E. Siapno, The effectiveness of soil conservation structures in steep cultivated mountain regions of the Philippines, in *Erosion, debris flows and environment in mountain regions*, edited by D.E. Walling, T.R. Davies, and B. Hasholt, pp. 399-405, IAHS Publ. no. 209, Wallingford, United Kingdom, 1992.

Darwin, C., *The origin of species by means of natural selection*, Murray, London, 1859.

Davies, B.E., Heavy metal contamination from base metal mining and smelting: implications for man and his environment, in *Applied Environmental Geochemistry*, edited by I. Thornton, pp. 425-462, Academic Press, London, 1983.

Davies, B.R., M.C. Thoms, K.F. Walker, J.H. O'Keefe, and J.A. Gore, Dryland rivers: their ecology, conservation, and management, in *The rivers handbook*, edited by P. Calow and G.E. Petts, pp. 484-511, Blackwell Scientific Publications, Oxford, UK, 1994.

Davies, T.R.H., Problems of bedload transport in braided gravel-bed rivers, in *Sediment transport in gravel-bed rivers,* edited by C.R. Thorne, J.C. Bathurst and R.D. Hey, pp. 793-828, John Wiley and Sons, Chichester, 1987.

Davies, T.R.H., Research of fluvial processes in mountains: a change of emphasis, in *Fluvial hydraulics of mountain regions*, edited by A. Armanini and G. DiSilvio, pp. 251-266, Springer-Verlag, Berlin, 1991.

Davis, W.M., The geographical cycle, *Journal of Geography*, 14, 481-504, 1899.

Davis, W.M., Base-level, grade, and peneplain, *Geographical Essays*, 18, 381-412, 1902.

Dawdy, D.R. and W.C. Wang, Prediction of gravel transport using Parker's algorithm, in *Hydraulic engineering '93*, edited by H.W. Shen, S.T. Su, and F. Wen, pp. 1523-1528, ASCE, 1993.

Day, D.G., Drainage density changes during rainfall, *Earth Surface Processes*, 3, 319-326, 1978.

Day, T.J., The channel geometry of mountain streams, in *Mountain geomorphology: geomorphological processes in the Canadian Cordillera*, edited by H.O. Slaymaker and H.J. McPherson, pp. 141-149, Tantalus Research Ltd., Vancouver, Canada, 1972.

Day, T.J., Field procedures and evaluation of a slug dilution gauging method in mountain streams, *Journal of Hydrology (New Zealand)*, 16, 113-133, 1977.

De Boer, D.H., Changing contributions of suspended sediment sources in small basins resulting from European settlement on the Canadian Prairies, *Earth Surface Processes and Landforms*, 22, 623-639, 1997.

DeByle, N.V., Broadcast burning of logging residues and the water repellency of soils, *Northwest Science*, 47, 77-87, 1973.

DeByle, N.V., Wildlife, in *Aspen: ecology and management in the western US*, edited by N.V. DeByle and R.P. Winokur, pp. 135-152, U.S. Fish and Wildlife Service, Rocky Mountain Forest and Range Experiment Station, Ft. Collins, Colorado, 1985.

DéCamps, H. and O. DéCamps, The relevance of the concept of health in managing riparian landscapes, *Ecological Society of America, 1999 Annual Meeting Abstracts*, p. 13, 1999.

DéCamps, H., M. Fortuné, F. Gazelle, and G. Pautou, Historical influence of man on the riparian dynamics of a fluvial landscape, *Landscape Ecology*, 1, 163-173, 1988.

DéCamps, H. and E. Tabacchi, Species richness in vegetation along river margins, in *Aquatic ecology: scale, pattern and process*, edited by P.S. Giller, A.G. Hildrew, and D.G. Raffaelli, pp. 1-20, Blackwell Scientific Publications, Oxford, 1994.

Dedkov, A.P. and V.I. Moszherin, Erosion and sediment yield in mountain regions of the world, in *Erosion, debris flows and environment in mountain regions*, edited by D.E. Walling, T.R. Davies, and B. Hasholt, pp. 29-36, IAHS Publ. no. 209, Wallingford, United Kingdom, 1992.

De Jong, C., The significance of extreme events in the development of mountain river beds, in *Variability in stream erosion and sediment transport*, edited by L.J. Olive, R.J. Loughran, and

J.A. Kesby, pp. 13-24, IAHS Publication no. 224, Wallingford, UK, 1994.

Dengler, L., A.K. Lehre, and C.J. Wilson, Bedrock geometry of unchannelized valleys, in *Erosion and sedimentation in the Pacific Rim*, edited by R.L. Beschta, T. Blinn, G.E. Grant, G.G. Ice, and F.J. Swanson, pp. 81-90, IAHS Publ. no. 165, 1987.

Dengler, L. and D.R. Montgomery, Estimating thickness of colluvial fill in unchanneled valleys from surface topography, *Bulletin of the Association of Engineering Geologists*, 26, 333-342, 1989.

Denning, A.S., J. Baron, M.A. Mast and M. Arthur, Hydrologic pathways and chemical composition of runoff during snowmelt in Loch Vale watershed, Rocky Mountain National Park, Colorado, USA, *Water, Air, Soil Pollution*, 59, 107-123, 1991.

Deroanne, C. and F. Petit, Longitudinal evaluation of the bed load size and of its mobilisation in a gravel bed river, in *Floods and landslides*, edited by R. Casale and C. Margottini, pp. 335-342, Springer-Verlag, Berlin, 1999.

Desloges, J.R. and M. Church, Geomorphic implications of glacier outburst flooding: Noieck River valley, British Columbia, *Canadian Journal of Earth Sciences*, 29, 551-564, 1992.

De Villiers, G.D.T., Rainfall variations in mountainous regions, in *Hydrology in mountainous regions I. Hydrological measurements; the water cycle*, edited by H. Lang and A. Musy, pp. 33-41, IAHS Publication no. 193, Wallingford, UK, 1990.

De Vries, M., On accuracy of bed-material sampling, *Journal of Hydraulic Research*, 8, 523-533, 1971.

Diepenbroek, M. and C. De Jong, Quantification of textural particle characteristics by image analysis of sediment surfaces - examples from active and paleosurfaces in steep, coarse grained mountain environments, in *Dynamics and geomorphology of mountain rivers*, edited by P. Ergenzinger and K.-H. Schmidt, pp. 301-314, Springer-Verlag, Berlin, 1994.

Dietrich, W., *Northwest passage: the great Columbia River*, University of Washington Press, Seattle, 448 pp., 1995.

Dietrich, W.E. and R. Dorn, Significance of thick deposits of colluvium on hillslopes: a case study involving the use of pollen analysis in the coastal mountains of northern California, *Journal of Geology*, 92, 147-158, 1984.

Dietrich, W.E. and T. Dunne, Sediment budget for a small catchment in mountainous terrain, *Zeitschrift für Geomorphologie*, 29, 191-206, 1978.

Dietrich, W.E. and T. Dunne, The channel head, in *Channel network hydrology*, edited by K. Beven and M.J. Kirkby, pp. 175-219, John Wiley and Sons, Chichester, 1993.

Dietrich, W.E., J.W. Kirchner, H. Ikeda, and F. Iseya, Sediment supply and the development of the coarse surface layer in gravel-bedded rivers, *Nature*, 340, 215-217, 1989.

Dietrich, W.E. and M.R. Montgomery, A digital terrain model for predicting debris flow source areas, *EOS*, 73, 227, 1992.

Dietrich, W.E. and P.J. Whiting, Boundary shear stress and sediment transport in river meanders of sand and gravel, in *River meandering*, edited by S. Ikeda and G. Parker, pp. 1-50, Am Geophys Union, Washington, D.C., 1989.

Dietrich, W.E., C.J. Wilson, D.R. Montgomery, and J. McKean, Analysis of erosion thresholds, channel networks, and landscape morphology using a digital terrain model, *Journal of Geology*, 101, 259-278, 1993.

Dietrich, W.E., C.J. Wilson, D.R. Montgomery, J. McKean, and R. Bauer, Erosion thresholds and land surface morphology, *Geology*, 20, 675-679, 1992.

Dill, L.M., R.C.Ydenberg, and A.H.G. Fraser, Food abundance and territory size in juvenile coho salmon (*Oncorhynchus kisutch*), *Canadian Journal of Zoology*, 59, 1801-1809, 1981.

Dinehart, R.L., Correlative velocity fluctuations over a gravel bed river, *Water Resources Research*, 35, 569-582, 1999.

Dingman, S.L., *Fluvial hydrology*, W.H. Freeman and Company, New York, 383 pp., 1991.

Dingwall, P.R., Erosion by overland flow on an alpine debris slope, in *Mountain geomorphology: geomorphological processes in the Canadian Cordillera*, edited by H.O. Slaymaker and H.J.

McPherson, pp. 113-120, Tantalus Research Ltd., Vancouver, Canada, 1972.

Diplas, P. and J.B. Fripp, Properties of various sediment sampling procedures, *ASCE Journal of Hydraulic Engineering*, 118, 955-970, 1992.

Diplas, P. and G. Parker, Deposition and removal of fines in gravel-bed streams, in *Dynamics of gravel-bed rivers*, edited by P. Billi, R.D. Hey, C.R. Thorne and P. Tacconi, pp. 313-329, John Wiley and Sons, Chichester, 1992.

Diplas, P. and A.J. Sutherland, Sampling techniques of gravel sized sediments, *ASCE Journal of Hydraulic Engineering*, 114, 484-501, 1988.

DiSilvio, G., Floods and sediment dynamics in mountain rivers, in *Coping with floods*, edited by G. Rossi, N. Harmancioglu and V. Yevjevich, pp. 375-392, Kluwer, The Netherlands, 1994.

Di Silvio, G. and S. Brunelli, Experimental investigations on bed-load and suspended transport in mountain streams, in *Fluvial hydraulics of mountain regions*, edited by A. Armanini and G. DiSilvio, pp. 443-457, Springer-Verlag, Berlin, 1991.

Di Silvio, G. and M. Peviani, Modelling short- and long-term evolution of mountain rivers: an application to the Torrent Mallero (Italy), in *Fluvial hydraulics of mountain regions*, edited by A. Armanini and G. DiSilvio, pp. 293-315, Springer-Verlag, Berlin, 1991.

Dittrich, A., F. Nestmann and P. Ergenzinger, Ratio of lift and shear forces over rough surfaces, in *Coherent flow structures in open channels*, edited by P.J. Ashworth, S.J. Bennett, J.L. Best and S.J. McLelland, pp. 125-146, John Wiley and Sons, Chichester, 1996.

Djorovic, M., Ten-years of sediment discharge measurement in the Jasenica research drainage basin, Yugoslavia, in *Erosion, debris flows and environment in mountain regions*, edited by D.E. Walling, T.R. Davies, and B. Hasholt, pp. 37-40, IAHS Publ. no. 209, Wallingford, United Kingdom, 1992.

Dodds, G.S. and F.L. Hisaw, Ecological studies of aquatic insects. IV. Altitudinal range and zonation of mayflies, stoneflies and caddisflies in the Colorado Rockies, *Ecology*, 6, 380-390, 1925.

Dolan, R., A. Howard, and D. Trimble, Structural control of the rapids and pools of the Colorado River in the Grand Canyon, *Science*, 202, 629-631, 1978.

Dolling, R.K., Occurrence of pools and riffles: an element in the quasi-equilibrium state of river channels, *Ontario Geography*, 2, 3-11, 1968.

Donnell, B.D., J.L. Finnie, J.V. Letter, Jr., W.H. McAnally, Jr., L.C. Roig, and W.A. Thomas, *Users guide to RMA2 WES version 4.3*, U.S. Army Corps of Engineers, Waterways Experiment Station Hydraulics Laboratory, 1997.

Douglas, I., Man, vegetation and the sediment yield of rivers, *Nature*, 215, 925-928, 1967.

Draft Report, *Dam removal success stories*, American Rivers and Trout Unlimited, Unpublished report at http://www.amrivers.org/success-intro.html, 1999.

Drake, T.G., R.L. Shreve, W.E. Dietrich, P.J. Whiting, and L.B. Leopold, Bedload transport of fine gravel observed by motion-picture photography, *Journal of Fluid Mechanics*, 192, 193-217, 1988.

Drever, J.I., *The geochemistry of natural waters*, Prentice-Hall, Englewood Cliffs, New Jersey, 388 pp., 1982.

Drever, J.I., *The geochemistry of natural waters*, 2nd ed., Prentice-Hall, Englewood Cliffs, New Jersey, 437 pp., 1988.

Drever, J.I. and D.R. Hurcomb, Neutralization of atmospheric acidity by chemical weathering in an alpine drainage basin in the North Cascade Mountains, *Geology*, 14, 221-224, 1986.

Driedger, C.L. and A.G. Fountain, Glacier outburst floods at Mount Rainier, Washington State, U.S.A., *Annals of Glaciology*, 13, 51-55, 1989.

Drury, T.A., T.B. Abbe, G.R. Pess, C. Petroff, and D.R. Montgomery, Experimental application of engineered log jams: North Fork Stillaguamish River, Washington, *EOS, Transactions, Am. Geophysical Union*, 79, F346, 1998.

Duckson, D.W., Jr. and L.J. Duckson, Morphology of bedrock step pool systems, *Water Resources Bulletin*, 31, 43-51, 1995.

Dunkerley, D.L., The development of armour in the Tambo River, Victoria, Australia, *Earth Surface Processes and Landforms*, 15, 405-412, 1990.

Dunne, T., Sediment yield and land use in tropical catchments, *Journal of Hydrology*, 42, 281-300, 1979.

Dunne, T., Formation and controls of channel networks, *Progress in Physical Geography*, 4, 211-239, 1980.

Dunne, T. and R.G. Black, An experimental investigation of runoff production in permeable soils, *Water Resources Research*, 6, 478-490, 1970a.

Dunne, T. and R.G. Black, Partial area contributions to storm runoff in a small New England watershed, *Water Resources Research*, 6, 1296-1311, 1970b.

Dunne, T., K.X. Whipple, and B.F. Aubry, Microtopography of hillslopes and initiation of channels by Horton overland flow, in *Natural and anthropogenic influences in fluvial geomorphology*, edited by J.E. Costa, A.J. Miller, K.W. Potter, and P.R. Wilcock, pp. 27-44, Geophysical Monograph 89, American Geophysical Union, Washington, D.C., 1995.

Dynesius, M. and C. Nilsson, Fragmentation and flow regulation of river systems in the northern third of the world, *Science*, 266, 753-762, 1994.

Earle, C.J., Asynchronous droughts in California streamflow as reconstructed from tree rings, *Quaternary Research*, 39, 290-299, 1993.

Easterbrook, D.J., *Surface processes and landforms*, Macmillan Publishing Company, New York, 520 pp., 1993.

Ebisemiju, F.S., The effects of environmental heterogeneity on the interdependence of drainage basin morphometric properties and its implications for applied studies, *Singapore Journal of Tropical Geography*, 8, 114-128, 1987.

Eckley, M.S. and D.L. Hinchliff, Glen Canyon Dam's quick fix, *Civil Engineering*, 56, 46-48, 1986.

Eddins, W.H. and T.J. Zembrzuski, Jr., Factors affecting accuracy of slope-area discharge determination of the Sept. 1992 flood in Raven Fork, western North Carolina, in *Hydraulic engineering '94*, edited by G.V. Cotroneo and R.R. Rumer, pp. 645-649, Proceed of the 1994 Conf, Hydraul Div, ASCE, New York, 1994.

Egashira, S. and K. Ashida, Flow resistance and sediment transportation in streams with step-pool bed morphology, in *Fluvial hydraulics of mountain regions*, edited by A. Armanini and G. DiSilvio, pp. 45-58, Springer-Verlag, 1991.

Einstein, H.A., Der Geschliebetrieb also Wahrscheinlichkeitsproblem. [Bedload transport as a probability problem.] *Mitteilungen der Versuchsantallt für Wasserbau an der Eidgenössischen Technischen Hochschule in Zürich*, 1937.

Einstein, H.A., Formulas for the transportation of bedload, *Trans., ASCE*, 107, 561-577, 1942.

Einstein, H.A., The bedload function for sediment transportation in open channel flows, *USDA Technical Bulletin 1026*, 70 pp., 1950.

Eisbacher, G.H., Mountain torrents and debris flows, *Episodes*, 1982, 12-17, 1982.

Eisbacher, G.H. and J.J. Clague, Destructive mass movements in high mountains: hazard and management, *Geological Survey of Canada, Paper 84-16*, 75 pp., 1984.

Elder, K., Modeling the spatial distribution of seasonal snow accumulation on Teton Glacier, Wyoming, USA, in *Biogeochemistry of seasonally snow-covered catchments*, edited by K.A. Tonnessen, M.W. Williams, and M. Tranter, pp. 445-454, IAHS Publ. no. 228, 1995.

Elder, K., R. Kattelmann, and R. Ferguson, Refinements in dilution gauging for mountain streams, in *Hydrology in mountainous regions I. Hydrological measurements; the water cycle*, edited by H. Lang and A. Musy, pp. 247-254, IAHS Publication no. 193, Wallingford, UK, 1990.

Elevatorski, E.A., *Hydraulic energy dissipaters*, McGraw-Hill Book Company, New York, 214 pp., 1959.

Elfström, A., Large boulder deposits and catastrophic floods. A case study of the Bäldakatj area, Swedish Lapland, *Geografiska Annaler*, 69A, 101-121, 1987.

Elliott, J.G. and R.S. Parker, Potential climate-change effects on bed-material entrainment, the Gunnison Gorge, Colorado, in *Managing water resources during global change*, pp. 751-759, Am. Water Resources Assoc., 1992.

Ellis, J.B., Sediment-water quality interactions in urban rivers, in *International geomorphology 1986*, edited by V. Gardiner, Part I, pp. 287-301, John Wiley and Sons, Chichester, 1987.

Ely, L.L., Y. Enzel, V.R. Baker, and D.R. Cayan, A 5000-year record of extreme floods and climate change in the southwestern United States, *Science*, 262, 410-412, 1993.

Ely, L.L., Y. Enzel, V.R. Baker, V.S. Kale, and S. Mishra, Changes in the magnitude and frequency of late Holocene monsoon floods on the Narmada River, central India, *Geological Society America Bulletin*, 108, 1134-1148, 1996.

Ely, L.L., R.H. Webb, and Y. Enzel, Accuracy of post-bomb ^{137}Cs and ^{14}C in dating fluvial deposits, *Quaternary Research*, 38, 196-204, 1992.

Elwood, J.W., J.D. Newbold, R.V. O'Neill, and W. Van Winkle, Resource spiraling: an operational paradigm for analyzing lotic ecosystems, in *Dynamics of lotic ecosystems*, edited by T.D. Fontaine and S.M. Bartell, pp. 3-27, Ann Arbor Science, Ann Arbor, MI, 1983.

Emmett, W.W., Overland flow, in *Hillslope hydrology*, edited by M.J. Kirkby, pp. 145-176, Wiley and Sons, Chichester, 1978.

Emmett, W.W., A field calibration of the sediment-trapping characteristics of the Helley-Smith bed-load sampler, *U.S. Geological Survey Professional Paper 1139*, 44 pp., 1980.

Emmett, W.W., R.L. Burrows, and E.F. Chacho, Jr., Coarse-particle transport in a gravel-bed river, *International Journal of Sediment Research*, 11, 8-21, 1996.

Enzel, Y., L.L. Ely, P.K. House, V.R. Baker, and R.H. Webb, Paleoflood evidence for a natural upper bound to flood magnitudes in the Colorado River basin, *Water Resources Research*, 29, 2287-2297, 1993.

Ergenzinger, P., Riverbed adjustments in a step-pool system: Lainbach, Upper Bavaria, in *Dynamics of gravel-bed rivers*, edited by P. Billi, R.D. Hey, C.R. Thorne and P. Tacconi, pp. 415-430, John Wiley and Sons, Chichester, 1992.

Ergenzinger, P., The susceptibility of valley slopes and river beds to erosion and accretion under the impact of climatic change - Alpine examples, in *Variability in stream erosion and sediment transport*, edited by L.J. Olive, R.J. Loughran, and J.A. Kesby, pp. 43-53, IAHS Publication no. 224, Wallingford, UK, 1994.

Ergenzinger, P. and C. De Jong, Monitoring and modeling the transport of coarse single particles in mountain rivers, in *Hydraulic engineering '94*, edited by G.V. Cotroneo and R.R. Rumer, p. 634, Proceed of the 1994 Conf Hydraulics Division, ASCE, New York, 1994.

Ergenzinger, P., C. De Jong, and G. Christaller, Interrelationships between bedload transfer and river-bed adjustment in mountain rivers: an example from Squaw Creek, Montana, in *Process models and theoretical geomorphology*, edited by M. J. Kirkby, pp. 141-158, John Wiley and Sons, Chichester, 1994a.

Ergenzinger, P., C. De Jong, J. Laronne, and I. Reid, Short term temporal variations in bedload transport rates: Squaw Creek, Montana, USA and Nahal Yatir and Nahal Estemoa, Israel, in *Dynamics and geomorphology of mountain rivers*, edited by P. Ergenzinger and K.-H. Schmidt, pp. 251-264, Springer-Verlag, 1994b.

Ergenzinger, P. and K.-H. Schmidt, Stochastic elements of bed load transport in a step-pool moun-tain river, in *Hydrology in mountainous regions II. Artificial reservoirs, water and slopes*, edit-ed by R.O. Sinniger and M. Monbaron, pp. 39-46, IAHS Publication no. 194, Wallingford, UK, 1990.

Ergenzinger, P. and K.-H. Schmidt, (eds.), *Dynamics and geomorphology of mountain rivers*, Springer-Verlag, Berlin, 1994.

Ericksen, G.E., G. Pflaker, and J.F. Concha, Preliminary report on the geologic events associated with the May 31, 1970 Peru earthquake, *U.S. Geological Survey Circular 639*, 25 pp., 1970.

Ersi, K., A. Ohmura and H. Lang, Simulation of runoff processes of a continental mountain glacier in the Tian Shan, China, in *Biogeochemistry of seasonally snow-covered catchments*, edited by K.A. Tonnessen, M.W. Williams, and M. Tranter, pp. 455-465, IAHS Publ. no. 228, 1995.

Ettema, R., Sampling armor-layer sediments, *ASCE Journal of Hydraulic Engineering*, 110, 992-996, 1984.

Evans, S.G., The maximum discharge of outburst floods caused by the breaching of man-made and natural dams, *Canadian Geotechnical Journal*, 23, 385-387, 1986.

Everest, F.H., R.L. Beschta, J.C. Scrivener, K.V. Koski, J.R. Sedell, and C.J. Cederholm, Fine sediment and salmonid production: a paradox, in *Streamside management: Forestry and fishery implications*, edited by E.O. Salo and T.W. Cundy, pp. 98-142, University of Washington, Institute of Forest Resources, Contrib. No. 57, 1987.

Everest, F.H. and D.W. Chapman, Habitat selection and spatial interaction by juvenile chinook salmon and steelhead trout in two Idaho streams, *Journal Fisheries Research Board Canada*, 29, 91-100, 1972.

Everitt, B.L., Use of the cottonwood in an investigation of the recent history of a flood plain, *American Journal Science*, 266, 417-439, 1968.

Everitt, B.L., Ecology of saltcedar - a plea for research, *Environmental Geology*, 3, 77-84, 1980.

Ewing, R., Postfire suspended sediment from Yellowstone National Park, Wyoming, *Journal Am Water Resources Association*, 32, 605-627, 1996.

Fabel, D., J. Harbor, and C. Steele, Valley-scale glacial erosion rates from ^{10}Be and ^{26}Al inheritance in bedrock, *EOS, Transactions, Am. Geophysical Union*, 79, F336, 1998.

Fahnestock, R.K., Morphology and hydrology of a glacial stream - White River, Mt. Rainier, Washington, *U.S. Geological Survey Professional Paper 422A*, 61 pp., 1963.

Fairchild, L.H., The importance of lahar initiation processes, in *Debris flows/avalanches: process, recognition, and mitigation*, edited by J.E. Costa and G.F. Wieczorek, pp. 51-61, Geological Society of America, Reviews of Engineering Geology, v. 7, Boulder, Colorado, 1987.

Fanok, S.F. and E.E. Wohl, Assessing the accuracy of paleohydrologic indicators, Harpers Ferry, West Virginia, *Journal American Water Resources Association*, 33, 1091-1102, 1997.

Farnworth, E.G. et al., *Impacts of sediment and nutrients on biota in surface waters of the United States*, Report No. EPA-60013-79-105, USEPA, Athens, Georgia, 1979.

Fausch, K.D., Profitable stream positions for salmonids: relating specific growth rate to net energy gain, *Canadian Journal of Zoology*, 62, 441-451, 1984.

Fausch, K.D. and T.G. Northcote, Large woody debris and salmonid habitat in a small coastal British Columbia stream, *Canadian Journal of Fisheries and Aquatic Sciences*, 49, 682-693, 1992.

Fengjing, L., M.W. Williams, Y. Daqing, and J. Melack, Snow and water chemistry of a headwater alpine basin, Urumqi River, Tian Shan, China, in *Biogeochemistry of seasonally snow-covered catchments*, edited by K.A. Tonnessen, M.W. Williams, and M. Tranter, pp. 207-219, IAHS Publ. no. 228, 1995.

Fenn, C.R., Sediment transfer processes in alpine glacier basins, in *Glacio-fluvial sediment transfer*, edited by A.M. Gurnell and M.J. Clark, pp. 59-85, John Wiley and Sons, Chichester, 1987.

Fenn, C.R. and A.M. Gurnell, Proglacial channel processes, in *Glacio-fluvial sediment transfer*, edited by A.M. Gurnell and M.J. Clark, pp. 423-472, John Wiley and Sons, Chichester, 1987.

Ferguson, R. and P. Ashworth, Slope-induced changes in channel character along a gravel-bed stream: the Allt Dubhaig, Scotland, *Earth Surface Processes and Landforms*, 16, 65-82, 1991.

Ferguson, R.I., Sediment load of the Hunza River, in *International Karakoram project*, edited by K.J. Miller, v. 2, pp. 581-598, Cambridge University Press, Cambridge, 1984.

Ferguson, R.I., Critical discharge for entrainment of poorly sorted gravel, *Earth Surface Processes and Landforms*, 19, 179-186, 1994.

Ferguson, R.I. and P.J. Ashworth, Spatial patterns of bedload transport and channel change in braided and near-braided rivers, in *Dynamics of gravel-bed rivers*, edited by P. Billi, R.D. Hey, C.R. Thorne and P. Tacconi, pp. 477-496, John Wiley and Sons, Chichester, 1992.

Ferguson, R.I., A.D. Kirkbride and A.G. Roy, Markov analysis of velocity fluctuations in gravel-bed rivers, in *Coherent flow structures*, edited by P.J. Ashworth, S.J. Bennett, J.L. Best and S.J. McLelland, pp. 165-183, John Wiley and Sons, Chichester, 1996.

Ferguson, R.I. and C. Paola, Bias and precision of percentiles of bulk grain size distributions, *Earth Surface Processes and Landforms*, 22, 1061-1077, 1997.

Ferguson, R.I. and S.J. Wathen, Tracer-pebble movement along a concave river profile: virtual velocity in relation to grain size and shear stress, *Water Resources Research*, 34, 2031-2038, 1998.

Fiebig, D.M., M.A. Lock and C. Neal, Soil water in the riparian zone as a source of carbon for a headwater stream, *Journal of Hydrology*, 116, 217-237, 1990.

Findlay, S., Importance of surface-subsurface exchange in stream ecosystems: the hyporheic zone, *Limnology and Oceanography*, 40, 159-164, 1995.

Finley, J.B., J.I. Drever and J.T. Turk, Sulfur isotope dynamics in a high-elevation catchment, West Glacier Lake, Wyoming, *Water, Air and Soil Pollution*, 79, 227-241, 1995.

Fischer, H., Geomorphology in Austria, in *The evolution of geomorphology*, edited by H.J. Walker and W.E. Grabau, pp. 45-49, John Wiley and Sons, New York, 1993.

Fischer, K.J. and M.D. Harvey, Geomorphic response of lower Feather River to 19th century hydraulic mining operations, in *Inspiration: come to the headwaters*, pp. 128-132, Proceedings, 15th Annual Conference of Association of State Floodplain Managers, June 10-14, 1991, Denver, Colorado, 1991.

Fisher, S.G., N.B. Grimm, E. Martí, R.M. Holmes, and J.B. Jones, Jr., Material spiraling in stream corridors: a telescoping ecosystem model, *Ecosystems*, 1, 19-34, 1998a.

Fisher, S.G., N.B. Grimm, E. Martí, and R. Gomez, Hierarchy, spatial configuration, and nutrient cycling in a desert stream, *Australian Journal of Ecology*, 23, 41-52, 1998b.

Flint, J.J., Development of headward growth of channel networks, *Geological Society of America Bulletin*, 84, 1087-1094, 1973.

Florsheim, J.L., E.A. Keller, and D.W. Best, Fluvial sediment transport in response to moderate storm flows following chaparral wildfire, Ventura County, southern California, *Geological Society of America Bulletin*, 103, 504-511, 1991.

Foley, M.G., Quaternary diversion and incision, Dearborn River, Montana, *Geological Society of America Bulletin*, 91, Part 1, 2152-2188, 1980a.

Foley, M.G., Bedrock incision by streams, *Geological Society of America Bulletin*, 91, Part 2, 2189-2213, 1980b.

Ford, D.C. and P.W. Williams, *Karst geomorphology and hydrology*, Unwin Hyman, London, 601 pp., 1989.

Forman, R.T.T. and M. Godron, *Landscape ecology*, John Wiley and Sons, New York, 1986.

Foster, I.D.L., H. Dalgleish, J.A. Dearing, and E.D. Jones, Quantifying soil erosion and sediment transport in drainage basins; some observations on the use of ^{137}Cs, in *Variability in stream erosion and sediment transport*, edited by L.J. Olive, R.J. Loughran, and J.A. Kesby, pp. 55-64, IAHS Publication no. 224, Wallingford, UK, 1994.

Fournier, F., Debit solide des cours d'eau. Essai d' estimation de la perte en terre subie par l'ensemble du globe terrestre, *International Association of Scientific Hydrology Publ. No. 53*, pp. 19-22 (in Knighton, 1984), 1960.

Frangi, J.L. and A.E. Lugo, Hurricane damage to a flood plain forest in the Luquillo Mountains of Puerto Rico, *Biotropica*, 23, 324-335, 1991.

Fripp, J.B. and P. Diplas, Surface sampling in gravel streams, *ASCE Journal of Hydraulic Engineering*, 119, 473-490, 1993.

Frissell, C.A., Groundwater processes and stream classification in the montane West, *Ecological Society of America, 1999 Annual Meeting Abstracts*, p. 17, 1999.

Frissell, C.A., W.J. Liss, C.E. Warren, and M.D. Hurley, A hierarchical framework for stream classification: viewing streams in a wateshed context, *Environmental Management*, 10, 199-214, 1986.

Froehlich, W., Sediment dynamics in the Polish Flysch Carpathians, in *Sediment and water quality in river catchments*, edited by I. Foster, A. Gurnell, and B. Webb, pp. 453-461, John Wiley and Sons, Chichester, 1995.

Froehlich, W., E. Gil, I. Kasza, and L. Starkel, Thresholds in the transformation of slopes and river channels in the Darjeeling Himalaya, India, *Mountain Research and Development*, 10, 301-312, 1990.

Froehlich, W. and L. Starkel, Normal and extreme monsoon rains - their role in the shaping of the Darjeeling Himalaya, *Studia Geomorphologica Carpatho-Balcanica*, 21, 129-158, 1987.

Froehlich, W. and D.E. Walling, The use of fallout radionuclides in investigations of erosion and sediment delivery in the Polish Flysh Carpathians, in *Erosion, debris flows and environment in mountain regions*, edited by D.E. Walling, T.R. Davies, and B. Hasholt, pp. 61-76, IAHS Publ. no. 209, Wallingford, United Kingdom, 1992.

Fujita, M., M. Michine, and K. Ashida, Simulation of reservoir sedimentation in mountain regions, in *Fluvial hydraulics of mountain regions*, edited by A. Armanini and G. DiSilvio, pp. 209-222, Springer-Verlag, Berlin, 1991.

Furbish, D.J., Flow structure in a bouldery mountain stream with complex bed topography, *Water Resources Research*, 29, 2249-2263, 1993.

Fushimi, H., K. Ikegami, and K. Higuchi, Nepal case study: catastrophic floods, in *Techniques for prediction of runoff from glacierized areas*, edited by G.J. Young, pp. 125-130, IAHS Publ. no. 149, Wallingford, United Kingdom, 1985.

Galay, V.J., Causes of river bed degradation, *Water Resources Research*, 19, 1057-1090, 1983.

Gallino, G.L. and T.C. Pierson, Polallie Creek debris flow and subsequent dam-break flood of 1980, East Fork Hood River basin, Oregon, *U.S. Geological Survey Water-Supply Paper 2273*, 22 pp., 1985.

Garcia-Ruiz, J.M., J. Arnaez-Vadillo, L.O. Izquierdo, and A. Gomez-Villar, Debris flows subsequent to a forest fire in the Najerilla River valley (Iberian system, Spain), *Pirineos*, 131, 3-23, 1988.

Gardner, J.S., Alpine mass-wasting in contemporary time: some examples from the Canadian Rocky Mountains, in *Space and time in geomorphology*, edited by C.E. Thorn, pp. 171-192, George Allen and Unwin, London, 1982.

Gardner, T.W., Experimental study of knickpoint and longitudinal profile evolution in cohesive, homogeneous material, *Geological Society of America Bulletin*, 94, 664-672, 1983.

Garr, C.E. and B.B. Fitzharris, Sensitivity of mountain runoff and hydro-electricity to changing climate, in *Mountain environments in changing climates*, edited by M. Beniston, pp. 366-381, Routledge, London, 1994.

Garrels, R.M. and F.T. Mackenzie, *Evolution of sedimentary rocks*, W.W. Norton, New York, 397 pp., 1971.

Gavrilovic, Z. and Z. Matovic, Review of disastrous torrent flood on the Vlasina River on June 26, 1988, including analysis of flood and the obtained results, in *Fluvial hydraulis of mountain regions*, edited by A. Armanini and G. DiSilvio, pp. 235-250, Springer-Verlag, Berlin, 1991.

Gazis, C.A., J.D. Blum, A.D. Jacobson and C.P. Chamberlain, Controls on the Strontium isotope geochemistry of the Indus River in northern Pakistan, *EOS, Transactions, Am. Geophys. Union, 79*, F337, 1998.

Gees, A., Flow measurement under difficult measuring conditions: field experience with the salt dilution method, in *Hydrology in mountainous regions I. Hydrological measurements; the water cycle*, edited by H. Lang and A. Musy, pp. 255-262, IAHS Publication no. 193, Wallingford, UK, 1990.

Gellis, A., The effects of Hurricane Hugo on suspended-sediment loads, Lago Loiza basin, Puerto Rico, *Earth Surface Processes and Landforms*, 18, 505-517, 1993.

Georgiev, B.V., Reliability of bed load measurements in mountain rivers, in *Hydrology in mountainous regions I: Hydrological measurements; the Water Cycle*, IAHS Publ no. 193, p. 263-270, 1990.

Germanoski, D., *The effects of sediment load and gradient on braided river morphology*, Unpublished PhD dissertation, Colorado State University, Ft. Collins, Colorado, 407 pp., 1989.

Germanoski, D. and M.D. Harvey, Asynchronous terrace development in degrading braided channels, *Physical Geography*, 14, 16-38, 1993.

Gerrard, J., *Mountain environments: an examination of the physical geography of mountains*, The MIT Press, Cambridge, 317 pp., 1990.

Gessler, J., *Der Geschiebetriebbeginn bei Mischungen Untersucht an Natürlichen Abpflästerungserscheinungen in Kanälen*, Mitteilungen der Versuchsanstalt für Wasserbau und Erdbau, Zurich, no. 69, 1965.

Ghose, B., S. Pandey, S. Singh, and G. Lal, Quantitative geomorphology of the drainage basins in the central Luni Basin in western Rajasthan, *Zeitschrift für Geomorphologie*, 1, 146-160, 1957.

Gibbs, R.J., Mechanisms controlling world water chemistry, *Science*, 170, 1088-1090, 1970.

Gilbert, G.K., *Report on the geology of the Henry Mountains*, Government Printing Office, Washington, D.C., 160 pp., 1877.

Gilbert, G.K., Niagara Falls and their history, *National Geographic Monograph*, 1, 203-236, 1896.

Gilbert, G.K., Transportation of debris by running water, *U.S. Geological Survey Professional Paper 86*, 221 pp., 1914.

Gilbert, G.K., Hydraulic-mining debris in the Sierra Nevada, *U.S. Geological Survey Professional Paper 105*, 1917.

Gilman, K. and M.D. Newson, *Soil pipes and pipeflow - a hydrological study in upland Wales*, Geobooks, Norwich, 1980.

Gintz, D., M.A. Hassan, and K.-H. Schmidt, Frequency and magnitude of bedload transport in a mountain river, *Earth Surface Processes and Landforms*, 21, 433-445, 1996.

Giorgi, F., C. Shields-Brodeur, and G.T. Bates, Regional climate change scenarios over the United States produced with a nested regional climate model: spatial and seasonal characteristics, *Journal of Climate*, 7, 375-399, 1994.

Givone, C. and X. Meignien, Influence of topography on spatial distribution of rain, in *Hydrology of mountainous areas*, edited by L. Molnar, pp. 57-65, IAHS Publication no. 190, 1990.

Glancy, P.A. and R.P. Williams, Problems with indirect determinations of peak streamflows in steep, desert stream channels, in *Hydraulic engineering '94*, edited by G.V. Cotroneo and R.R. Rumer, pp. 635-639, Proceed of the 1994 Conf, Hydraul Div, ASCE, New York, 1994.

Glock, W.S., The development of drainage systems: a synoptic view, *Geographical Review*, 21, 475-482, 1931.

Glysson, G.D., U.S. Geological Survey bedload sampling policy, in *Hydraulic engineering '93*, edited by H.W. Shen, S.T. Su, and F. Wen, pp. 701-706, ASCE, 1993.

Goetzmann, W.H., *New lands, new men: America and the second great age of discovery*, Penguin Books, New York, 528 pp., 1986.

Goldman, S., K. Jackson, and T. Bursktynsky, *Erosion and sediment control handbook*, McGraw Hill, New York, 1986.

Goldrick, G. and P. Bishop, Differentiating the roles of lithology and uplift in the steepening of bedrock river long profiles: an example from southeastern Australia, *Journal of Geology*, 103, 227-231, 1995.

Goldsmith, E. and N. Hildyard, *The social and environmental effects of large dams*, Sierra Club Books, San Francisco, 404 pp., 1984.

Gomez, B., Temporal variations in bedload trasnport rates: the effect of progressive bed armouring, *Earth Surface Processes and Landforms*, 8, 41-54, 1983.

Gomez, B., Bedload, in *Glacio-fluvial sediment transfer*, edited by A.M. Gurnell and M.J. Clark, pp. 355-376, John Wiley and Sons, Chichester, 1987.

Gomez, B. and M. Church, An assessment of bed load sediment transport formulae for gravel bed rivers, *Water Resources Research*, 25, 1161-1186, 1989.

Gomez, B., Roughness of stable, armored gravel beds, *Water Resources Research*, 29, 3631-3642, 1993.

Gomez, B., R.L. Naff, and D.W. Hubbell, Temporal variations in bedload transport rates associated with the migration of bedforms, *Earth Surface Processes and Landforms*, 14, 135-156, 1989.

Gomez, B. and B.M. Troutman, Evaluation of process errors in bed load sampling using a dune model, *Water Resources Research*, 33, 2387-2398, 1997.

Goodman, I.A., M.E. Jensen, and D.P. Lettenmaier, Watershed classification to assess vulnerability to disturbance, *Ecological Society of America, 1999 Annual Meeting Abstracts*, p. 18, 1999.

Gordon, N., Summary of technical testimony in the Colorado Water Division 1 trial, *USDA Forest Service General Technical Report RM-GTR-270*, 140 pp., 1995.

Gore, J.A. and A.M. Milner, Island biogeographic theory: can it be used to predict lotic recovery rates?, *Environmental Management*, 14, 1491-1501, 1990.

Gottesfeld, A.S. and L.M.J. Gottesfeld, Floodplain dynamics of a wandering river, dendrochronology of the Morice River, British Columbia, Canada, *Geomorphology*, 3, 159-179, 1990.

Gough, L.P., Understanding our fragile environment: lessons from geochemical studies, *U.S. Geological Survey Circular 1105*, 34 pp., 1993.

Graf, J.B., Measured and predicted velocity and longitudinal dispersion at steady and unsteady flow, Colorado River, Glen Canyon Dam to Lake Mead, *Water Resources Bulletin*, 31, 265-281, 1995.

Graf, W., Flow resistance over a gravel bed: its consequence on initial sediment movement, in *Fluvial hydraulics of mountain regions*, edited by A. Armanini and G. DiSilvio, pp. 17-32, Springer-Verlag, Berlin, 1991.

Graf, W.L., Fluvial adjustments to the spread of tamarisk in the Colorado Plateau region, *Geological Society of America Bulletin*, 89, 1491-1501, 1978.

Graf, W.L., Mining and channel response, *Annals Assoc. Am. Geographers*, 69, 262-275, 1979.

Graf, W.L., *Fluvial processes in dryland rivers*, Springer-Verlag, Berlin, 346 pp., 1988.

Graf, W.L., Transport and deposition of plutonium-contaminated sediments by fluvial processes, Los Alamos Canyon, New Mexico, *Geological Society of America Bulletin*, 108, 1342-1355, 1996.

Graham, W.F. and R.A. Duce, Atmospheric pathways of the phosphorus cycle, *Geochimica Cosmochimica Acta*, 43, 1195-1208, 1979.

Grant, G.E., Hydraulics and sediment transport dynamics controlling step-pool formation in high gradient streams: a flume experiment, in *Dynamics and geomorphology of mountain rivers*, edited by P. Ergenzinger and K.-H. Schmidt, pp. 241-250, Springer-Verlag, Berlin, 1994.

Grant, G., Critical flow constrains flow hydraulics in mobile-bed streams: a new hypothesis, *Water Resources Research*, 33, 349-358, 1997.

Grant, G.E. and T. Mizuyama, Origin of step-pool sequences in high gradient streams: a flume experiment, in *Japan-US Workshop on Snow Avalanche, Landslide, Debris Flow Prediction and Control*, edited by M. Tominaga, pp. 523-532, Japan Science and Technology Agency, National Research Institute for Earth Science and Disaster Prevention, Tsukuba, 1991.

Grant, G.E. and F.J. Swanson, Morphology and processes of valley floors in mountain streams, western Cascades, Oregon, in *Natural and anthropogenic influences in fluvial geomorphology*, edited by J.E. Costa, A.J. Miller, K.W. Potter and P.R. Wilcock, pp. 83-101, Geophysical Monograph 89, American Geophysical Union, Washington, D.C., 1995.

Grant, G.E., F.J. Swanson, and M.G. Wolman, Pattern and origin of stepped-bed morphology in high-gradient streams, western Cascades, Oregon, *Geological Society of America Bulletin*, 102, 340-352, 1990.

Grass, A.J, Structural features of turbulent flow over smooth and rough boundaries, *Journal of Fluid Mechanics*, 50, 233-255, 1971.

Gray, D.H. and W.F. Megahan, Forest vegetation removal and slope stability in the Idaho batholith, *USDA Forest Service Research Paper INT-271*, 23 pp., 1981.

Gregory, K.J., Lichens and the determination of river channel capacity, *Earth Surface Processes*, 1, 273-285, 1976.

Gregory, K.J., The hydrogeomorphology of alpine proglacial areas, in *Glacio-fluvial sediment transfers*, edited by A.M. Gurnell and M.J. Clark, pp. 87-107, John Wiley and Sons, Chichester, 1987.

Gregory, K.J. and V. Gardiner, Drainage density and climate, *Zeitschrift für Geomorphologie*, 19, 287-298, 1975.

Gregory, S., Spatial and temporal patterns of woody debris retention and transport (abstract), *Bulletin, North American Benthological Society*, 8, 75, 1991.

Gregory, S.V., *Primary production in Pacific Northwest streams*, Unpublished PhD dissertation, Oregon State University, Corvallis, 1980.

Griffiths, G.A., Stochastic estimation of bed load yield in pool-and-riffle mountain streams, *Water Resources Research*, 16, 931-937, 1980.

Griffiths, G.A., Flow resistance in coarse gravel bed rivers, *ASCE Journal of Hydraulics Division*, 107, 899-918, 1981.

Griffiths, G.A., Form resistance in gravel channels with mobile beds, *ASCE Journal of Hydraulic Engineering*, 115, 340-355, 1987.

Griffiths, G.A., Form resistance in gravel channels with mobile beds, *Journal of Hydraulic Engineering*, 115, 340-355, 1989.

Grimm, M.M., *Paleoflood history and geomorphology of Bear Creek Basin, Colorado*, Unpublished MS thesis, Colorado State University, Ft. Collins, Colorado, 126 pp., 1993.

Grimm, M.M., E.E. Wohl, and R.D. Jarrett, Coarse-sediment distribution as evidence of an elevation limit for flash flooding, Bear Creek, Colorado, *Geomorphology*, 14, 199-210, 1995.

Grimm, N.B. and S.G. Fisher, Responses of arid-land streams to changing climate, in *Global climate change and freshwater ecosystems*, edited by P. Firth and S.G. Fisher, pp. 211-233, Springer-Verlag, New York, 1992.

Grimm, N.B., H.M. Valett, E.H. Stanley and S.G. Fisher, Contribution of the hyporheic zone to stability of an arid-land stream, *Verh. Internat. Verein. Limnol.*, 24, 1595-1599, 1991.

Grimshaw, D.L., J. Lewin, and R. Fuge, Seasonal and short-term variations in the concentration and supply of dissolved zinc to polluted aquatic environments, *Environmental Pollution*, 11, 1-7, 1976.

Grodek, T., M. Inbar, and A.P. Schick, Step pool geometry and flow characteristics in low-sediment storage channel beds, in *Hydraulic engineering '94*, edited by G.V. Cotroneo and R.R. Rumer, v. 2, pp. 819-823, ASCE, Proceedings of the 1994 Conference, 1994.

Grötzbach, E. and C. Stadel, Mountain peoples and cultures, in *Mountains of the world: a global priority*, edited by B. Messerli and J.D. Ives, pp. 17-38, The Parthenon Publishing Group, London, 1997.

Gupta, A., Large floods as geomorphic events in the humid tropics, in *Flood geomorphology*, edited by V.R. Baker, R.C. Kochel, and P.C. Patton, pp. 301-315, John Wiley and Sons, New York, 1988.

Gupta, A., Magnitude, frequency, and special factors affecting channel form and processes in the seasonal tropics, in *Natural and anthropogenic influences in fluvial geomorphology*, edited by J.E. Costa, A.J. Miller, K.W. Potter, and P.R. Wilcock, pp. 125-136, Geophysical Monograph 89, American Geophysical Union, Washington, D.C., 1995.

Gupta, R.P. and B.C. Joshi, Landslide hazard zoning using the GIS approach - a case study from Ramganga Catchment, Himalayas, *Engineering Geology*, 28, 119-132, 1990.

Gurnell, A.M., Fluvial sediment yield from alpine, glacierized catchments, in *Glacio-fluvial sediment transfer*, edited by A.M. Gurnell and M.J. Clark, pp. 415-420, John Wiley and Sons, Chichester, 1987a.

Gurnell, A.M., Suspended sediment, in *Glacio-fluvial sediment transfer*, edited by A.M. Gurnell and M.J. Clark, pp. 305-354, John Wiley and Sons, Chichester, 1987b.

Gurnell, A.M., Sediment yield from alpine glacier basins, in *Sediment and water quality in river catchments*, edited by I. Foster, A. Gurnell, and B. Webb, pp. 407-435, John Wiley and Sons, Chichester, 1995.

Gurnell, A.M., The hydrogeomorphological effects of beaver dam-building activity, *Progress in Physical Geography*, 22, 167-189, 1998.

Gurnell, A.M., M.J. Clark, and C.T. Hill, The geomorphological impact of modified river discharge and sediment transport regimes downstream of hydropower scheme meltwater intake structures, in *Hydrology in mountainous regions II. Artificial reservoirs, water and slopes*, edited by R.O. Sinniger and M. Monbaron, pp. 165-170, IAHS Publ. no. 194, Wallingford, UK, 1990.

Gurnell, A.M. and J. Warburton, The significance of suspended sediment pulses for estimating suspended sediment load and identifying suspended sediment sources in Alpine glacier basins, in *Hydrology in mountainous regions I. Hydrological measurements, the water cycle*, edited by H. Lang and A. Musy, pp. 463-470, IAHS Publication no. 193, Wallingford, UK, 1990.

Gutiérrez, F., M. Gutiérrez, and C. Sancho, Geomorphological and sedimentological analysis of a catastrophic flash flood in the Arás drainage basin (Central Pyrenees, Spain), *Geomorphology*, 22, 265-283, 1998.

Guyot, J.L., J. Bourges, and J. Cortez, Sediment transport in the Rio Grande, an Andean river of the Bolivian Amazon drainage basin, in *Variability in stream erosion and sediment transport*, edited by L.J. Olive, R.J. Loughran and J.A. Kesby, pp. 223-231, IAHS Publication no. 224, Wallingford, UK, 1994.

Gyalistras, D., C. Schaer, H.C. Davies, and H. Wanner, *Future Alpine climate, in A view from the alps: regional perspectives on climate change*, edited by P. Cebon et al., MIT Press, Boston, 1997.

Habersack, H.M. and H.P. Nachtnebel, Analysis of sediment transport developments in relation to human impacts, in *Variability in stream erosion and sediment transport*, edited by L.J. Olive, R.J. Loughran and J.A. Kesby, pp. 385-393, IAHS Publ. no. 224, Wallingford, UK, 1994.

Hack, J.T., Studies of longitudinal stream profiles in Virginia and Maryland, *U.S. Geological Survey Professional Paper 294-B*, p. 45-97, 1957.

Hack, J.T., Interpretation of erosional topography in humid temperate regions, *American Journal of Science*, 258A, 80-97, 1960.

Hack, J.T. and J.C. Goodlett, Geomorphology and forest ecology of a mountain region in the central Appalachians, *U.S. Geological Survey Professional Paper 347*, 66 pp., 1960.

Haeberli, W., Frequency and characteristics of glacier floods in the Swiss Alps, *Annals of Glaciology*, 4, 85-90, 1983.

Haigh, M.J., J.S. Rawat, and H.S. Bisht, Hydrological impact of deforestation in the central Himalaya, in *Hydrology of mountainous areas*, edited by L. Molnar, pp. 419-433, IAHS Publ. no. 190, Wallingford, UK, 1990.

Hamilton, L.S. and L.A. Bruijnzeel, Mountain watersheds - integrating water, soils, gravity, vegetation, and people, in *Mountains of the world: a global priority*, edited by B. Messerli and J.D. Ives, pp. 337-370, The Parthenon Publishing Group, London, 1997.

Hammann, K. and A. Dittrich, Measurement systems to determine the velocity field in and close to the roughness sublayer, in *Dynamics and geomorphology of mountain rivers*, edited by P. Ergenzinger and K.-H. Schmidt, pp. 265-288, Springer-Verlag, Berlin, 1994.

Hancock, G.S., R.S. Anderson and K.X. Whipple, Beyond power: bedrock river incision process and form, in *Rivers over rock: fluvial processes in bedrock channels*, edited by K.J. Tinkler and E.E. Wohl, pp. 35-60, Am. Geophys. Union Geophysical Monograph 107, 1998.

Harbor, D.J., Landscape evolution at the margin of the Basin and Range, *Geology*, 25, 1111-1114, 1997.

Harden, D.R., Controlling factors in the distribution and development of incised meanders in the central Colorado Plateau, *Geological Society of America Bulletin*, 102, 233-242, 1990.

Harmon, M.E., J.F. Franklin, and F.J. Swanson, Ecology of coarse woody debris in temperate ecosystems, *Advances in Ecological Research*, 15, 133-302, 1986.

Harr, R.D., Effects of clearcutting on rain on snow runoff in western Oregon: a new look at old studies, *Water Resources Research*, 22, 1095-1100, 1986.

Harris, R.R., Occurrence of vegetation on geomorphic surfaces in the active floodplain of a California alluvial stream, *The American Midland Naturalist*, 118, 393-405, 1987.

Harris, R.R., Associations between stream-valley geomorphology and riparian vegetation as a basis for landscape analysis in the eastern Sierra Nevada, California, USA, *Environmental Management*, 12, 219-228, 1988.

Hartman, G., Habitat selection by European beaver (*Castor fiber*) colonizing a boreal landscape, *Journal of Zoology, London*, 240, 317-325, 1996.

Hartman, G.F. and J.C. Scrivener, Impacts of forestry practices on a coastal stream ecosystem,

Carnation Creek, British Columbia, *Canadian Bulletin of Fisheries and Aquatic Sciences*, 223, 148 pp., 1990.

Harvey, A.M., Sediment supply to upland streams; influence on channel adjustment, in *Sediment transport in gravel-bed rivers*, edited by C.R. Thorne, J.C. Bathurst, and R.D. Hey, pp. 121-150, John Wiley and Sons, Chichester, 1987.

Harvey, A.M., Controls on sedimentary style on alluvial fans, in *Dynamics of gravel-bed rivers*, edited by P. Billi, R.D. Hey, C.R. Thorne and P. Tacconi, pp. 519-535, John Wiley and Sons, Chichester, 1992.

Harvey, A.M., D.H. Hitchcock, and D.J. Hughes, Event frequency and morphological adjustment of fluvial systems in upland Britain, in *Adjustments of the fluvial system*, edited by D.D. Rhodes and G.P. Williams, pp. 139-167, George Allen and Unwin, London, 1979.

Harvey, J.W. and K.E. Bencala, The effect of streambed topography on surface-subsurface water exchange in mountain catchments, *Water Resources Research*, 29, 89-98, 1993.

Harvey, M.D., *Steepland channel response to episodic erosion*, Unpublished PhD dissertation, Colorado State University, Ft. Collins, Colorado, 266 pp., 1980.

Harvey, M.D., R.A. Mussetter, and E.J. Wick, A physical process-biological response model for spawning habitat formation for the endangered Colorado squawfish, *Rivers*, 4, 114-131, 1993.

Harvey, M.D., J. Pitlick, and J. Laird, Temporal and spatial variability of sediment storage and erosion in Ash Creek, Arizona, in *Erosion and sedimentation in the Pacific Rim*, edited by R.L. Beschta, T. Blinn, G.E. Grant, G.G. Ice, and F.J. Swanson, pp. 281-282, IAHS Publ. no. 165, 1987.

Harvey, M.D., C.C. Watson, and S.A. Schumm, Channelized streams: an analog for the effects of urbanization, *1983 International Symposium on Urban Hydrology, Hydraulics and Sediment Control*, University of Kentucky, p. 401-409, 1983.

Haschenburger, J.K., A probability model of scour and fill depths in gravel-bed channels, *Water Resources Research*, 35, 2857-2869, 1999.

Haschenburger, J.K. and M. Church, Bed material transport estimated from the virtual velocity of sediment, *Earth Surface Processes and Landforms*, 23, 791-808, 1998.

Hasegawa, K. and S. Kanbayashi, Formation mechanism of step-pool systems in steep rivers and guide lines for the design of construction, *Annual Journal of Hydraulic Engineering (Japan)*, 40, 893-900, 1996.

Hasegawa, K. and T. Mizugaki, Analysis of blocking phenomena in bifurcated channels found in mountainous rivers, in *Hydraulic engineering '94*, edited by G.V. Cotroneo and R.R. Rumer, pp. 829-833, ASCE, Proceedings of the 1994 Conference, New York, 1994.

Haslam, S.M., *River pollution: an ecological perspective*, Belhaven Press, London, 218 pp., 1990.

Hassan, M.A., Bed material and bedload movement in two ephemeral streams, *Special Publications International Association of Sedimentologists*, 17, 37-49, 1993.

Hassan, M.A. and M. Church, The movement of individual grains on the streambed, in *Dynamics of gravel-bed rivers*, edited by P. Billi, R.D. Hey, C.R. Thorne and P. Tacconi, pp. 159-175, John Wiley and Sons, Chichester, 1992.

Hassan, M.A., M. Church, and A.P. Schick, Distance of movement of coarse particles in gravel bed streams, *Water Resources Research*, 27, 503-511, 1991.

Hassan, M.A. and I. Reid, The influence of microform bed roughness elements on flow and sediment transport in gravel bed rivers, *Earth Surface Processes and Landforms*, 15, 739-750, 1990.

Hassan, M.A., A.P. Schick, and J.B. Laronne, The recovery of flood-dispersed coarse sediment particles, in *Channel processes - water, sediment, catchment controls*, edited by A.P. Schick, pp. 153-162, Catena Supplement, 5, 1984.

Hassan, M.A., A.P. Schick, and P.A. Shaw, The transport of gravel in an ephemeral sandbed river, *Earth Surface Processes and Landforms*, 24, 623-640, 1999.

Haupt, H.F., Infiltration, overland flow and soil movement on frozen and snow covered plots, *Water Resources Research*, 3, 145-161, 1967.

Hawkes, H.A., River zonation and classification, in *River ecology*, edited by B.A. Whitton, pp. 312-374, University of California Press, Berkeley, 1975.

Hawkins, C.P., J.L. Kershener, P.A. Bisson, M.D. Bryant, L.M. Decker, S.V. Gregory, D.A. McCullough, C.K. Overton, G.H. Reeves, R.J. Steedman, and M.K. Young, A hierarchical approach to classifying stream habitat features, *Fisheries*, 18, 3-12, 1993.

Hayden, B.P., Flood climates, in *Flood geomorphology*, edited by V.R. Baker, R.C. Kochel, and P.C. Patton, pp. 13-26, John Wiley and Sons, New York, 1988.

Hayward, J.A., Mountain stream sediments, in *Physical hydrology: New Zealand experience*, edited by D.L. Murray and P. Ackroyd, pp. 193-212, New Zealand Hydrological Society Inc., North Wellington, 1979.

Hayward, J.A., *Hydrology and stream sediments from Torlesse Stream catchment*, Tussock Grasslands and Mountain Lands Institute, Lincoln College, New Zealand, Special Publication No. 17, 1980.

Hayward, J.A. and A.J. Sutherland, The Torlesse stream vortex-tube sediment trap, *Journal of Hydrology (New Zealand)*, 13, 41-53, 1974.

He, Q. and P. Owens, Determination of suspended sediment provenance using Caesium-137, unsupported Lead-210 and Radium-226: a numerical mixing model approach, in *Sediment and water quality in river catchments*, edited by I. Foster, A. Gurnell, and B. Webb, pp. 207-227, John Wiley and Sons, Chichester, 1995.

Heede, B.H., Influences of a forest on the hydraulic geometry of two mountain streams, *Water Resources Bulletin*, 8, 523-530, 1972.

Heede, B.H., Dynamics of selected mountain streams in the western United States of America, *Zeitschrift für Geomorphologie*, 25, 17-32, 1981.

Heede, B.H., Increased flows after timber harvest accelerate stream disequilibrium, in *Erosion control: a global perspective*, pp. 449-454, Proceedings of the Conference 22, International Erosion Control Association, Orlando, Florida, 1991a.

Heede, B.H., Response of a stream in disequilibrium to timber harvest, *Environmental Management*, 15, 251-255, 1991b.

Heede, B.H. and J.N. Rinne, Hydrodynamic and fluvial morphologic processes: implications for fisheries management and research, *North American Journal of Fisheries Management*, 10, 249-268, 1990.

Helley, E.J. and V.C. LaMarche, Jr., Historic flood information for northern California streams from geological and botanical evidence, *U.S. Geological Survey Prof Paper 485-E*, E1-E16, 1973.

Hem, J.D., A. Demayo, and R.A. Smith, Hydrogeochemistry of rivers and lakes, in *Surface water hydrology*, edited by M.G. Wolman and H.C. Riggs, pp. 189-231, Geological Society of America, Boulder, Colorado, 1990.

Henriksen, A., Acidification of fresh waters - a large scale titration, in *Ecological impact of acid precipitation*, edited by D. Drablos and A. Tollan, pp. 68-74, SNSF Project, Oslo-Ås, 1980.

Hewitt, K., Natural dams and outburst floods of the Karakoram Himalaya, in *Hydrological aspects of alpine and high mountain areas*, edited by J.W. Glen, pp. 259-269, IAHS Publication no. 138, 1982.

Hewitt, K., Risk and disasters in mountain lands, in *Mountains of the world: a global priority*, edited by B. Messerli and J.D. Ives, pp. 371-408, The Parthenon Publishing Group, London, 1997.

Hewitt, K., Catastrophic landslides and their effects on the Upper Indus streams, Karakoram Himalaya, northern Pakistan, *Geomorphology*, 26, 47-80, 1998.

Hey, R.D., Flow resistance in gravel-bed rivers, *ASCE Journal of Hydraulics Div*, 105, 365-279, 1979.

Hey, R.D., River dynamics, flow regime and sediment transport, in *Sediment transport in gravel-bed rivers*, edited by C.R. Thorne, J.C. Bathurst, and R.D. Hey, pp. 17-40, John Wiley and Sons, Chichester, 1987.

Hey, R.D., Bar form resistance in gravel-bed rivers, *ASCE Journal Hydraulic Engineering*, 114, 1498-1508, 1988.

Hey, D.L. and N.S. Philippi, Flood reduction through wetland restoration: the upper Mississippi River basin as a case history, *Restoration Ecology*, 3, 4-17, 1995.

Hey, R.D. and C.R. Thorne, Accuracy of surface samples from gravel bed material, *ASCE Journal of Hydraulic Engineering*, 109, 842-851, 1983.

Hey, R.D., C.R. Thorne, and J.C. Bathurst, (eds.), *Gravel-bed rivers*, John Wiley and Sons, Chichester, 1982.

Higgins, R.J., G. Pickup, and P.S. Cloke, Estimating the transport and deposition of mining waste at Ok Tedi, in *Sediment transport in gravel-bed rivers*, edited by C.R. Thorne, J.C. Bathurst, and R.D. Hey, pp. 949-976, John Wiley and Sons, Chichester, 1987.

Hildrew, A.G. and P.S. Giller, Patchiness, species interactions and disturbance in the stream benthos, in *Aquatic ecology: scale, pattern and process*, edited by P.S. Giller, A.G. Hildrew and D.G. Raffaelli, pp. 21-62, Blackwell Scientific Publications, Oxford, 1994.

Hill, B.R., E.H. Decarlo, C.C. Fuller and M.F. Wong, Using sediment 'fingerprints' to assess sediment-budget errors, North Halawa Valley, Oahu, Hawaii, 1991-92, *Earth Surface Processes and Landforms*, 23, 493-508, 1998.

Hilmes, M.M., *Changes in channel morphology associated with placer mining along the Middle Fork of the South Platte River, Fairplay, Colorado*, Unpublished MS thesis, Colorado State University, Ft. Collins, Colorado, 261 pp., 1993.

Hilmes, M.M. and E.E. Wohl, Changes in channel morphology associated with placer mining, *Physical Geography*, 16, 223-242, 1995.

Hilton, S. and T.E. Lisle, Measuring the fraction of pool volume filled with fine sediment, *USDA Forest Service Research Note PSW-RN-414*, 11 pp., 1993.

Hirsch, R.M., J.F. Walker, J.C. Day, and R. Kallio, The influence of man on hydrologic systems, in *Surface water hydrology*, edited by M.G. Wolman and H.C. Riggs, pp. 329-359, Geological Society of America, Boulder, Colorado, 1990.

Hirschboeck, K.K., Hydroclimatically-defined mixed distributions in partial duration flood series, in *Hydrologic frequency modeling*, edited by V.P. Singh, pp. 195-205, D. Reidel, Boston, 1987.

Hirschboeck, K.K., Flood hydroclimatology, in *Flood geomorphology*, edited by V.R. Baker, R.C. Kochel, and P.C. Patton, pp. 27-49, John Wiley and Sons, New York, 1988.

Hjulström, F., Studies of the morphological activity of rivers as illustrated by the River Fyris, *Bulletin of the Geological Institute, University of Uppsala*, 25, 221-527, 1935.

Hodgkins, R., Seasonal trend in suspended-sediment transport from an Arctic glacier, and implications for drainage system structure, *Annals of Glaciology*, 22, 147-151, 1996.

Hodgkins, R., Glacier hydrology in Svalbard, Norwegian High Arctic, *Quaternary Science Reviews*, 16, 957-973, 1997.

Hodgkins, R., M. Tranter, and J.A. Dowdeswell, Solute provenance, transport and denudation in a High Arctic glacierized catchment, *Hydrological Processes*, 11, 1813-1832, 1997.

Hodgkins, R., M. Tranter, and J.A. Dowdeswell, The hydrochemistry of runoff from a 'cold-based' glacier in the High Arctic (Scott Turnerbreen, Svalbard), *Hydrological Processes*, 12, 87-103, 1998.

Hoey, T., Temporal variations in bedload transport rates and sediment storage in gravel-bed rivers, *Progress in Physical Geography*, 16, 319-338, 1992.

Hoey, T.B. and A.J. Sutherland, Channel morphology and bedload pulses in braided rivers: A laboratory study, *Earth Surface Processes and Landforms*, 16, 447-462, 1991.

Hoffman, P.F. and J.P. Grotzinger, Orographic precipitation, erosional unloading, and tectonic style, *Geology*, 21, 195-198, 1993.

Hofmann, L. and R.E. Ries, Relationship of soil and plant characteristics to erosion and runoff on pasture and range, *Journal of Soil and Water Conservation*, 46, 143-147, 1991.

Hogan, D.L., *Channel morphology of unlogged, logged and debris torrented streams in the Queen Charlotte Islands*, British Columbia Ministry of Forests and Lands, Land Management Report No. 49, 94 pp., 1986.

Hohberger, K. and G.. Einsele, Die Bedeutung des Lösungsabtrags verschiedener Gesteine für die

Landschaftsentwicklung in Mitteleuropa, *Zeitschrift für Geomorphologie*, 23, 361-382, 1979. (In Selby, 1982)

Holland, H.D., *The chemistry of the atmosphere and oceans*, Wiley and Sons, New York, 351 pp., 1978.

Holland, W.N. and G. Pickup, Flume study of knickpoint development in stratified sediment, *Geological Society of America Bulletin*, 87, 76-82, 1976.

Holmes, R.M., S.G. Fisher and N.B. Grimm, Parafluvial nitrogen dynamics in a desert stream ecosystem, *J. N. Am. Benthological Society*, 13, 468-478, 1994.

Holtan, H.N. and M.H. Kirkpatrick, Rainfall infiltration and hydraulics of flow in runoff computation, *Transactions American Geophysical Union*, 31, 771-779, 1950.

Hooke, J.M. and C.E. Redmond, Use of cartographic sources for analysing river channel change with examples from Britain, in *Historical change of large alluvial rivers: western Europe*, edited by G.E. Petts, pp. 79-73, John Wiley and Sons, Chichester, 1989.

Hooke, J.M. and C.E. Redmond, Causes and nature of river planform changes, in *Dynamics of gravel-bed rivers*, edited by P. Billi, R.D. Hey, C.R. Thorne and P. Tacconi, pp. 557-571, 1992.

Hooke, R. LeB., Processes on arid-region alluvial fans, *Journal of Geology*, 75, 438-460, 1967.

Hooke, R. LeB. and W.L. Rohrer, Geometry of alluvial fans: effect of discharge and sediment size, *Earth Surface Processes*, 4, 147-166, 1979.

Horton, R.E., Drainage basin characteristics, *Transactions, American Geophysical Union*, 13, 350-361, 1932.

Horton, R.E., Erosional development of streams and their drainage basins; hydrophysical approach to quantitative morphology, *Geological Society of America Bulletin*, 56, 275-370, 1945.

Houghton, B.F., J.H. Latter, and W.R. Hackett, Volcanic hazard assessment for Ruapehu composite volcano, Taupo volcanic zone, New Zealand, *Bulletin of Volcanology*, 49, 737-751, 1987.

Hovius, N., C.P. Stark, M.A. Tutton, and L.D. Abbott, Landslide-driven drainage network evolution in a pre-steady-state mountain belt: Finisterre Mountains, Papua New Guinea, *Geology*, 26, 1071-1074, 1998.

Howard, A.D., Drainage analysis in geologic interpretation: a summation, *American Association of Petroleum Geologists Bulletin*, 51, 2246-2259, 1967.

Howard, A.D., Simulation of stream networks by headward growth and branching, *Geographical Analysis*, 3, 29-50, 1971.

Howard, A.D., Thresholds in river regimes, in *Thresholds in geomorphology*, edited by D.R. Coates and J.D. Vitek, pp. 227-258, George Allen and Unwin, London, 1980.

Howard, A.D., Modelling fluvial systems: rock-, gravel- and sand-bed channels, in *River channels: environment and process*, edited by K. Richards, pp. 69-94, Blackwell, New York, 1987.

Howard, A.D., A detachment-limited model of drainage basin evolution, *Water Resources Research*, 30, 2261-2285, 1994.

Howard, A.D., Long profile development of bedrock channels: interaction of weathering, mass wasting, bed erosion, and sediment transport, in *Rivers over rock: fluvial processes in bedrock channels*, edited by K.J. Tinkler and E.E. Wohl, pp. 297-319, Am. Geophys. Union Geophysical Monograph 107, 1998.

Howard, A.D., W.E. Dietrich, and M.A. Seidl, Modelling fluvial erosion on regional to continental scales, *Journal of Geophysical Research*, 99 (B7), 13,971-13,986, 1994.

Hubbell, D.W., Bed load sampling and analysis, in *Sediment transport in gravel-bed rivers*, edited by C.R. Thorne, J.C. Bathurst, and R.D. Hey, pp. 89-118, John Wiley and Sons, Chichester, 1987.

Hudson, J.A., R.C. Johnson, and J.R. Blackie, Choice and calibration of streamflow structures for two mountain experimental basins, in *Hydrology in mountainous regions I. Hydrological measurements; the water cycle*, edited by H. Lang and A. Musy, pp. 275-282, IAHS Publication no. 193, Wallingford, UK, 1990.

Huet, M., Biologie, profils en long et en travers des eaux courantes, *Bulletin Francais de Pisciculture*, 175, 41-53, 1954.

Hughes, F.M.R., Environmental change, disturbance, and regeneration in semi-arid floodplain forests, in *Environmental change in drylands: biogeographical and geomorphological perspectives*, edited by A.C. Millington and K. Pye, pp. 321-345, John Wiley and Sons, New York, 1994.

Hughes, G.M., Polluted fish respiratory physiology, in *Effects of pollutants on aquatic organisms*, edited by A.P.M. Lockwood, pp. 163-183, Cambridge University Press, Cambridge, 1976.

Hultberg, H., H. Apsimon, R.M. Church, P. Grenffelt, M.J. Mitchell, F. Moldan and H.B. Ross, Sulphur, in *Biogeochemistry of small catchments: a tool for environmental research*, edited by B. Moldan and J. Cerny, pp. 229-254, John Wiley and Sons, Chichester, 1994.

Hungr, O., G.C. Morgan, D.F. Van Dine, and D.R. Lister, Debris flow defenses in British Columbia, in *Debris flows/avalanches: process, recognition, and mitigation*, edited by J.E. Costa and G.F. Wieczorek, pp. 201-236, Geological Society of America, Reviews in Engineering Geology, v. 7, Boulder, Colorado, 1987.

Hupp, C.R., Plant ecological aspects of flood geomorphology and paleoflood history, in *Flood geomorphology*, edited by V.R. Baker, R.C. Kochel, and P.C. Patton, pp. 335-356, John Wiley and Sons, New York, 1988.

Hupp, C.R., Vegetation patterns in relation to basin hydrogeomorphology, in *Vegetation and erosion*, edited by J.B. Thornes, pp. 217-237, John Wiley and Sons, Chichester, 1990.

Hupp, C.R. and W.R. Osterkamp, Riparian vegetation and fluvial geomorphic processes, *Geomorphology*, 14, 277-295, 1996.

Hupp, C.R. and A. Simon, Bank accretion and the development of vegetated depositional surfaces along modified alluvial channels, *Geomorphology*, 4, 111-124, 1991.

Hutton, J., *The theory of the Earth*, vols. 1 and 2, William Creech, Edinburgh, 1795.

Hyatt, J.A. and P.M. Jacobs, Distribution and morphology of sinkholes triggered by flooding following Tropical Storm Alberto at Albany, Georgia, USA, *Geomorphology*, 17, 305-316, 1996.

Hydrologic Engineering Center, *HEC-6, scour and deposition in rivers and reservoirs, user's manual*, U.S. Army Corps of Engineers, 1977.

Hydrologic Engineering Center, *HEC-RAS river analysis system v. 2.0 user's manual*, U.S. Army Corps of Engineers, Davis, California, 1997.

Hynes, N., *The ecology of running waters*, University of Toronto Press, Toronto, Canada, 555 pp., 1970.

Hynes, N., The stream and its valley, *International Assoc. Theor. Applied Limnol.*, 19, 1-15, 1975.

Ichim, I. and M. Radoane, On the high erosion rate in the Vrancea region, Romania, in *International geomorphology 1986*, edited by V. Gardiner, Part I, pp. 783-790, John Wiley and Sons, Chichester, 1987.

Iida, T. and K. Okunishi, Development of hillslopes due to landslides, *Zeitschrift für Geomorphologie*, 46, 67-77, 1983.

Ikeda, H., Flume experiments on the causes of superior mobility of sediment mixtures, *Annual Report of the Institute of Geoscience, University of Tsukuba (Japan)*, No. 10, p. 53-56, 1984.

Ikeda, H. and F. Iseya, Thresholds in the mobility of sediment mixtures, in *International geomorphology*, edited by V. Gardiner, pp. 561-570, Part I, John Wiley and Sons, 1986.

Ikeda, H. and F. Iseya, *Experimental study of heterogeneous sediment transport*, University of Tsukuba (Japan), Environmental Research Center Paper No. 12, 50 pp., 1988.

Ikeda, H., F. Iseya, and Y. Kodama, Sedimentation on an alluvial cone in the Upper Oi River, central Japan, *Bulletin of the Tsukuba University Forests (Japan)*, 9, 149-173, 1993.

Ilies, J., Versuch einer allegemein biozonitischen Gliederung der Fliessgewasser, *Verhandlungen der Internationalen Vereinigung für Theoretische und Angewandte Limnologie*, 13, 834-844, 1961.

Ilies, J. and L. Botosaneanu, Problèmes et méthodes de la classification et de la zonation écologique des eaux courantes considérées surtout du point de vue faunistique, *Mitteilungen der Internationalen Vereinigung für Theoretische und Angewandte Limnologie*, 12, 1-57, 1963. [English summary]

Inbar, M., Effects of a high magnitude flood in a Mediterranean climate: a case study in the Jordan River basin, in *Catastrophic flooding*, edited by L. Mayer and D. Nash, pp. 333-353, Allen and Unwin, Boston, 1987.

Inbar, M. and A.P. Schick, Bedload transport associated with high stream power, Jordan River, Israel, *Proceedings, National Academy of Sciences, USA*, 76, 2515-2517, 1979.

Inbar, M., M. Tamir, and L. Wittenberg, Runoff and erosion processes after a forest fire in Mount Carmel, a Mediterranean area, *Geomorphology*, 24, 17-33, 1998.

Inman, D.L. and S.A. Jenkins, Climate change and the episodicity of sediment flux of small California rivers, *Journal of Geology*, 107, 251-270, 1999.

Innes, J.L., Debris flows, *Progress in Physical Geography*, 7, 469-501, 1983.

Iseya, F. and H. Ikeda, Pulsations in bedload transport rates induced by a longitudinal sediment sorting: a flume study using sand and gravel mixtures, *Geografiska Annaler*, 69A, 15-27, 1987.

Iseya, F., H. Ikeda, H. Maita, and Y. Kodama, Fluvial deposits in a torrential gravel-bed stream by extreme sediment supply: sedimentary structure and depositional mechanism, in *Third International Workshop on Gravel-bed Rivers*, Firenze, Italy, 1990.

Ismail, W.R. and Z.A. Rahaman, The impact of quarrying activity on suspended sediment concentration and sediment load of Sungai Relau, Pulau Pinang, Malaysia, *Malaysian Journal of Tropical Geography*, 25, 45-57, 1994.

Iso, N., K. Yamakawa, H. Yonezawa, and T. Matsubara, Accumulation rates of alluvial cones, constructed by debris-flow deposits, in the drainage basins of the Takahara River, Gifu prefecture, central Japan, *Geographical Review Japan*, 53, 699-720, 1980.

Iverson, R.M. and R.G. Lahusen, Momentum transport in debris flows: large-scale experiments, *EOS*, 73 227, 1992.

Iverson, R.M. and M.E. Reid, Gravity-driven groundwater flow and slope failure potential. 1. Elastic effective-stress model. And 2. Effects of slope morphology, material properties, and hydraulic heterogeneity, *Water Resources Research*, 28, 925-950, 1992.

Ives, J.D., Introduction: a description of the Front Range in, *Geoecology of the Colorado Front Range: a study of alpine and subalpine environments*, edited by J.D. Ives, pp. 1-7, Westview Press, Boulder, Colorado, 1980.

Ives, J.D., Mountain environments, *Progress in Physical Geography*, 9, 425-433, 1985.

Ives, J.D., Glacial lake outburst floods and risk engineering in the Himalaya, *International Centre for Integrated Mountain Development (ICIMOD) Occasional Paper No. 5*, Kathmandu, Nepal, 42 pp., 1986.

Ives, J.D. and R.G. Barry, (eds.), *Arctic and alpine environments*, Methuen, London, 999 pp., 1974.

Ives, J.D. and B. Messerli, *The Himalayan dilemma: reconciling development and conservation*, Routledge, London, 295 pp., 1989.

Ives, J.D., B. Messerli, and E. Spiess, Mountains of the world - a global priority, in *Mountains of the world: a global priority*, edited by B. Messerli and J.D. Ives, pp. 1-15, The Parthenon Publishing Group, London, 1997.

Jackson, L.E., Jr., R.A. Kostaschuk, and G.M. MacDonald, Identification of debris flow hazard on alluvial fans in the Canadian Rocky Mountains, in *Debris flows/avalanches: process, recognition, and mitigation*, edited by J.E. Costa and G.F. Wieczorek, pp. 115-124, Geological Society of America, Reviews in Engineering Geology, v. 7, Boulder, Colorado, 1987.

Jackson, W.L. and R.L. Beschta, A model of two-phase bedload transport in an Oregon Coast Range stream, *Earth Surface Processes and Landforms*, 7, 517-527, 1982.

Jacobson, R.B., J.P. McGeehin, E.D. Cron, C.E. Carr, J.M. Harper, and A.D. Howard, Landslides triggered by the storm of November 3-5, 1985, Wills Mountain anticline, West Virginia and Virginia, *U.S. Geological Survey Bulletin 1981*, part C, C1-C33, 1993.

Jaeggi, M.N.R., Interaction of bed load transport with bars, in *Sediment transport in gravel-bed rivers*, edited by C.R. Thorne, J.C. Bathurst, and R.D. Hey, pp. 829-841, John Wiley and Sons, Chichester, 1987.

Jaeggi, M. and B. Zarn, Stream channel restoration and erosion control for incised channels in alpine environments, in *Incised river channels: processes, forms, engineering and management*, edited by S.E. Darby and A. Simon, pp. 343-369, Wiley, Chichester, 1999.

James, L.A., Sustained reworking of hydraulic mining sediment in California: G.K. Gilbert's sediment wave model reconsidered, *Zeitschrift für Geomorphologie*, 88, 49-66, 1993.

James, L.A., Channel changes wrought by gold mining: northern Sierra Nevada, California, in *Effects of human-induced changes on hydrologic systems*, pp. 629-638, American Water Resources Association, 1994.

Janda, R.J., K.M. Scott, K.M. Nolan, and H.A. Martinson, Lahar movement, effects, and deposits, in *The 1980 eruptions of Mount St. Helens, Washington*, edited by P.W. Lipman and D.R. Mullineaux, pp. 461-478, U.S. Geological Survey Professional Paper 1250, 1981.

Japanese Ministry Of Construction, *Sabo*, Ministry of Construction, Kobe, Japan, 36 pp., 1993.

Jarrett, R.D., Hydraulics of high-gradient streams, *ASCE Journal Hydraulics Division*, 110, 1519-1539, 1984.

Jarrett, R.D., Determination of roughness coefficients for streams in Colorado, *U.S. Geological Survey Water-Resources Investigations Report 85-4004*, 54 pp., 1985.

Jarrett, R.D., Errors in slope-area computations of peak discharges in mountain streams, *Journal Hydrology*, 96, 53-67, 1987.

Jarrett, R.D., Hydrology and paleohydrology used to improve the understanding of flood hydrometeorology in Colorado, in *Design of hydraulic structures 89*, edited by M.L. Albertson and R.A. Kia, pp. 9-16, Proceed. of the 2nd International Symposium on Design of Hydraulic Structures, Ft. Collins, CO, 26-29 June 89, A.A. Balkema, Rotterdam, 1989.

Jarrett, R.D., Hydrologic and hydraulic research in mountain rivers, *Water Resources Bulletin*, 26, 419-429, 1990a.

Jarrett, R.D., Paleohydrologic techniques used to define the spatial occurrence of floods, *Geomorphology*, 3, 181-195, 1990b.

Jarrett, R.D., Wading measurements of vertical velocity profiles, *Geomorphology*, 4, 243-247, 1991.

Jarrett, R.D., Hydraulics of mountain rivers, in *Channel flow resistance: centennial of Manning's formula*, edited by B.C. Yen, pp. 287-298, Water Resource Publications, Littleton, CO, 1992.

Jarrett, R.D., Flood elevation limits in the Rocky Mountains, in *Engineering hydrology*, edited by C.Y. Kuo, pp. 180-185, ASCE Hydraulics Division, 1993.

Jarrett, R.D., Historic-flood evaluation and research needs in mountainous areas, in *Hydraulic engineering '94*, edited by G.V. Cotroneo and R.R. Rumer, pp. 875-879, Proceed of the 1994 Conf, Hydraul Div, ASCE, New York, 1994.

Jarrett, R.D., J.P. Capesius, D. Jarrett, and J.F. England, Jr., 1995: where the past (paleoflood hydrology) meets the present, understanding maximum flooding, *Geological Society of America Annual Meeting, Abstracts with Programs*, p. A-110, 1996.

Jarrett, R.D. and J.E. Costa, Hydrology, geomorphology, and dam-break modeling of the July 15, 1982, Lawn Lake Dam and Cascade Dam failures, Larimer County, Colorado, *U.S. Geological Survey Prof Paper 1369*, 1986.

Jarrett, R.D. and J.E. Costa, Evaluation of the flood hydrology in the Colorado Front Range using precipitation, streamflow, and paleoflood data, *U.S. Geological Survey Water Resources Investigations Report 87-4117*, 37 pp., 1988.

Jeník, J., The diversity of mountain life, in *Mountains of the world: a global priority*, edited by B. Messerli and J.D. Ives, pp. 199-231, The Parthenon Publishing Group, London, 1997.

Jenkins, A., N.E. Peters and A. Rodhe, Hydrology, in *Biogeochemistry of small catchments: a tool for environmental research*, edited by B. Moldan and J. Cerny, pp. 31-54, John Wiley and Sons, Chichester, 1994.

Jiongxin, X., Underlying gravel layers in a large sand bed river and their influence on downstream-dam channel adjustment, *Geomorphology*, 17, 351-359, 1996.

Johnejack, K.R. and W.F. Megahan, Sediment transport in headwater channels in Idaho, in *Proceedings of the Fifth Federal Interagency Sedimentation Conference*, edited by S.-S. Fan and Y.-H. Kuo, pp. 4-155 to 4-161, Las Vegas, Nevada, 1991.

Johnson, A.M. and J.R. Rodine, Debris flow, in *Slope instability*, edited by D. Brunsden and D.B. Prior, pp. 257-361, John Wiley and Sons, 1984.

Johnson, B.L., W.B. Richardson, and T.J. Naimo, Past, present, and future concepts in large river ecology, *BioScience*, 45, 134-141, 1995.

Johnson, C.E., M.I. Litaor, M.F. Billett and O.P. Bricker, Chemical weathering in small catchments: climatic and anthropogenic influences, in *Biogeochemistry of small catchments: a tool for environmental research,* edited by B. Moldan and J. Cerny, pp. 323-341, John Wiley and Sons, Chichester, 1994.

Johnson, K.A. and N. Sitar, Hydrologic conditions leading to debris-flow initiation, *Canadian Geotechnical Journal*, 27, 789-801, 1990.

Johnson, M.G. and R.L.Beschta, Logging, infiltration and surface erodibility in western Oregon, *Journal of Forestry*, 78, 334-337, 1980.

Johnson, R.R., The lower Colorado River: a western system, in *Strategies for protection and management of floodplain wetlands and other riparian ecosystems*, pp. 41-55, USDA Forest Service General Technical Report WO-12, 1978.

Johnson, S.L., A.P. Covich, T.A. Crowl, A. Estrada-Pinto, J. Bithorn, and W.A. Wurstbaugh, Do seasonality and disturbance influence reproduction in freshwater atyid shrimp in headwater streams, Puerto Rico? *Verhandlungen International Verein. Limnol.*, 26, 2076-2081, 1998.

Johnston, C.E., E.D. Andrews, and J. Pitlick, In situ determination of particle friction angles of fluvial gravels, *Water Resources Research*, 34, 2017-2030, 1998.

Jolly, I.D., The effects of river management on the hydrology and hydroecology of arid and semi-arid floodplains, in *Floodplain processes*, edited by M.G. Anderson, D.E. Walling, and P.D. Bates, pp. 577-609, John Wiley and Sons, Chichester, 1996.

Jones, J.A.A., *The nature of soil piping: a review of research*, Geobooks, Norwich, 1981.

Jones, J.B., Jr., S.G. Fisher and N.B. Grimm, Nitrification in the hyporheic zone of a desert stream ecosystem, *J. N. Am. Benthological Society*, 14, 249-258, 1995a.

Jones, J.B., Jr., S.G. Fisher and N.B. Grimm, Vertical hydrologic exchange and ecosystem metabolism in a Sonoran desert stream, *Ecology*, 76, 942-952, 1995b.

Jones, P.D., K.R. Briffa, and J.R. Pilcher, Riverflow reconstruction from tree rings in southern Britain, *Journal of Climatology*, 4, 461-472, 1984.

Jowett, I.G., Instream flow methods: a comparison of approaches, *Regulated Rivers: Research and Management*, 13, 115-127, 1997.

Jubb, R.A., The J.G. Strydom Dam: Pongolo River: northern Zululand. The importance of floodplains below it, *Piscator*, 86, 104-109, 1972.

Julien, P.Y., *Erosion and sedimentation*, Cambridge University Press, New York, 280 pp., 1995.

Junk, W.J., P.B. Bayley, and R.E. Sparks, The flood pulse concept in river-floodplain systems, *Canadian Special Publications Fisheries and Aquatic Sciences*, 106, 110-127, 1989.

Kaizuka, S. and T. Suzuki, Geomorphology in Japan, in *The evolution of geomorphology*, edited by H.J. Walker and W.E. Grabau, pp. 255-271, Wiley and Sons, New York, 1993.

Kalliola, R. and M. Puhakka, River dynamics and vegetation mosaicism: a case study of the River Kamajohka, northernmost Finland, *Journal of Biogeography*, 15, 703-719, 1988.

Kaplinski, M., J. Bennett, J. Cain, J.E. Hazel, M. Manone, R. Parnell, and L.E. Stevens, Fluvial habitats developed on Colorado River sandbars in Grand Canyon, *EOS, Transactions, American Geophysical Union*, v. 79, no. 45, p. F344, 1998.

Karr, J.R., Biological integrity: a long-neglected aspect of water resource management, *Ecological Applications*, 1, 66-84, 1991.

Karr, J.R. and I.J. Schlosser, *Impact of nearstream vegetation and stream morphology on water quality and stream biota*, Report No. EPA-600/3-77-097, USEPA, Athens, Georgia, 1977.

Kasran, B., Effect of logging on sediment yield in a hill Dipterocarp forest in Peninsular Malaysia, *Journal of Tropical Forest Sciences*, 1, 56-66, 1988.

Kattelmann, R., Floods in the high Sierra Nevada, California, USA, in *Hydrology in mountainous regions II. Artificial reservoirs, water and slopes*, edited by R.O. Sinniger and M. Monbaron, pp. 39-46, IAHS Publication no. 194, Wallingford, UK, 1990.

Kattelmann, R., A review of watershed degradation and rehabilitation throughout the Sierra Nevada, in *Watershed restoration management: physical, chemical, and biological considerations*, edited by J.J. McDonell, J.B. Stribling, L.R. Neville and D.J. Leopold, pp. 199-207, Am. Water Resources Association, Herndon, Virginia, 1996.

Kattenberg, A. et al., Climate models - projections of future climate, in *Climate change 1995 - the science of climate change*, edited by J.T. Houghton et al., pp. 285-357, Cambridge University Press, Cambridge, 1996.

Kauffman, J.B. and W.C. Krueger, Livestock impacts on riparian ecosystems and streamside management implications ... a review, *Journal of Range Management*, 37, 430-438, 1984.

Kearney, M.S. and J.C. Stevenson, Island land loss and marsh vertical accretion rate evidence for historical sea-level changes in Chesapeake Bay, *Journal of Coastal Research*, 7, 403-415, 1991.

Keller, E.A., Bed-load movement experiments: Dry Creek, California, *Journal of Sedimentary Petrology*, 40, 1339-1344, 1970.

Keller, E.A., Areal sorting of bedload material, the hypothesis of velocity reversal, *Geological Society of America Bulletin*, 82, 279-280, 1971.

Keller, E.A. and J.L. Florsheim, Velocity-reversal hypothesis: a model approach, *Earth Surface Processes and Landforms*, 18, 733-740, 1993.

Keller, E.A. and W.N. Melhorn, Rhythmic spacing and origin of pools and riffles, *Geological Society of America Bulletin*, 89, 723-730, 1978.

Keller, E.A. and F.J. Swanson, Effects of large organic material on channel form and fluvial processes, *Earth Surface Processes*, 4, 361-380, 1979.

Keller, E.A. and T. Tally, Effects of large organic debris on channel form and fluvial processes in the coastal redwood environment, in *Adjustments of the fluvial system*, edited by D.D. Rhodes and G.P. Williams, pp. 169-197, Kendall/Hunt Publishing Company, Dubuque, Iowa, 1979.

Kellerhals, R. and D.I. Bray, Sampling procedures for coarse fluvial sediments, *ASCE Journal of Hydraulics Division*, 97, 1165-1180, 1971.

Kelsey, H.M., R. Lamberson, and M.A. Madej, Modelling the transport of stored sediment in a gravel bed river, northwestern California, in *Drainage basin sediment delivery*, edited by R.F. Hadley, pp. 367-391, IAHS Publ. no. 15, 1986.

Kendall, C., M.G. Sklash and T.D. Bullen, Isotope tracers of water and solute sources in catchments, in *Solute modelling in catchment systems*, edited by S.T. Trudgill, pp. 261-303, John Wiley and Sons, Chichester, 1995.

Kennedy, J.F., The mechanics of dunes and antidunes in erodible-bed channels, *Journal of Fluid Mechanics*, 16, 521-544, 1963.

Keppeler, E.T., The summer flow and water yield response to timber harvest, in *Proceedings of the conference on coastal watersheds: the Caspar Creek story*, edited by R.R. Ziemer, pp. 35-43, Pacific Southwest Research Station, USDA, Albany, California, 1998.

Keppeler, E.T. and D. Brown, Subsurface drainage processes and management impacts, in *Proceedings of the conference on coastal watersheds: the Caspar Creek story*, edited by R.R. Ziemer, pp. 25-34, Pacific Southwest Research Station, USDA, Albany, California, 1998.

Ketcheson, G.L. and W.F. Megahan, Sediment tracing in step-pool granitic streams in Idaho, in *Proceedings of the Fifth Federal Interagency Sedimentation Conference*, edited by S.-S. Fan and Y.-H. Kuo, pp. 4-147 to 4-154, Las Vegas, Nevada, 1991.

Khosrowshahi, F.B., Sediment transport in mountain streams, in *Hydrology in mountainous regions. II- Artificial reservoirs, water and slopes*, pp. 59-66, IAHS Publ. no. 194, 1990.

Kieffer, S.W., The 1983 hydraulic jump in Crystal Rapid: implications for river-running and geomorphic evolution in the Grand Canyon, *Journal of Geology*, 93, 385-406, 1985.

Kieffer, S.W., The rapids and waves of the Colorado River, Grand Canyon, Arizona, *U.S. Geological Survey Open-File Report 87-096*, 69 pp., 1987.

Kieffer, S.W., Geologic nozzles, *Reviews of Geophysics*, 27, 3-38, 1989.

Kieffer, S.W., J.B. Graf, and J.C. Schmidt, Hydraulics and sediment transport of the Colorado River, in *Geology of the Grand Canyon, northern Arizona*, edited by D.P. Elston, G.H. Billingsley, and R.A. Young, pp. 48-66, Am Geophys Union, Washington, D.C., 1989.

King, T.V.V., ed., Environmental considerations of active and abandoned mine lands: lessons from Summitville, Colorado, *U.S. Geological Survey Bulletin 2220*, 38 pp., 1995.

Kirkbride, A., Observations of the influence of bed roughness on turbulence structure in depth limited flows over gravel beds, in *Turbulence: perspectives on flow and sediment transport*, edited by N.J. Clifford, J.R. French, and J. Hardisty, pp. 185-196, John Wiley and Sons, Chichester, 1993.

Kirkby, M., Hillslope runoff processes and models, *Journal of Hydrology*, 100, 315-339, 1988.

Kirkby, M.J. 1967. Measurement and theory of soil creep. Journal of Geology 75: 359-378.

Kite, J.S. and R.C. Linton, Depositional aspects of the November 1985 flood on Cheat River and Black Fork, West Virginia, in Geomorphic studies of the storm and flood of Nov. 3-5, 1985, in the upper Potomac and Cheat River basins in West Virginia and Virginia, edited by R.B. Jacobson, pp. D1-D24, *U.S. Geological Survey Bulletin 1981*, 1993.

Klaghofer, E. and W. Summer, Estimation of soil erosion from a lower Alpine catchment, in *Hydrology in mountainous regions II. Artificial reservoirs, water and slopes*, edited by R.O. Sinniger and M. Monbaron, pp. 67-74, IAHS Publication no. 194, Wallingford, UK, 1990.

Klein, J.M. and H.E. Taylor, Mount St. Helens, Washington, volcanic eruption; Part 2, Chemical variations in surface waters affected by volcanic activity, *EOS, Am. Geophys. Union Transactions*, 61, 956, 1980.

Klein, R., R. Sonnevil, and D. Short, Effects of woody debris removal on sediment storage in a northwestern California stream, in *Erosion and sedimentation in the Pacific Rim*, edited by R.L. Beschta, T. Blinn, G.E. Grant, G.G. Ice and F.J. Swanson, pp. 403-404, IAHS Publ. no. 165, 1987.

Klemes, V., The modelling of mountain hydrology: the ultimate challenge, in *Hydrology of mountainous areas*, edited by L. Molnar, pp. 29-43, IAHS Publication no. 190, Wallingford, UK, 1990.

Klimek, K., Man's impact on fluvial processes in the Polish Western Carpathians, *Geografiska Annaler*, 69A, 221-225, 1987.

Klingeman, P.C. and R.T. Milhous, Oak Creek vortex bedload sampler, *AGU, 17th Annual Pacific Northwest Regional Meeting*, Tacoma, Washington, 1970.

Knighton, A.D., River adjustment to changes in sediment load: the effects of tin mining on the Ringarooma River, Tasmania, 1875-1984, *Earth Surface Processes and Landforms*, 14, 333-359, 1989.

Knighton, A.D., Downstream variation in stream power, *Geomorphology*, 29, 293-306, 1999.

Knighton, D., *Fluvial forms and processes*, Edward Arnold, London, 218 pp., 1984.

Knighton, D., *Fluvial forms and processes: a new perspective*, Arnold, London, 383 pp., 1998.

Knuepfer, P.L.K., Estimating ages of late Quaternary stream terraces from analysis of weathering rinds and soils, *Geological Society of America Bulletin*, 100, 1224-1236, 1988.

Kobashi, S. and M. Suzuki, The critical rainfall (danger index) for disasters caused by debris flows and slope failures, in *Erosion and sedimentation in the Pacific Rim*, edited by R.L. Beschta, T. Blinn, G.E. Grant, G.G. Ice and F.J. Swanson, pp. 201-211, IAHS Publ. no. 165, 1987.

Kochel, R.C., Holocene debris flows in central Virginia, in *Debris flows/avalanches: process, recognition, and mitigation*, edited by J.E. Costa and G.F. Wieczorek, pp. 139-155, Geological Society of America, Reviews in Engineering Geology, v. 7, Boulder, Colorado, 1987.

Kochel, R.C., Geomorphic impact of large floods: review and new perspectives on magnitude and frequency, in *Flood geomorphology*, edited by V.R. Baker, R.C. Kochel and P.C. Patton, pp. 169-187, John Wiley and Sons, New York, 1988.

Kochel, R.C., R.A. Johnson and S. Valastro, Repeated episodes of Holocene debris avalanching in central Virginia, *Geological Society of America Abstracts with Programs*, 14, 31, 1982.

Kochel, R.C., D.F. Ritter, and J. Miller, Role of tree dams in the construction of pseudo-terraces and variable geomorphic response to floods in Little River Valley, Virginia, *Geology*, 15, 718-721, 1987.

Komar, P.D., Selective grain entrainment by a current from a bed of mixed sizes: a reanalysis, *Journal Sedimentary Petrology*, 57, 203-211, 1987a.

Komar, P.D., Selective grain entrainment and the empirical evaluation of flow competence, *Sedimentology*, 34, 1165-1176, 1987b.

Komar, P.D., Flow-competence evaluation of the hydraulic parameters of floods: an assessment of the technique, in *Floods: hydrological, sedimentological, and geomorphological implications*, edited by K. Beven and P.A. Carling, pp. 107-134, John Wiley and Sons, Chichester, 1989.

Komar, P.D. and P.A. Carling, Grain sorting in gravel-bed streams and the choice of particle sizes for flow-competence evaluations, *Sedimentology*, 38, 489-502, 1991.

Komar, P.D. and Z. Li, Pivoting analyses of the selective entrainment of sediments by shape and size with application to grain threshold, *Sedimentology*, 33, 425-436, 1986.

Komar, P.D. and S.-M. Shih, Equal mobility versus changing bedload grain sizes in gravel-bed streams, in *Dynamics of gravel-bed rivers*, edited by P. Billi, R.D. Hey, C.R. Thorne, and P. Tacconi, pp. 73-106, John Wiley and Sons, Chichester, 1992.

Kondolf, G.M., Lag in stream channel adjustment to livestock exclosure, White Mountains, California, *Restoration Ecology*, 1, 226-230, 1993.

Kondolf, G.M., S.S. Cook, H.R. Maddux, and W.R. Persons, Spawning gravels of rainbow trout in Glen and Grand Canyons, Arizona, *Journal of the Arizona-Nevada Academy of Science*, 23, 19-28, 1989.

Kondolf, G.M., M.J. Sale, and M.G. Wolman, Modification of fluvial gravel size by spawning salmonids, *Water Resources Research*, 29, 2265-2274, 1993.

Kondolf, G.M. and P.R. Wilcock, The flushing flow problem: Defining and evaluating objectives, *Water Resources Research*, 32, 2589-2599, 1996.

Köppen, W., Das geographische system der Klimate, in *Handbuch der Klimatologie*, edited by W. Köppen and R. Geiger, 1. Bornträger, Berlin, 44 pp., 1936.

Koster, E.H., Transverse ribs: their characteristics, origin, and paleohydraulic singificance, in *Fluvial sedimentology*, edited by A.D. Miall, pp. 161-186, Canadian Soc. Petrol. Geologists, 1978.

Kostka, Z. and L. Holko, Problems of the water balance determination in mountainous catchments, in *FRIEND: Flow regimes from international experimental and network data*, edited by P. Senna, A. Gustard, N.W. Arnell, and G.A. Cole, pp. 433-438, IAHS Publication no. 221, Wallingford, UK, 1994.

Krigstrom, A., Geomorphological studies of sandur plains and their braided rivers in Iceland, *Geografiska Annaler*, 44, 328-346, 1962.

Krzyszkowski, D. and R. Stachura, Neotectonically controlled fluvial features, Walbrzych Upland, Middle Sudeten Mountains, southwestern Poland, *Geomorphology*, 22, 73-91, 1998.

Kuhle, M., S. Meiners, and L. Iturrizaga, Glacier-induced hazards as a consequence of glacigenic mountain landscapes, in particular glacier- and moraine-dammed lake outbursts and Holocene debris production, in *Geomorphological hazards in high mountain areas*, edited by J. Kalvoda and C.L. Rosenfeld, pp. 63-96, Kluwer Academic Publishers, The Netherlands, 1998.

Kuhn, T.S., *The structure of scientific revolutions*, The University of Chicago Press, Chicago, 210 pp., 1962.

Kuhnle, R.A., Bed load transport during rising and falling stages on two small streams, *Earth Surface Processes and Landforms*, 17, 191-197, 1992a.

Kuhnle, R.A., Fractional transport rates of bedload on Goodwin Creek, in *Dynamics of gravel-bed rivers*, edited by P. Billi, R.D. Hey, and C.R. Thorne, pp. 141-155, John Wiley and Sons, Chichester, 1992b.

Kuhnle, R.A. and J.B. Southard, Bedload transport fluctuations in a gravel bed laboratory channel, *Water Resources Research*, 24, 247-260, 1988.

Kundzewicz, Z.W., Water resources for sustainable development, *Hydrological Sciences Journal*, 42, 467-480, 1997.

Kurashige, Y., Mechanisms of suspended sediment supply to headwater rivers, *Trans., Japanese Geomorphological Union*, 15A, 109-129, 1994.

Kurashige, Y., Process-based model of grain lifting from river bed to estimate suspended-sediment concentration in a small headwater basin, *Earth Surface Processes and Landforms*, 21, 1163-1173, 1996.

Kurashige, Y., Monitoring of thickness of river-bed sediment in the Pankenai River, Hokkaido, Japan, *Transactions, Japanese Geomorphological Union*, 20, 21-33, 1999.

Laenen, A. and J.C. Risley, Precipitation-runoff and streamflow-routing models for the Willamette River Basin, Oregon, *U.S. Geological Survey Water-Resources Investigations Report 95-4284*, 197 pp., 1997.

Lagasse, P.F., Geomorphic response of the Rio Grande to dam construction, *New Mexico Geological Society, Special Publication No. 10*, p. 27-46, 1981.

Laity, J.E. and M.C. Malin, Sapping processes and the development of theater-headed valley networks on the Colorado Plateau, *Geological Society of America Bulletin*, 96, 203-217, 1985.

Lake, J.S., Fish of the Murray River, in *The book of the Murray*, edited by G.C. Lawrence and G.K. Smith, pp. 213-223, Adelaide, Australia, 1975.

LaMarche, V.C., Jr., Rates of slope degradation as determined from botanical evidence, White Mountains, California, *U.S. Geological Survey Professional Paper 352-I*, 1968.

Lamb, H.R., M. Tranter, G.H. Brown, B.P. Hubbard, M.J. Sharp, S. Gordon, C.C. Smart, I.C. Willis and M.K. Nielsen, The composition of subglacial meltwaters sampled from boreholes at the Haut Glacier d'Arolla, Switzerland, in *Biogeochemistry of seasonally snow-covered catchments*, edited by K.A. Tonnessen, M.W. Williams and M. Tranter, pp. 395-403, IAHS Publ. no. 228, 1995.

Lance, J.C., S.C. McIntyre, J.W. Naney, and S.S. Rousseva, Measuring sediment movement at low erosion rates using Cesium-137, *Soil Science Society of America Journal*, 50, 1303-1309, 1986.

Landers, M.N., J.S. Jones, and R.E. Trent, Brief summary of national bridge scour data base, in *Hydraulic engineering '94*, edited by G.V. Cotroneo and R.R. Rumer, pp. 41-45, Proceedings of the Am. Soc. Civil Engineers Conference, 1994.

Lane, S.N., K.F. Bradbrook, K.S. Richards, P.A. Biron, and A.G. Roy, The application of computational fluid dynamics to natural river channels: three-dimensional versus two-dimensional approaches, *Geomorphology*, 29, 1-20, 1999.

Lang, H. and A. Musy, (eds.), *Hydrology in mountainous regions I. Hydrological measurements; the water cycle*, IAHS Publication no. 193, Wallingford, UK, 810 pp., 1990.

Langbein, W.B. and L.B. Leopold, Quasi-equilibrium states in channel morphology, *American Journal of Science*, 262, 782-794, 1964.

Langbein, W.B. and L.B. Leopold, River meanders - theory of minimum variance, *U.S. Geological Survey Professional Paper 422H*, 15 pp., 1966.

Langbein, W.B. and L.B. Leopold, River channel bars and dunes - theory of kinematic waves, *U.S. Geological Survey Professional Paper 422L*, 1968.

Langbein, W.B. and S.A. Schumm, Yield of sediment in relation to mean annual precipitation, *Transactions, American Geophysical Union*, 39, 1076-1084, 1958.

Lapointe, M.F., Y. Secretan, S.N. Driscoll, N. Bergeron, and M. Leclerc, Response of the Ha!Ha! River to the flood of July 1996 in the Saguenay Region of Quebec: large-scale avulsion in a glaciated valley, *Water Resources Research*, 34, 2382-2392, 1998.

Laronne, J.B. and M.A. Carson, Interrelationships between bed morphology and bed-material transport for a small, gravel-bed channel, *Sedimentology*, 23, 67-85, 1976.

Laronne, J.B. and M.J. Duncan, Bedload transport paths and gravel bar formation, in *Dynamics of gravel-bed rivers*, edited by P. Billi, R.D. Hey, C.R. Thorne and P. Tacconi, pp. 177-202, John Wiley and Sons, Chichester, 1992.

Laronne, J.B., I. Reid, Y. Yitschak, and L.E. Frostick, Recording bedload discharge in a semiarid channel, Nahal Yatir, Israel, in *International Symposium on Erosion and Sediment Transport*

Monitoring Programmes in River Basins, edited by J. Bogen, D.E. Walling, and T. Day, p. 210, IAHS, Oslo, 1992.

Larsen, E.E., W.C. Bradley, and M. Ozima, Development of the Colorado River system in north-western Colorado during the late Cenozoic, in *Canyondlands Country*, edited by J.E. Fassett, pp. 97-102, A Guidebook of the Four Corners Geological Society, 8th Field Conference, Canyonlands, Utah, 1975.

Larsen, M.C. and J.E. Parks, How wide is a road? The association of roads and mass-wasting in a forested montane environment, *Earth Surface Processes and Landforms*, 22, 835-848, 1997.

Larsen, M.C. and A. Simon, A rainfall intensity-duration threshold for landslides in a humid-tropical environment, Puerto Rico, *Geografiska Annaler*, 75A, 13-23, 1993.

Lauer, W., (ed.), *Natural environments and man in tropical mountain ecosystems*, Franz Steiner Verlag, Wiesbaden, 1984.

Lawrence, D.E., Woody debris budgets in 'burn' and 'reference' headwater streams: long-term predictions for debris accumulation processes and geomorphic heterogeneity (abstract), *Bulletin, North American Benthological Society*, 8, 75, 1991.

Leeder, M.R. and P.H. Bridges, Flow separation in meander bends, *Nature*, 253, 338-339, 1975.

Lehre, A.K., Sediment budget of a small California Coast Range drainage basin near San Francisco, in *Erosion and sediment transport in Pacific Rim steeplands*, edited by T.R.H. Davies and A.J. Pierce, pp. 123-139, IAHS Publication no. 132, Wallingford, UK, 1981.

Lekach, J. and A.P. Schick, Suspended sediment in desert floods in small catchments, *Israel Journal of Earth-Sciences*, 31, 144-156, 1982.

Lekach, J. and A.P. Schick, Evidence for transport of bedload in waves: analysis of fluvial sediment samples in a small upland stream channel, *Catena* 10, 267-279, 1983.

Lenzi, M.A., L. Marchi, and G.R. Scussel, Measurement of coarse sediment transport in a small Alpine stream, in *Hydrology in mountainous regions I. Hydrological measurements; the water cycle*, edited by H. Lang and A. Musy, pp. 283-290, IAHS Publication no. 193, Wallingford, UK, 1990.

Leopold, L.B., An improved method for size distribution of stream bed gravel, *Water Resources Research*, 6, 1357-1366, 1970.

Leopold, L.B., Sediment size that determines channel morphology, in *Dynamics of gravel-bed rivers*, edited by P. Billi, R.D. Hey, C.R. Thorne and P. Tacconi, pp. 297-311, John Wiley and Sons, Chichester, 1992.

Leopold, L.B. and W.B. Bull, Base level, aggradation, and grade, *Proceedings, American Philosophical Society*, 123, 168-202, 1979.

Leopold, L.B. and W.W. Emmett, Bedload measurements, East Fork River, Wyoming, *Proceed., National Academy of Sciences, US*, 73, 1000-1004, 1976.

Leopold, L.B., W.W. Emmett, and R.M. Myrick, Channel and hillslope processes in a semiarid area, New Mexico, *U.S. Geological Survey Professional Paper 352-G*, p. 193-243, 1966.

Leopold, L.B. and W.B. Langbein, The concept of entropy in landscape evolution, *U.S. Geological Survey Professional Paper 500-A*, 1962.

Leopold, L.B. and T. Maddock, The hydraulic geometry of stream channels and some physiographic implications, *U.S. Geological Survey Professional Paper 252*, 57 pp., 1953.

Leopold, L.B. and J.P. Miller, Ephemeral streams - hydraulic factors and their relation to the drainage net, *U.S. Geological Survey Professional Paper 282-A*, p. 1-37, 1956.

Leopold, L.B. and M.G. Wolman, River channel patterns - braided, meandering and straight, *U.S. Geological Survey Professional Paper 282B*, p. 39-85, 1957.

Leopold, L.B., M.G. Wolman, and J.P. Miller, *Fluvial processes in geomorphology*, W.H. Freeman and Company, San Francisco, California, 522 pp., 1964.

Lepistö, A., P. Seuna, and L. Bengtsson, The environmental tracer approach in storm runoff studies in forested catchments, in *FRIEND: Flow regimes from international experimental and network data*, edited by P. Seuna, A. Gustard, N.W. Arnell and G.A. Cole, pp. 369-379, IAHS Publication no. 221, Wallingford, UK, 1994.

Lewin, J., Initiation of bed forms and meanders in coarse-grained sediment, *Geological Society of America Bulletin*, 87, 281-285, 1976.

Lewin, J., B.E. Davies, and P.J. Wolfenden, Interactions between channel change and historic mining sediments, in *River channel changes*, edited by K.J. Gregory, pp. 353-367, John Wiley and Sons, Chichester, 1977.

Lewis, J., Evaluating the impacts of logging activities on erosion and suspended sediment transport in the Caspar Creek watersheds, in *Proceedings of the conference on coastal watersheds: the Caspar Creek story*, edited by R.R. Ziemer, pp. 55-69, Pacific Southwest Research Station, USDA, Albany, California, 1998.

Li, R.M., Water and sediment routing from watersheds, in *Modeling of rivers*, edited by H.W. Shen, p. 9-1 to 9-88, John Wiley and Sons, New York, 1979.

Li, Z. and P.D. Komar, Laboratory measurements of pivoting angles for applications to selective entrainment of gravel in a current, *Sedimentology*, 33, 413-423, 1986.

Ligon, F.K., W.E. Dietrich, and W.J. Trush, Downstream ecological effects of dams: a geomorphic perspective, *BioScience*, 45, 183-192, 1995.

Likens, G.E., F.H. Bormann, R.S. Pierce, J.S. Eaton, and N.M. Johnson, *Biogeochemistry of a forested ecosystem*, Springer-Verlag, New York, 146 pp., 1977.

Limbrey, S. 1983. Archaeology and palaeohydrology, in *Background to palaeohydrology: a perspective*, edited by K.J. Gregory, pp. 189-212, John Wiley and Sons, Chichester, 1983.

Limerinos, J.T., Determination of the Manning coefficient from measured bed roughness in natural channels, *U.S. Geological Survey Water Supply Paper 1898-B*, 47 pp., 1970.

Liniger, H., Water and soil resource conservation and utilization on the northwest side of Mount Kenya, *Mountain Research and Development*, 12, 363-373, 1992.

Lisle, T.E., A sorting mechanism for a riffle-pool sequence: summary, *Geological Society of America Bulletin*, 90, 616-617, 1979.

Lisle, T.E., Effects of aggradation and degradation on riffle-pool morphology in natural gravel channels, northwestern California, *Water Resources Research*, 18, 1643-1651, 1982.

Lisle, T.E., Stabilization of a gravel channel by large streamside obstructions and bedrock bends, Jacoby Creek, northwestern California, *Geological Society of America Bulletin*, 97, 999-1011, 1986.

Lisle, T.E., Overview: channel morphology and sediment transport in steepland streams, in *Erosion and sedimentation in the Pacific Rim*, edited by R.L. Beschta, T. Blinn, G.E. Grant, G.G. Ice and F.J. Swanson, pp. 287-297, Proceedings of the Corvallis Symp, Aug. 1987, IAHS Publ. no. 165, 1987.

Lisle, T.E., Particle size variations between bed load and bed material in natural gravel bed channels, *Water Resources Research*, 31, 1107-1118, 1995.

Lisle, T.E. and S. Hilton, The volume of fine sediment in pools: an index of sediment supply in gravel-bed streams, *Water Resources Bulletin*, 28, 371-383, 1992.

Lisle, T.E. and S. Hilton, Fine bed material in pools of natural gravel bed channels, *Water Resources Research*, 35, 1291-1304, 1999.

Lisle, T.E., H. Ikeda, and F. Iseya, Formation of stationary alternate bars in a steep channel with mixed-size sediment: a flume experiment, *Earth Surface Processes and Landforms*, 16, 463-469, 1991.

Lisle, T.E. and M.A. Madej, Spatial variation in armouring in a channel with high sediment supply, in *Dynamics of gravel-bed rivers*, edited by P. Billi, R.D. Hey, C.R. Thorne and P. Tacconi, pp. 277-293, John Wiley and Sons, Chichester, 1992.

Lisle, T.E. and M.B. Napolitano, Effects of recent logging on the main channel of North Fork Caspar Creek, in *Proceedings of the conference on coastal watersheds: the Caspar Creek story*, edited by R.R. Ziemer, pp. 81-85, Pacific Southwest Research Station, USDA, Albany, California, 1998.

Lisle, T.E., J.E. Pizzuto, H. Ikeda, F. Iseya and Y. Kodama, Evolution of a sediment wave in an experimental channel, *Water Resources Research*, 33, 1971-1981, 1997.

Liu, C.-M., The effectivness of check dams in controlling upstream channel stability in northeastern Taiwan, in *Erosion, debris flows and environment in mountain regions*, edited by D.E. Walling, T.R. Davies, and B. Hasholt, pp. 423-428, IAHS Publ. no. 209, Wallingford, United Kingdom, 1992.

Lliboutry, L., B.M. Arnao, A. Pautre, and B. Schneider, Glaciological problems set by the control of dangerous lakes in Cordillera Blanca, Peru: I. Historical failures of morainic dams, their causes and prevention, *Journal of Glaciology*, 18, 239-254, 1977.

Lock, M.A., R.R. Wallace, J.W. Costerton, R.M. Ventullo, and S.E. Charton, River epilithon: toward a structural-functional model, *Oikos*, 42, 10-22, 1984.

Loughran, R.J. and B.L. Campbell, The identification of catchment sediment sources, in *Sediment and water quality in river catchments*, edited by I. Foster, A. Gurnell, and B. Webb, pp. 189-205, John Wiley and Sons, Chichester, 1995.

Luce, C.H. and T.A. Black, Sediment production from forest roads in western Oregon, *Water Resources Research*, 35, 2561-2570, 1999.

Lugt, H.J., *Vortex flow in nature and technology*, Wiley and Sons, New York, 297 pp., 1983.

Lustig, L.K., Sediment yield of the Castaic watershed, western Los Angeles County, California - a quantitative geomorphic approach, *U.S. Geological Survey Professional Paper 422-F*, 23 pp., 1965.

Lvovich, M.I. and G.M. Chernogaeva, The water balance of Moscow, in *Effects of urbanization and industrialization on the hydrological regime and on water quality*, pp. 48-51, IAHS Publ. No. 123, 1977.

MacDonald, L.H., D.M. Anderson, and W.E. Dietrich, Paradise threatened: land use and erosion on St. John, U.S. Virgin Islands, *Environmental Management*, 21, 851-863, 1997.

MacDonald, L.H. and J.A. Hoffman, Causes of peak flows in northwestern Montana and northeastern Idaho, *Water Resources Bulletin*, 31, 79-86, 1995.

MacGregor, K.C., R.S. Anderson, S.P. Anderson and E.D. Waddington, Glacially driven evolution of long valley profiles and implications for alpine landscape evolution, *EOS, Transactions, Am. Geophysical Union*, 79, F337, 1998.

Mackenthun, K.M. and W.M. Ingram, Pollution and life in the water, in *Organism-substrate relationships in streams*, edited by K.W. Cummins, C.A. Tryon, and R.T. Hartman, pp. 136-145, Special Publication No. 4, Pymatuning Laboratory of Ecology, University of Pittsburgh, 1966.

Mackin, J.H., Concept of the graded river, *Geological Society of America Bulletin*, 59, 463-512, 1948.

Madej, M.A. and V. Ozaki, Channel response to sediment wave propagation and movement, Redwood Creek, California, USA, *Earth Surface Processes and Landforms*, 21, 911-927, 1996.

Madsen, S.W., *Channel response associated with predicted water and sediment yield increases in northwestern Montana*, Unpublished MS thesis, Colorado State University, Ft. Collins, 230 pp., 1995.

Magilligan, F.J., Thresholds and the spatial variability of flood power during extreme floods, *Geomorphology*, 5, 373-390, 1992.

Maizels, J.K., Palaeovelocity and palaeodischarge determination for coarse gravel deposits, in *Background to palaeohydrology*, edited by K.J. Gregory, pp. 101-139, John Wiley and Sons, Chichester, 1983.

Maizels, J., Sedimentology and palaeohydrology of Holocene flood deposits in front of a jökulhlaup glacier, South Iceland, in *Floods: Hydrological, Sedimentological and Geomorphological Implications*, edited by K. Beven and P. Carling, pp. 239-251, John Wiley and Sons, Chichester, 1989.

Major, J.J., T.C. Pierson and R.L. Dinehart, Sediment yield following severe volcanic disturbance — two-decade perspective from Mount St. Helens, *Geological Society of America, 1999 Annual Meeting, Abstracts with Programs*, 31, A-200, 1999.

Malanson, G.P. and D.R. Butler, Woody debris, sediment, and riparian vegetation of a subalpine river, Montana, USA, *Arctic and Alpine Research*, 22, 183-194, 1990.

Malanson, G.P. and D.R. Butler, Floristic variation among gravel bars in a subalpine river, Montana, USA, *Arctic and Alpine Research*, 23, 273-278, 1991.

Marchand, J.P., R.D. Jarrett, and L.L. Jones, Velocity profile, water-surface slope, and bed-material size for selected streams in Colorado, *U.S. Geological Survey Open-File Report 84-733*, 1984.

Marcus, W.A., S.C. Ladd, J.A. Stoughton, and J.W. Stock, Pebble counts and the role of user-dependent bias in documenting sediment size distribution, *Water Resources Research*, 31, 2625-2631, 1995.

Marcus, W.A., K. Roberts, L. Harvey, and G. Tackman, An evaluation of methods for estimating Manning's n in small mountain streams, *Mountain Research and Development*, 12, 227-239, 1992.

Margalef, R., Ideas for a synthetic approach to the ecology of running waters, *Int. Rev. Gesamten Hydrobiol.*, 45, 133-153, 1960.

Marinucci, M.R., F. Giorgi, M. Benitson, M. Wild, P. Tschuck, and A. Bernasconi, High resolution simulation of January and July climate over the western Alpine region with a nested regional modeling system, *Theoretical and Applied Climatology*, 51, 119-138, 1995.

Mark, R.K., Map of debris-flow probability, San Mateo County, California, *U.S. Geological Survey Miscellaneous Investigations Series Map I-1257-M*, 1992.

Markham, A. and G. Day, Sediment transport in the Fly River basin, Papua New Guinea, in *Variability in stream erosion and sediment transport*, edited by L.J. Olive, R.J. Loughran and J.A. Kesby, pp. 233-239, IAHS Publication no. 224, Wallingford, UK, 1994.

Marlow, C.B. and T.M. Pogacnik, Time of grazing and cattle-induced damage to streambanks, in *Riparian ecosystems and their management; reconciling conflicting uses*, pp. 279-284, First North American Riparian Conference, Tucson, Arizona, USDA Forest Service General Technical Report RM-120, 1985.

Marron, D.C., Colluvium in bedrock hollows on steep slopes, Redwood Creek drainage basin, northwestern California, in *Soils and geomorphology*, edited by P.D. Jungerius, pp. 59-68, Catena Supplement 6, Braunschweig, 1985.

Martinez-Castroviejo, R., Advances in fluvial geomorphology of mountain environments, *Pirineos*, 132, 65-88, 1988.

Mast, M.A., C. Kendall, D.H. Campbell, D.W. Clow and J. Back, Determination of hydrologic pathways in an alpine-subalpine basin using isotopic and chemical tracers, Loch Vale watershed, Colorado, USA, in *Biogeochemistry of seasonally snow-covered catchments*, edited by K.A. Tonnessen, M.W. Williams and M. Tranter, pp. 263-270, IAHS Publ. no. 228, 1995.

Matthes, G.H., Macroturbulence in natural stream flow, *Transactions, American Geophysical Union*, 28, 255-265, 1947.

McCabe, G.J., Jr. and L.E. Hay, Hydrological effects of hypothetical climate change in the East River basin, Colorado, USA, *Hydrological Sciences Journal*, 40, 303-318, 1995.

McClain, M.E., G. Pinay, and R.M. Holmes, Contrasting biogeochemical cycles of riparian forests in temperate, wet tropical, and arid regions, *Ecological Society of America, 1999 Annual Meeting Abstracts*, p. 26, 1999.

McDonnell, J.J., M.K. Stewart and I.F. Owens, Effect of catchment-scale subsurface mixing on stream isotopic response, *Water Resources Research*, 27, 3065-3073, 1991.

McLean, S.R. and J.D. Smith, Turbulence measurements in the boundary layer over a sand wave field, *Journal of Geophysical Research*, 84, 7791-7808, 1979.

McLeay, D.J., I.K. Birtwell, G.F. Hartman, and G.L. Ennis, Responses of Arctic grayling (*Thymallus arcticus*) to acute and prolonged exposure to Yukon placer mining sediment, *Canadian Journal of Fisheries and Aquatic Sciences*, 44, 658-673, 1987.

McNeil, W.J., Effect of the spawning bed environment on reproduction of pink and chum salmon, *U.S. Fish and Wildlife Service Bulletin*, 65, 495-523, 1966.

Meade, R.H., T. Dunne, J.E. Richey, U. deM. Santos, and E. Salati, Storage and remobilization of suspended sediment in the lower Amazon River of Brazil, *Science*, 228, 488-490, 1985.

Megahan, W.F. and C.C. Bohn, Progressive, long-term slope failure following road construction and logging on noncohesive, granitic soils of the Idaho Batholith, in *Headwaters Hydrology*, pp. 501-510, American Water Resources Association, 1989.

Megahan, W.F. and W.J. Kidd, Effects of logging and logging roads on erosion and sediment deposition from steep terrain, *Journal of Forestry*, 70, 136-141, 1972.

Mei-e, R. and Z. Xianmo, Anthropogenic influences on changes in the sediment load of the Yellow River, China, during the Holocene, *The Holocene*, 4, 314-320, 1994.

Meigs, A., Bedrock landsliding accompanying deglaciation: three possible examples from the Chugach/St. Elias Range, Alaska, *EOS, Transactions, Am. Geophysical Union*, 79, F337, 1998.

Mejia-Navarro, M. and E.E. Wohl, Geological hazard and risk evaluation using GIS: methodology and model applied to Medellín, Colombia, *Bulletin of the Association of Engineering Geologists*, 31, 459-481, 1994.

Mejia-Navarro, M., E.E. Wohl, and S.D. Oaks, Geological hazards, vulnerability, and risk assessment using GIS: model for Glenwood Springs, Colorado, *Geomorphology*, 10, 331-354, 1994.

Meko, D.M., Inferences from tree rings on low frequency variations in runoff in the Interior Western United States, in *Proceedings Sixth Annual Pacific Climate Workshop*, edited by J.L. Betancourt and A.M. MacKay, pp. 123-127, March 5-8, 1989. CA Dept of Water Resources, Interagency Ecological Studies Program Tech Rep 23, 1990.

Melack, J.M. and J.O. Sickman, Snowmelt induced chemical changes in seven streams in the Sierra Nevada, California, in *Biogeochemistry of seasonally snow-covered catchments*, edited by K.A. Tonnessen, M.W. Williams and M. Tranter, pp. 221-234, IAHS Publ. no. 228, 1995.

Meleason, M.A., S.V. Gregory, and J.P. Bolte, Simulation of large-wood dynamics in small streams of the Pacific Northwest, *Ecological Society of America, 1999 Annual Meeting Abstracts*, p. 147, 1999.

Melis, T.S., R.H. Webb, P.G. Griffiths, and T.W. Wise, Magnitude and frequency data for historic debris flows in Grand Canyon National Park and vicinity, Arizona, *U.S. Geological Survey Water-Resources Investigations Report 94-4214*, 285 pp., 1995.

Melosh, H.J., The mechanics of large rock avalanches, in *Debris flows/avalanches: process, recognition, and mitigation*, edited by J.E. Costa and G.F. Wieczorek, pp. 41-49, Geological Society of America, Reviews in Engineering Geology, v. 7, Boulder, Colorado, 1987.

Melton, M.A., Intravalley variation in slope angles related to microclimate and erosional environment, *Geological Society of America Bulletin*, 71, 133-144, 1960.

Menges, E.S. and D.M. Waller, Plant strategies in relation to elevation and light in floodplain herbs, *The American Naturalist*, 122, 454-473, 1983.

Merefield, J.R., Sediment mineralogy and the environmental impact of mining, in *Sediment and water quality in river catchments*, edited by I. Foster, A. Gurnell, and B. Webb, pp. 145-160, John Wiley and Sons, Chichester, 1995.

Merritt, D. M.., *The effects of mountain reservoir operations on the distributions and dispersal mechanisms of riparian plants, Colorado Front Range*, unpublished Ph.D. dissertation, Colorado State University, Fort Collins, CO, 160 pp., 1999.

Merritts, D.J. and M. Ellis, Introduction to special section on tectonics and topography, *Journal of Geophysical Research*, 99 (B6), 12,135-12,141, 1994.

Merritts, D.J. and K.R. Vincent, Geomorphic response of coastal streams to low, intermediate, and high rates of uplift, Mendocino triple junction region, northern California, *Geological Society of America Bulletin*, 100, 1373-1388, 1989.

Merritts, D.J., K.R. Vincent, and E.E. Wohl, Long river profiles, tectonisim, and eustasy: a guide to interpreting fluvial terraces, *Journal of Geophysical Research*, 99 (B7), 14,031-14,050, 1994.

Mertes, L.A.K., Documentation and significance of the perirheic zone on inundated floodplains, *Water Resources Research*, 33, 1749-1762, 1997.

Messerli, B. and J.D. Ives, *Mountain ecosystems: stability and instability*, International Mountain

Society, Boulder, Colorado, 1984.

Messerli, B. and J.D. Ives, (eds.), *Mountains of the world: a global priority*, The Parthenon Publishing Group, London, 1997.

Meyer, G.A. and P.M. Watt, Hydrological controls on the geomorphic and ecological impacts of a tailings dam-break flood on Soda Butte Creek, Montana and Yellowstone National Park, *Geological Society of America, 1999 Annual Meeting, Abstracts with Programs*, 31, A-253, 1999.

Meyer-Peter, E. and R. Müller, Formulas for bed load transport, in *Report on second meeting of the International Association of Hydraulic Structures Research*, pp. 39-64, Stockholm, Sweden, 1948.

Michalik, A. and W. Bartnik, An attempt at determination of incipient bed load motion in mountain streams, in *Dynamics and geomorphology of mountain rivers*, edited by P. Ergenzinger and K.-H. Schmidt, pp. 289-299, Springer-Verlag, Berlin, 1994.

Middleton, G.V. and J.B. Southard, *Mechanics of sediment movement*, SEPM Short Course No. 3, Providence, Rhode Island, 401 pp., 1984.

Mikos, M., The downstream fining of gravel-bed sediments in the Alpine Rhine River, in *Dynamics and geomorphology of mountain rivers*, edited by P. Ergenzinger and K.-H. Schmidt, pp. 93-108, Springer-Verlag, Berlin, 1994.

Milhous, R.T., *Sediment transport in a gravel-bottomed stream*, Unpublished PhD dissertation, Oregon State University, Corvallis, 232 pp., 1973.

Milhous, R.T., Effect of sediment transport and flow regulation on the ecology of gravel-bed rivers, in *Gravel-bed rivers*, edited by R.D. Hey, C.R. Thorne, and J.C. Bathurst, pp. 819-841, John Wiley and Sons, Chichester, 1982.

Millar, R.G. and M.C. Quick, Flow resistance of high-gradient gravel channels, in *Hydraulic engineering '94*, edited by G.V. Cotroneo and R.R. Rumer, pp. 717-721, Proceed of the 1994 Conf, Hydraul Div, ASCE, New York, 1994.

Miller, A.J., Flood hydrology and geomorphic effectiveness in the central Appalachians, *Earth Surface Processes and Landforms*, 15, 119-134, 1990a.

Miller, A.J., Fluvial response to debris associated with mass wasting during extreme floods, *Geology*, 18, 599-602, 1990b.

Miller, A.J., Debris-fan constrictions and flood hydraulics in river canyons: some implications from two-dimensional flow modelling, *Earth Surface Processes and Landforms*, 19, 681-697, 1994.

Miller, A.J., Valley morphology and boundary conditions influencing spatial variations of flood flow, in *Natural and anthropogenic influences in fluvial geomorphology*, edited by J.E. Costa, A.J. Miller, K.W. Potter and P.R. Wilcock, pp. 57-81, Geophysical Monograph 89, American Geophysical Union, Washington, D.C., 1995.

Miller, A.J. and B.L. Cluer, Modeling considerations for simulation of flow in bedrock channels, in *Rivers over rock: fluvial processes in bedrock channels*, edited by K.J. Tinkler and E.E. Wohl, pp. 61-104, American Geophysical Union Geophysical Monograph 107, 1998.

Miller, A.J. and D.J. Parkinson, Flood hydrology and geomorphic effects on river channels and floodplains: the flood of November 4-5, 1985, in the South Branch Potomac River basin of West Virginia, in Geomorphic studies of the storm and flood of November 3-4, 1985, in the Upper Potomac and Cheat River Basins in West Virginia and Virginia, edited by R.B. Jacobson, pp. E1-E96, *U.S. Geological Survey Bulletin 1981*, 1993.

Miller, E.K., C.D. Carson, A.J. Friedland and J.D. Blum, Chemical and isotopic tracers of snowmelt flowpaths in a subalpine watershed, in *Biogeochemistry of seasonally snow-covered catchments*, edited by K.A. Tonnessen, M.W. Williams and M. Tranter, pp. 349-353, IAHS Publ. no. 228, 1995.

Miller, J., R. Barr, D. Grow, P. Lechler, D. Richardson, K. Waltman, and J. Warwick, Effects of the 1997 flood on the transport and storage of sediment and mercury within the Carson River Valley, west-central Nevada, *Journal of Geology*, 107, 313-327, 1999.

Miller, J.R., The influence of bedrock geology on knickpoint development and channel-bed degradation along downcutting streams in south-central Indiana, *Journal of Geology*, 99, 591-605, 1991.

Miller, J.R. and J.B. Ritter, An examination of the Rosgen classification of natural rivers: Discussion, *Catena*, 27, 295-299, 1996.

Miller, R.A., J. Troxell, and L.B. Leopold, Hydrology of two small river basins in Pennsylvania before urbanization, *U.S. Geological Survey Professional Paper 701-A*, 57 pp., 1971.

Miller, T.E., Geologic and hydrologic controls on karst and cave development in Belize, *Journal of Cave and Karst Studies*, 58, 100-120, 1996.

Miller, W.R. and J.I. Drever, Chemical weathering and related controls on surface water chemistry in the Absaroka Mountains, Wyoming, *Geochimica Cosmochimica Acta*, 41, 1693-1702, 1977.

Milliman, J.D. and J.P.M. Syvitski, Geomorphic/tectonic control of sediment discharge to the ocean: the importance of small mountainous rivers, *Journal of Geology*, 100, 525-544, 1992.

Mills, H.H., Hollow form as a function of boulder size in the Valley and Ridge province, southwestern Virginia, *Geology*, 17, 595-598, 1989.

Milner, A.M., System recovery, in *The rivers handbook*, edited by P. Calow and G.E. Petts, v. 2, pp. 76-97, Blackwell Scientific Publications, Oxford, UK,, 1994.

Milner, N.J., J. Scullion, P.A. Carling, and D.T. Crisp, The effects of discharge on sediment dynamics and consequent effects on invertebrates and salmonids in upland rivers, in *Advances in applied biology*, edited by T.H. Coaker, v. 6, pp. 153-220, Academic Press, London, 1991.

Mimikou, M.A., P.S. Hadjisavva, and Y.S. Kouvopoulos, Regional effects of climate change on water resources systems, in *Hydrology for the water management of large river basins*, edited by F.H.M. Van de Ven et al., pp. 173-182, IAHS Publication no. ——, Wallingford, UK, 1991.

Minshall, G.W., Stream ecosystem theory: a global perspective, *Journal North American Benthological Society*, 7, 263-288, 1988.

Minshall, G.W., K.W. Cummins, R.C. Petersen, C.E. Cushing, D.A. Bruns, J.R. Sedell, and R.L. Vannote, Developments in stream ecosystem theory, *Canadian Journal of Fisheries and Aquatic Sciences*, 42, 1045-1055, 1985.

Minshall, G.W., R.C. Peterson, K.W. Cummins, T.L. Bott, J.R. Sedell, C.E. Cushing, and R.L. Vannote, Interbiome comparison of stream ecosystem dynamics, *Ecological Monographs*, 53, 1-25, 1983.

Mitchell, D.K. and F.J. Pazzaglia, A field-based test of the stream power incision law, *Geological Society of America, 1999 Annual Meeting, Abstracts with Programs*, 31, A-255, 1999.

Miyabuchi, Y. and F. Nakamura, Seasonal variation of erosion processes at the headwater basin of Oboppu River in Tarumae Volcano, Hokkaido, *Trans., Japanese Geomorphological Union*, 12, 367-377, 1991.

Mizutani, T., Drainage basin characteristics affecting sediment discharge from steep mountain basins, in *Erosion and sedimentation in the Pacific Rim*, edited by R.L. Beschta, T. Blinn, G.E. Grant, G.G. Ice, and F.J. Swanson, pp. 397-398, Proceed of the Corvallis Symp, Aug. 1987, IAHS Publ. no. 165, 1987.

Mizuyama, T., Sediment yield and river bed change in mountain rivers, in *Fluvial hydraulics of mountain regions*, edited by A. Armanini and G. DiSilvio, pp. 147-161, Springer-Verlag, Berlin, 1991.

Mizuyama, T., Structural and non-structural debris-flow countermeasures, in *Hydraulic engineering '93*, edited by H.W. Shen, S.T. Su and F. Wen, pp. 1914-1919, ASCE, 1993.

Mizuyama, T., S. Kobashi, and G. Ou, Prediction of debris flow peak discharge, *International Symposium, Interpraevent 1992-Bern*, p. 99-108, 1992.

Mizuyama, T., K. Kosugi, I. Sato, and S. Kobashi, Runoff through underground pipes in hollows, in *Proceedings of the International Symposium on Forest Hydrology*, pp. 233-240, Tokyo, Japan, Oct. 1994, 1994.

Mizuyama, T., A. Yazawa, A. and K. Ido, Computer simulation of debris flow deposit processes, in *Erosion and sedimentation in the Pacific Rim*, edited by R.L. Beschta, T. Blinn, G.E. Grant, G.G. Ice and F.J. Swanson, pp. 179-190, IAHS Publ. no. 165, 1987.

Moldan, B. and J. Cerny, Small catchment research, in *Biogeochemistry of small catchments: a tool for environmental research*, edited by B. Moldan and J. Cerny, pp. 1-29, John Wiley and Sons, Chichester, 1994.

Mollo-Christensen, E., Physics of turbulent flow, *AIAA Journal*, 9, 1217-1228, 1971.

Molnar, L., (ed.), *Hydrology of mountain areas*, IAHS Publ. no. 190, Wallingford, UK, 452 pp., 1990.

Montgomery, D.R., Valley incision and the uplift of mountain peaks, *Journal of Geophysical Research*, 99 (B7), 13,913-13,921, 1994.

Montgomery, D.R., T.B. Abbe, J.M. Buffington, N.P. Peterson, K.M. Schmidt, and J.D. Stock, Distribution of bedrock and alluvial channels in forested mountain drainage basins, *Nature*, 381, 587-589, 1996a.

Montgomery, D.R. and J.M. Buffington, Channel-reach morphology in mountain drainage basins, *Geological Society of America Bulletin*, 109, 596-611, 1997.

Montgomery, D.R., J.M. Buffington, N.P. Peterson, D. Schuett-Hames, and T.P. Quinn, Stream-bed scour, egg burial depths, and the influence of salmonid spawning on bed surface mobility and embryo survival, *Canadian Journal of Fisheries and Aquatic Sciences*, 53, 1061-1070, 1996b.

Montgomery, D.R., J.M. Buffington, R.D. Smith, K.M. Schmidt, and G. Pess, Pool spacing in forest channels, *Water Resources Research*, 31, 1097-1105, 1995.

Montgomery, D.R. and W.E. Dietrich, Where do channels begin?, *Nature*, 336, 232-234, 1988.

Montgomery, D.R. and W.E. Dietrich, Source areas, drainage density, and channel initiation, *Water Resources Research*, 25, 1907-1918, 1989.

Montgomery, D.R. and W.E. Dietrich, Channel initiation and the problem of landscape scale, *Science*, 255, 826-830, 1992.

Montgomery, D.R. and W.E. Dietrich, A physically based model for the topographic control on shallow landsliding, *Water Resources Research*, 30, 1153-1171, 1994a.

Montgomery, D.R. and W.E. Dietrich, Landscape dissection and drainage area-slope thresholds, in *Process models and theoretical geomorphology*, edited by M.J. Kirkby, pp. 221-246, John Wiley and Sons, Chichester, 1994b.

Montgomery, D.R., G.E. Grant, and K. Sullivan, Watershed analysis as a framework for implementing ecosystem management, *Water Resources Bulletin*, 31, 369-386, 1995.

Montgomery, D.R., M.S. Panfil, and S.K. Hayes, Channel-bed mobility response to extreme sediment loading at Mount Pinatubo, *Geology*, 27, 271-274, 1999.

Montgomery, D.R., R.H. Wright, and T. Booth, Debris flow hazard mitigation for colluvium-filled swales, *Bulletin of the Association of Engineering Geologists*, 28, 303-323, 1991.

Moog, D.B. and P.J. Whiting, Annual hysteresis in bed load rating curves, *Water Resources Research*, 34, 2393-2399, 1998.

Moon, B.P. and M.J. Selby, Rock mass strength and scarp forms in southern Africa, *Geografiska Annaler*, 65A, 135-145, 1983.

Moore, N. and P. Diplas, Effects of particle shape on bedload transport, in *Hydraulic engineering '94*, edited by G.V. Cotroneo and R.R. Rumer, pp. 800-804, Proceed of the 1994 Conf, Hydraul Div., ASCE, New York, 1994.

Morisawa, M., *Rivers: form and processes*, Longman, London, 222 pp., 1985.

Morisawa, M.E., Quantitative geomorphology of some watersheds in the Appalachian Plateau, *Geological Society of America Bulletin*, 73, 1025-1046, 1962.

Morisawa, M. and E. LaFlure, Hydraulic geometry, stream equilibrium, and urbanization, in *Adjustments of the fluvial system*, edited by D.D. Rhodes and G.P. Williams, pp. 333-350, George Allen and Unwin, London, 1979.

Morrice, J.A., H.M. Valett, C.N. Dahm, and M.E. Campana, Alluvial characteristics, groundwater-surface water exchange and hydrological retention in headwater streams, *Hydrological Processes*, 11, 253-267, 1997.

Morris, S.E., The significance of rainsplash in the surficial debris cascade of the Colorado Front Range foothills, *Earth Surface Processes and Landforms*, 11, 11-22, 1986.

Moschen, H., Overflow weirs as gauging stations in mountain brooks, in *Hydrology in mountain-*

ous regions I. Hydrological measurements; the water cycle, edited by H. Lang and A. Musy, pp. 291-298, IAHS Publication no. 193, Wallingford, UK, 1990.

Mosley, M.P., Rainsplash and the convexity of badland divides, *Zeitschrift für Geomorphologie*, 18, 10-25, 1973.

Mosley, M.P., Erosion in the southeastern Ruahine Range; its implications for downstream river control, *New Zealand Journal of Forestry*, 23, 21-48, 1978.

Mosley, M.P. and D.S. Tindale, Sediment variability and bed material sampling in gravel-bed rivers, *Earth Surface Processes and Landforms*, 10, 465-482, 1985.

Moss, A.J., The physical nature of the common sandy and pebbly deposits. Part II, *American Journal of Science*, 261, 297-343, 1963.

Moss, A.J., Bed-load sediments, *Sedimentology*, 18, 159-219, 1972.

Moss, J.H., The relation of river terrace formation to glaciation in the Shoshone River basin, western Wyoming, in *Glacial geomorphology*, edited by D.R. Coates, pp. 293-314, State University of New York at Binghamton, Publications in Geomorphology, 1974.

Moss, J.H. and W.E. Bonini, Seismic evidence supporting a new interpretation of the Cody Terrace near Cody, Wyoming, *Geological Society of America Bulletin*, 72, 547-556, 1961.

Mountain Agenda, *Mountains of the world: challenges for the 21st century*, A contribution to chapter 13, Agenda 21, Paul Haupt Verlag, Switzerland, 36 pp., 1997.

Murphy, M.L. and J.D. Hall, Varied effects of clear-cut logging on predators and their habitat in small streams of the Cascade Mountains, Oregon, *Canadian Journal of Fisheries and Aquatic Sciences*, 38, 137-145, 1981.

Mussetter, R.A., M.D. Harvey and R.D. Tenney, Geologic and geomorphic associations with Colorado pikeminnow spawning, lower Yampa River, Colorado, *Geological Society of America, 1999 Annual Meeting, Abstracts with Programs*, 31, A-483, 1999.

Myers, T.J. and S. Swanson, Aquatic habitat condition index, stream type, and livestock bank damage in northern Nevada, *Water Resources Bulletin*, 27, 667-677, 1991.

Myers, T.J. and S. Swanson, Variation of stream stability with stream type and livestock bank damage in northern Nevada, *Water Resources Bulletin*, 28, 743-754, 1992.

Myers, T.J. and S. Swanson, Long-term aquatic habitat restoration: Mahogany Creek, Nevada, as a case study, *Water Resources Bulletin*, 32, 241-252, 1996a.

Myers, T.J. and S. Swanson, Temporal and geomorphic variations of stream stability and morphology: Mahogany Creek, Nevada, *Water Resources Bulletin*, 32, 253-265, 1996b.

Nadler, C.T. and S.A. Schumm, Metamorphosis of South Platte and Arkansas Rivers, eastern Colorado, *Physical Geography*, 2, 95-115, 1981.

Naef, F. and G.R. Bezzola, Hydrology and morphological consequences of the 1987 flood event in the upper Reuss valley, in *Hydrology in mountainous regions II. Artificial reservoirs, water and slopes*, edited by R.O. Sinniger and M. Monbaron, pp. 339-346, IAHS Publication no. 194, Wallingford, UK, 1990.

Naef, F., P. Horat, A.G. Milnes, and E. Hoehn, Anomalous hydrological behaviour of an Alpine stream (Varuna, Poschiavo, southern Switzerland) and its interpretation in terms of the geology of the catchment, in *Hydrology in mountainous regions II. Artificial reservoirs, water and slopes*, edited by R.O Sinniger and M. Monbaron, pp. 347-354, IAHS Publication no. 194, Wallingford, UK, 1990.

Naiman, R.J. and H. DéCamps, The ecology of interfaces: riparian zones, *Annual Review of Ecology and Systematics*, 28, 621-658, 1997.

Naiman, R.J., C.A. Johnston, and J.C. Kelley, Alteration of North American streams by beaver, *BioScience*, 38, 753-762, 1988.

Naiman, R.J., D.G. Lonzarich, T.J. Beechie, and S.C. Ralph, General principles of classification and the assessment of conservation potential in rivers, in *River conservation and management*, edited by P.J. Boon, P. Calow and G.E. Petts, pp. 93-123, John Wiley and Sons, Chichester, 1992.

Naiman, R.J., J.M. Melillo, and J.E. Hobbie, Ecosystem alteration of boreal forest streams by beaver *(Castor canadensis)*, *Ecology*, 67, 1254-1269, 1986.

Naiman, R.J. and J.R. Sedell, Relationships between metabolic parameters and stream order in Oregon, *Canadian Journal of Fisheries and Aquatic Sciences*, 37, 834-847, 1979.

Nakagawa, H., T. Tsujimoto, and Y. Shimizu, Turbulent flow with small relative submergence, in *Fluvial hydraulics of mountain regions*, edited by A. Armanini and G. DiSilvio, pp. 33-44, Springer-Verlag, Berlin, 1991.

Nakamura, F., T. Araya, and S. Higashi, Influence of river channel morphology and sediment production on residence time and transport distance, in *Erosion and sedimentation in the Pacific Rim*, edited by R.L. Beschta, T. Blinn, G.E. Grant, G.G. Ice, and F.J. Swanson, pp. 355-364, IAHS Publ. no. 165, 1987.

Nakamura, F., H. Maita, and T. Araya, Sediment routing analyses based on chronological changes in hillslope and riverbed morphologies, *Earth Surface Processes and Landforms*, 20, 333-346, 1995.

Nakamura, F. and F.J. Swanson, Effects of coarse woody debris on morphology and sediment storage of a mountain stream system in western Oregon, *Earth Surface Processes and Landforms*, 18, 43-61, 1993.

Nakano, S., K. Maekawa, and S. Yamamoto, Change of the life cycle of Japanese charr following artificial lake construction by damming, *Nippon Suisan Gakkaishi*, 56, 1901-1905, 1990.

Nanson, G.C., Bedload and suspended-load transport in a small, steep mountain stream, *American Journal of Science*, 274, 471-486, 1974.

Nanson, G.C. and H.F. Beach, Forest succession and sedimentation on a meandering-river floodplain, northeastern British Columbia, Canada, *Journal of Biogeography*, 4, 229-251, 1977.

Nanson, G.C. and R.W. Young, Downstream reduction of rural channel size with contrasting urban effects in small coastal streams of southeastern Australia, *Journal of Hydrology*, 52, 239-255, 1981.

Napolitano, M.B., Persistence of historical logging impacts on channel form in mainstem North Fork Caspar Creek, in *Proceedings of the conference on coastal watersheds: the Caspar Creek story*, edited by R.R. Ziemer, pp. 97-101, Pacific Southwest Research Station, USDA, Albany, California, 1998.

Nash, L.L. and P.H. Gleick, Sensitivity of streamflow in the Colorado basin to climatic changes, *Journal of Hydrology*, 125, 221-241, 1991.

National Academy, *Restoration of aquatic ecosystems: science, technology, and public policy*, National Academy Press, Washington, D.C., 552 pp., 1992.

National Research Council, *Opportunities in the hydrologic sciences*, National Academy Press, Washington, D.C., 348 pp., 1991.

Neal, C., A. Avila, and F. Roda, Modelling the long-term impacts of atmospheric pollution deposition and repeated forestry cycles on stream water chemistry for a holm oak forest in northeastern Spain, *Journal of Hydrology*, 168, 51-71, 1995.

Neal, C., T. Hill, S. Alexander, B. Reynolds, S. Hill, A.J. Dixon, M. Harrow, M. Neal, and C.J. Smith, Stream water quality in acid sensitive UK upland areas; an example of potential water quality remediation based on groundwater manipulation, *Hydrology and Earth System Sciences*, 1, 185-196, 1997.

Neary, D.G. and L.W. Swift, Jr., Rainfall thresholds for triggering a debris avalanching event in the southern Appalachian Moutains, in *Debris flows/avalanches: process, recognition, and mitigation*, edited by J.E. Costa and G.F. Wieczorek, pp. 81-92, Geological Society of America, Reviews in Engineering Geology, v. 7, Boulder, Colorado, 1987.

Needham, D.J. and R.D. Hey, Dynamic modelling of bed waves, in *Dynamics of gravel-bed rivers,* edited by P. Billi, R.D. Hey, C.R. Thorne and P. Tacconi, pp. 401-414, John Wiley and Sons, Chichester, 1992.

Needham, J.G. and J.T. Lloyd, *The life of inland waters*, Charles C. Thomas Publishers, Springfield, Illinois, 438 pp., 1930.

Nelson, J.M., R.L. Shreve, S.R. McLean, and T.G. Drake, Role of near-bed turbulence structure in bed transport and bed form mechanics, *Water Resources Research*, 31, 2071-2086, 1995.

Newbury, R. and M. Gaboury, Exploration and rehabilitation of hydraulic habitats in streams using principles of fluvial behaviour, *Freshwater Biology*, 29, 195-210, 1993.

Newson, M.D. and G.J. Leeks, Transport processes at the catchment scale, in *Sediment transport in gravel-bed rivers*, edited by C.R. Thorne, J.C. Bathurst, and R.D. Hey, pp. 187-223, John Wiley and Sons, Chichester, 1987.

Nezat, C.A., E.Y. Graham, N.L. Green, W.B. Lyons, K. Neumann, A.E. Carey, and M. Hicks, The physical and chemical controls on rare earth element concentrations in dissolved load, suspended load, and river channel sediments of the Hokitika River, New Zealand, *Geological Society of America, 1999 Annual Meeting, Abstracts with Programs*, 31, A-256, 1999.

Nicholas, A.P. and G.H. Sambrook Smith, Numerical simulation of three-dimensional flow hydraulics in a braided channel, *Hydrological Processes*, 13, 913-929, 1999.

Nienow, P., M. Sharp, and I. Willis, Seasonal changes in the morphology of the subglacial drainage system, Haut Glacier d'Arolla, Switzerland, *Earth Surface Processes and Landforms*, 23, 825-843, 1998.

Nihlgard, B.J., W.T. Swank, and M.J. Mitchell, Biological processes and catchment studies, in *Biogeochemistry of small catchments: a tool for environmental research*, edited by B. Moldan and J. Cerny, pp. 133-161, John Wiley and Sons, Chichester, 1994.

Nik, A.R., Water yield changes after forest conversion to agricultural landuse in Peninsular Malaysia, *Journal of Tropical Forest Science*, 1, 67-84, 1988.

Nikora, V.I., D.G. Goring, and B.J.F. Biggs, On gravel-bed roughness characterization, *Water Resources Research*, 34, 517-527, 1998.

Nilsson, C., A. Ekblad, M. Dynesius, S. Backe, M. Gardfjell, B. Carlberg, S. Hellqvist, and R. Jansson, A comparison of species richness and traits of riparian plants between a main river channel and its tributaries, *Journal of Ecology*, 82, 281-295, 1994.

Nilsson, C., A. Ekblad, M. Gardfjell, and B. Carlberg, Long-term effects of river regulation on river margin vegetation, *Journal of Applied Ecology*, 28, 963-987, 1991.

Nolan, K.M. and D.C. Marron, Contrast in stream-channel response to major storms in two mountainous areas of California, *Geology*, 13, 135-138, 1985.

Nolan, K.M., D.C. Marron, and L.M. Collins, Stream channel response to the January 3-5, 1982, storm in the Santa Cruz Mountains, west central California, *U.S. Geological Survey Open-File Report 84-248*, 1984.

Nott, J. and D. Price, Plunge pools and paleoprecipitation, *Geology*, 22, 1047-1050, 1994.

Nott, J., R. Young, and I. McDougall, Wearing down, wearing back, and gorge extension in the long-term denudation of a highland mass: quantitative evidence from the Shoalhaven Catchment, southeastern Australia, *Journal of Geology*, 104, 224-232, 1996.

Nunnally, N.R., Improving channel efficiency without sacrificing fish and wildlife habitat: the case for stream restoration, in *Strategies for protection and management of floodplain wetlands and other riparian ecosystems*, pp. 394-399, USDA Forest Service General Technical Report WO-12, 1978.

O'Brien, A.K., K.C. Rice, O.P. Bricker, M.M. Kennedy, and R.T. Anderson, Use of geochemical mass balance modelling to evaluate the role of weathering in determining stream chemistry in five mid-Atlantic watersheds on different lithologies, *Hydrological Processes*, 11, 719-744, 1997.

O'Brien, J.S., A case study of minimum streamflow for fishery habitat in the Yampa River, in *Sediment transport in gravel-bed rivers*, edited by C.R. Thorne, J.C. Bathurst, and R.D. Hey, pp. 921-946, John Wiley and Sons, Chichester, 1987.

O'Brien, J.S., Hydraulic modeling and mapping of mud and debris flows, in *Hydraulic engineering '93*, edited by H.W. Shen, S.T. Su and F. Wen, v. 2, pp. 1762-1767, ASCE, 1993.

O'Brien, J.S. and P.Y. Julien, Laboratory analysis of mudflow properties, *ASCE Journal of Hydraulic Engineering*, 114, 877-887, 1988.

O'Connor, J.E., Hydrology, hydraulics, and geomorphology of the Bonneville Flood, *Geological Society America Special Paper 274*, 83 pp., 1993.

O'Connor, J.E. and J.E. Costa, Geologic and hydrologic hazards in glacierized basins in North America resulting from 19th and 20th century global warming, *Natural Hazards*, 8, 121-140, 1993.

O'Connor, J.E., L.L. Ely, E.E. Wohl, L.E. Stevens, T.S. Melis, V.S. Kale, and V.R. Baker, A 4500-year record of large floods on the Colorado River in the Grand Canyon, Arizona, *Journal Geology*, 102, 1-9, 1994.

O'Connor, J.E. and J.E. Costa, Geologic and hydrologic hazards in glacierized basins in North America resulting from 19th and 20th century global warming, *Natural Hazards*, 8, 121-140, 1993.

O'Connor, J.E. and R.H. Webb, Hydraulic modeling for paleoflood analysis, in *Flood geomorphology*, edited by V.R. Baker, R.C. Kochel, and P.C. Patton, pp. 393-402, John Wiley and Sons, New York, 1988.

O'Connor, J.E., R.H. Webb, and V.R. Baker, Paleohydrology of pool-and-riffle pattern development: Boulder Creek, Utah, *Geological Society of America Bulletin*, 97, 410-420, 1986.

Odum, H.T., Trophic structure and productivity of Silver Springs, Florida, *Ecological Monographs*, 27, 55-112, 1957.

OFDA (US Office of Foreign Disaster Assistance), *Disaster history: significant data on major disasters worldwide, 1900-present*, Agency for International Development, Washington, D.C., 1988.

Oguchi, T., Average erosional conditions of Japanese mountains estimated from the frequency and magnitude of landslides, in *Proceedings of the International Symposium on Forest Hydrology*, pp. 399-406, Tokyo, Japan, Oct. 1994, 1994.

Oguchi, T., Factors affecting the magnitude of post-glacial hillslope incision in Japanese mountains, *Catena*, 26, 171-186, 1996a.

Oguchi, T., Late Quaternary hillslope erosion rates in Japanese mountains estimated from landform classification and morphometry, *Zeitschrift für Geomorphologie*, 106, 169-181, 1996b.

Oguchi, T., Channel incision and sediment production in Japanese mountains in relation to past and future climatic change, in *Proceedings of the Conference on Management of Landscapes Disturbed by Channel Incision*, edited by S.S.Y. Wang, E.J. Langendoen and F.D. Shields, Jr., pp. 867-872, 1997a.

Oguchi, T., Drainage density and relative relief in humid steep mountains with frequent slope failure, *Earth Surface Processes and Landforms*, 22, 107-120, 1997b.

Oguchi, T., Late Quaternary sediment budget in alluvial-fan-source-basin systems in Japan, *Journal of Quaternary Science*, 12, 381-390, 1997c.

Oguchi, T. and H. Ohmori, Analysis of relationships among alluvial fan area, source basin area, basin slope, and sediment yield, *Zeitschrift für Geomorphologie*, 38, 405-420, 1994.

Ohmori, H. and H. Shimazu, Distribution of hazard types in a drainage basin and its relation to geomorphological setting, *Geomorphology*, 10, 95-106, 1994.

Ohsumi Works Office, *Debris flow at Sakurajima 2*, Kyushu Regional Construction Bureau, Ministry of Construction, Japan, 81 pp., 1995.

Okuda, S., *Observation on the motion of debris flow and its geomorphological effects*, International Geographical Union, Community Field Experiment Geomorphology, Paris, 24 pp., 1978.

Okunishi, K., S. Okuda, and H. Suwa, A large-scale debris avalanche as an episode in slope-channel processes, in *Erosion and sedimentation in the Pacific Rim*, edited by R.L. Beschta, T. Blinn, G.E. Grant, G.G. Ice, and F.J. Swanson, pp. 225-232, IAHS Publ. no. 165, 1987.

Olley, J.M. and A.S. Murray, Origins of variability in the ^{230}Th/^{232}Th ratio in sediments, in *Variability in stream erosion and sediment transport*, edited by L.J. Olive, R.J. Loughran and A.J. Kesby, pp. 65-70, IAHS Publication no. 224, Wallingford, UK, 1994.

O'Loughlin, E.M., Prediction of surface saturation zones in natural catchments by topographic analysis, *Water Resources Research*, 22, 794-804, 1986.

Olson, R. and W.A. Hubert, *Beaver: water resources and riparian habitat manager*, University of Wyoming, Laramie, 48 pp., 1994.

O'Neal, J.S. and T.H. Sibley, A biological evaluation of stream rehabilitation: comparison of the effects of large woody debris and engineered alternative, *Ecological Society of America, 1999 Annual Meeting Abstracts*, p. 160, 1999.

O'Neill, M.P. and A.D. Abrahams, Objective identification of pools and riffles, *Water Resources Research*, 20, 921-926, 1984.

Orsborn, J.F. and J.W. Anderson, Stream improvements and fish response: a bio-engineering assessment, *Water Resources Bulletin*, 22, 381-388, 1986.

Osborne, L.L. and M.J. Wiley, Influence of tributary spatial position on the structure of warmwater fish communities, *Canadian Journal of Fisheries and Aquatic Sciences*, 49, 671-681, 1992.

Osterkamp, W.R. and C.R. Hupp, Geomorphic and vegetative characteristics along three northern Virginia streams, *Geological Society of America Bulletin*, 95, 1093-1101, 1984.

Osterkamp, W.R. and C.R. Hupp, Dating and interpretation of debris flows by geologic and botanical methods at Whitney Creek Gorge, Mount Shasta, California, in *Debris flows/avalanches: process, recognition, and mitigation*, edited by J.E. Costa and G.F. Wieczorek, pp. 157-163, Geological Society of America, Reviews in Engineering Geology, v. 7, Boulder, Colorado, 1987.

Osterkamp, W.R., C.R. Hupp, and J.C. Blodgett, Magnitude and frequency of debris flows, and areas of hazard on Mount Shasta, northern California, *U.S. Geological Survey Professional Paper 1396-C*, 21 pp., 1986.

Osterkamp, W.R. and T.J. Toy, The healing of disturbed hillslopes by gully gravure, *Geological Society of America Bulletin*, 106, 1233-1241, 1994.

Oswood, M.W., A.M. Milner, and J.G. Irons, III, Climate change and Alaskan rivers and streams, in *Global climate change and freshwater ecosystems*, edited by P. Firth and S.G. Fisher, pp. 192-210, Springer-Verlag, New York, 1992.

Ouchi, S., Response of alluvial rivers to slow active tectonic movement, *Geological Society of America Bulletin*, 96, 504-515, 1985.

Ouchi, S. and T. Mizuyama, Volume and movement of Tombi Landslide in 1858, Japan, *Transactions, Japanese Geomorphological Union*, 10, 27-51, 1989.

Overton, C.K., M.A. Radko, and R.L. Nelson, Fish habitat conditions: using the Northern/Intermountain Region's inventory procedures for detecting differences on two differently managed watersheds, *USDA Forest Service General Technical Report INT-300*, 14 pp., 1993.

Owen, L.A. and M.C. Sharma, Rates and magnitudes of paraglacial fan formation in the Garhwal Himalaya: implications for landscape evolution, *Geomorphology*, 26, 171-184, 1998.

Owens, P. and O. Slaymaker, Late Holocene sediment yields in small alpine and subalpine drainage basins, British Columbia, in *Erosion, debris flows and environment in mountain regions*, edited by D.E. Walling, T.R. Davies, and B. Hasholt, pp. 147-154, IAHS Publ. no. 209, Wallingford, United Kingdom, 1992.

Palmer, M.A., A.E. Bely, and K.E. Berg, Response of invertebrates to lotic disturbance: a test of the hyporheic refuge hypothesis, *Oecologia*, 89, 182-194, 1992.

Palmer, T., *Lifelines: the case for river conservation*, Island Press, Washington, D.C., 254 pp., 1994.

Paola, C., G. Parker, R. Seal, S.K. Sinha, J.B. Southard, and P.R. Wilcock, Downstream fining by selective deposition in a laboratory flume, *Science*, 258, 1757-1760, 1992.

Park, C.C., Man-induced changes in stream channel capacity, in *River channel changes*, edited by K.J. Gregory, pp. 121-144, John Wiley and Sons, Chichester, 1977.

Parker, G., Surface-based bedload transport relation for gravel rivers, *Journal of Hydraulic Research*, 28, 417-436, 1990.

Parker, G., Downstream variation of grain size in gravel rivers: abrasion versus selective sorting, in *Fluvial hydraulics of mountain regions*, edited by A. Armanini and G. DiSilvio, pp. 347-360, Springer-Verlag, Berlin, 1991.

Parker, G., Some speculations on the relation between channel morphology and channel-scale flow structures, in *Coherent flow structures in open channels*, edited by P.J. Ashworth, S.J. Bennett,

J.L. Best and S.J. McLelland, pp. 423-458, John Wiley and Sons, Chichester, 1996.

Parker, G., Y. Cui, J. Imran, and W.E. Dietrich, Flooding in the lower Ok Tedi, Papua New Guinea due to the disposal of mine tailings and its amelioration, in *International Seminar on Recent Trends of Floods and their Preventive Measures*, pp. 21-48, 20-21 June 1996, Sapporo, Japan, Post-seminar proceedings, 1997.

Parker, G. and P.C. Klingeman, On why gravel bed streams are paved, *Water Resources Research*, 18, 1409-1423, 1982.

Parker, G., P.C. Klingeman, and D.G. McLean, Bedload and size distribution in gravel-bed streams, *ASCE Journal of the Hydraulics Division*, 108, 544-571, 1982.

Parker, G. and A.W. Peterson, Bar resistance of gravel-bed streams, *ASCE Journal Hydraulics Division*, 106, 1559-1575, 1980.

Parker, M., *Beaver, water quality, and riparian systems*, Wyoming Water and Streamside Zone Conferences, Wyoming Water Research Center, University of Wyoming, Laramie, 1986.

Parker, R.S., Experimental study of drainage basin evolution and its hydrologic implications, *Colorado State University Hydrology Papers 90*, 58 pp., 1977.

Parrett, C., Fire-related debris flows in the Beaver Creek drainage, Lewis and Clark County, Montana, *U.S. Geological Survey Water-Supply Paper 2330*, p. 57-67, 1987.

Parrett, C. and S.R. Holnbeck, Relation between largest known flood discharge and elevation in Montana, in *Hydraulic engineering '94*, edited by G.V. Cotroneo and R.R. Rumer, pp. 870-874, Proceedings of the 1994 ASCE Conference, 1994.

Parriaux, A. and G.F. Nicoud, Hydrological behavior of glacial deposits in mountainous areas, in *Hydrology of mountainous areas*, edited by L. Molnar, pp. 291-312, IAHS Publ. no. 190, Wallingford, UK, 1990.

Patrick, R., *Rivers of the United States*, v. 2, chp. 7, pp. 195-228, Chemical and physical characteristics, Wiley and Sons, New York, 1995.

Patton, P.C., Drainage basin morphometry and floods, in *Flood geomorphology*, edited by V.R. Baker, R.C. Kochel, and P.C. Patton, pp. 51-64, John Wiley and Sons, New York, 1988a.

Patton, P.C., Geomorphic response of streams to floods in the glaciated terrain of southern New England, in *Flood geomorphology*, edited by V.R. Baker, R.C. Kochel and P.C. Patton, pp. 261-277, John Wiley and Sons, New York, 1988b.

Patton, P.C. and V.R. Baker, Morphometry and floods in small drainage basins subject to diverse hydrogeomorphic controls, *Water Resources Research*, 12, 941-952, 1976.

Patton, P.C. and P.J. Boison, Processes and rates of formation of Holocene alluvial terraces in Harris Wash, Escalante River basin, south-central Utah, *Geological Society of America Bulletin*, 97, 369-378, 1986.

Patton, P.C. and S.A. Schumm, Gully erosion, northern Colorado: a threshold phenomenon, *Geology*, 3, 88-90, 1975.

Payne, B.A. and M.F. Lapointe, Channel morphology and lateral stability: effects on distribution of spawning and rearing habitat for Atlantic salmon in a wandering cobble-bed river, *Canadian Journal of Fisheries and Aquatic Sciences*, 54, 2627-2736, 1997.

Pazzaglia, F.J., T.W. Gardner and D.J. Merritts, Bedrock fluvial incision and longitudinal profile development over geologic time scales determined by fluvial terraces, in *Rivers over rock: fluvial processes in bedrock channels*, edited by K.J. Tinkler and E.E. Wohl, pp. 207-235, Am. Geophys. Union Geophysical Monograph 107, 1998.

Pearce, A.J. and A.I. McKerchar, Upstream generation of storm runoff, in *Physical hydrology: New Zealand experience*, edited by D.L. Murray and P. Ackroyd, pp. 165-192, New Zealand Hydrological Society, Inc., Wellington North, 1979.

Pearlstine, L., H. McKellar, and W. Kitchens, Modelling the impacts of a river diversion on bottomland forest communities in the Santee River floodplain, South Carolina, *Ecological Modelling*, 29, 283-302, 1985.

Peart, M.R. and A.W. Jayawardena, Some observations on bedload movement in a small stream in Hong Kong, in *Variability in stream erosion and sediment transport*, edited by L.J. Olive, R.J.

Loughran, and J.A. Kesby, pp. 71-76, IAHS Publication no. 224, Wallingford, UK, 1994.

Pennak, R.W., Towards a classification of lotic habitats, *Hydrobiologia*, 38, 321-334, 1971.

Pereira, H.C., *Policy and practice in the management of tropical watersheds*, Westview Press, Boulder, Colorado, 237 pp., 1989.

Personius, S.F., H.M. Kelsey, and P.C. Graben, Evidence for regional stream aggradation in the central Oregon Coast Range during the Pleistocene-Holocene transition, *Quaternary Research*, 40, 297-308, 1993.

Pess, G.R., T.B. Abbe, T.A. Drury, and D.R. Montgomery, Biological evaluation of engineered log jams: North Fork Stillaguamish River, Washington, *EOS, Transactions Am. Geophys. Union*, 79, F346, 1998.

Peters, N.E., Hydrologic studies, in *Biogeochemistry of small catchments: a tool for environmental research*, edited by B. Moldan and J. Cerny, pp. 207-228, John Wiley and Sons, Chichester, 1994.

Petit, F., The relationship between shear stress and the shaping of the bed of a pebble-loaded river, La Rulles-Ardenne, *Catena*, 14, 453-468, 1987.

Petit, F., The evaluation of grain shear stress from experiments in a pebble-bedded flume, *Earth Surface Processes and Landforms*, 14, 499-508, 1989.

Petit, F., Evaluation of grain shear stresses required to initiate movement of particles in natural rivers, *Earth Surface Processes and Landforms*, 15, 135-148, 1990.

Petts, G.E., Channel response to flow regulation: the case of the River Derwent, Derbyshire, in *River channel changes*, edited by K.J. Gregory, pp. 145-164, John Wiley and Sons, Chichester, 1977.

Petts, G.E., *Impounded rivers: perspectives for ecological management*, John Wiley and Sons, Chichester, 326 pp., 1984.

Petts, G.E., Historical analysis of fluvial hydrosystems, in *Historical change of large alluvial rivers: western Europe*, edited by G.E. Petts, pp. 1-18, John Wiley and Sons, Chichester, 1989.

Philbrick, S.S., Horizontal configuration and the rate of erosion of Niagara Falls, *Geological Society of America Bulletin*, 81, 3723-3732, 1970.

Phillips, L.F. and S.A. Schumm, Effect of regional slope on drainage networks, *Geology*, 15, 813-816, 1987.

Phillips, P.J. and J.M. Harlin, Spatial dependency of hydraulic geometry exponents in a subalpine stream, *Journal of Hydrology*, 71, 277-283, 1984.

Phipps, R.L., Collecting, preparing, crossdating, and measuring tree increment cores, *U.S. Geological Survey Water- Resources Investigations Report 85-4148*, 48 pp., 1985.

Pickup, G., R.J. Higgins, and I. Grant, Modelling sediment transport as a moving wave - the transfer and deposition of mining waste, *Journal of Hydrology*, 60, 281-301, 1983.

Piégay, H. and A.M. Gurnell, Large woody debris and river geomorphological pattern: examples from S.E. France and S. England, *Geomorphology*, 19, 99-116, 1997.

Pierson, T.C., Erosion and deposition by debris flows at Mt. Thomas, North Canterbury, New Zealand, *Earth Surface Processes*, 5, 227-247, 1980.

Pinay, G., H, DéCamps, E. Chauvet, and E. Fustec, Functions of ecotones in fluvial systems, in *Ecology and management of aquatic-terrestrial ecotones*, edited by R.J. Naiman and H. DéCamps, UNESCO, Paris and The Parthenon Publishing Group, Carnforth, 1990.

Pircher, W., The contribution of hydropower reservoirs to flood control in the Austrian Alps, in *Hydrology in mountainous regions II. Artificial reservoirs, water and slopes*, edited by R.O. Sinniger and M. Monbaron, pp. 3-10, IAHS Publication no. 194, Wallingford, UK, 1990.

Pitlick, J., *The response of coarse-bed rivers to large floods in California and Colorado*, Unpublished PhD dissertation, Colorado State University, Ft. Collins, 137 pp., 1988.

Pitlick, J. 1994a. Coarse sediment transport and the maintenance of fish habitat in the upper Colorado River, in *Hydraulic engineering '94*, edited by G.V. Cotroneo and R.R. Rumer, pp. 855-859, Proceed. of the 1994 Conf, Hydraul Div, ASCE, New York, 1994a.

Pitlick, J., Relation between peak flows, precipitation, and physiography for five mountainous regions in the western USA, *Journal of Hydrology*, 158, 219-240, 1994b.

Pitlick, J. and M.M. Van Steeter, Geomorphology and endangered fish habitats of the upper Colorado River. 2. Linking sediment transport to habitat maintenance, *Water Resources Research*, 34, 303-316, 1998.

Pitlick, J.C. and C.R. Thorne, Sediment supply, movement and storage in an unstable gravel-bed river, in *Sediment transport in gravel-bed rivers*, edited by C.R. Thorne, J.C. Bathurst, and R.D. Hey, pp. 151-183, John Wiley and Sons, Chichester, 1987.

Platts, W.S., Effects of livestock grazing, *USDA Forest Service General Technical Report PNW-124*, 25 pp., 1981.

Platts, W.S., W.F. Megahan, and G.W. Minshall, Methods for evaluating stream, riparian, and biotic conditions, *USDA Forest Service General Technical Report INT-138*, 70 pp., 1983.

Platts, W.S., R.J. Torquemada, M.L. McHenry, and C.K. Graham, Changes in salmon spawning and rearing habitat from increased delivery of fine sediment to the South Fork Salmon River, Idaho, *Transactions American Fisheries Society*, 118, 274-283, 1989.

Poff, N.L., Regional hydrologic response to climate change: an ecological perspective, in *Global climate change and freshwater ecosystems*, edited by P. Firth and S.G. Fisher, pp. 88-115, Springer-Verlag, New York, 1992.

Poff, N.L., A hydrogeography of unregulated streams in the United States and an examination of scale-dependence in some hydrological descriptors, *Freshwater Biology*, 36, 71-91, 1996.

Poff, N.L., Landscape filters and species traits: towards mechanistic understanding and prediction in stream ecology, *Journal of the North American Benthological Society*, 16, 391-409, 1997.

Poff, N.L. and J.D. Allan, Functional organization of stream fish assemblages in relation to hydrological variability, *Ecology*, 76, 606-627, 1995.

Poff, N.L., J.D. Allan, M.B. Bain, J.R. Karr, K.L. Prestegaard, B.D. Richter, R.E. Sparks, and J.C. Stromberg, The natural flow regime: a paradigm for river conservation and restoration, *BioScience*, 47, 769-784, 1997.

Poff, N.L. and J.V. Ward, Implications of streamflow variability and predictability for lotic community structure: a regional analysis of streamflow patterns, *Canadian Journal of Fisheries and Aquatic Sciences*, 46, 1805-1818, 1989.

Poff, N.L. and J.V. Ward, Physical habitat template of lotic ecosystems: recovery in the context of historical pattern of spatiotemporal heterogeneity, *Environmental Management*, 14, 629-645, 1990.

Poff, N.L. and E. Wohl, An integrated hydrologic-geomorphic aquatic classification for fluvial ecosystems, *Ecological Society of America, 1999 Annual Meeting Abstracts*, p. 31, 1999.

Ponton, J.R., Hydraulic geometry in the Green and Birkenhead basins, British Columbia, in *Mountain geomorphology: geomorphological processes in the Canadian Cordillera*, edited by H.O. Slaymaker and H.J. McPherson, pp. 151-160, Tantalus Research Ltd., Vancouver, Canada, 1972.

Poole, G.C., C.A. Frissell, and S.C. Ralph, In-stream habitat unit classification: inadequacies for monitoring and some consequences for management, *Journal of the American Water Resources Association*, 33, 879-896, 1997.

Post, A. and L.R. Mayo, Glacier dammed lakes and outburst floods in Alaska, *U.S. Geological Survey Hydrologic Investigations Atlas HA-455*, 3 sheets, 1971.

Powell, D.M., Patterns and processes of sediment sorting in gravel-bed rivers, *Progress in Physical Geography*, 22, 1-32, 1998.

Powell, J.W., *Exploration of the Colorado River of the West (1869-72)*, U.S. Govt. Printing Office, Washington, D.C., 1875.

Powell, J.W., *Report on the geology of the eastern portion of the Uinta Mountains*, U.S. Govt. Printing Office, Washington, D.C., 1876.

Power, M.E., A. Sun, M. Parker, W.E. Dietrich, and J.T. Wootton, Hydraulic food-chain models: an approach to the study of food-web dynamics in large rivers, *BioScience*, 45, 159-167, 1995.

Press, F. and R. Siever, *Earth*, 4th ed. W.H. Freeman and Company, San Francisco, 656 pp., 1986.

Prestegaard, K.L., Bar resistance in gravel bed streams at bankfull stage, *Water Resources Research*, 19, 472-476, 1983a.

Prestegaard, K.L., Variables influencing water-surface slopes in gravel-bed streams at bankfull stage, *Geological Society of America Bulletin*, 94, 673-678, 1983b.

Price, L.W., *Mountains and man: a study of process and environment*, University of California Press, Berkeley, 506 pp., 1981.

Price, M.F. and R.G. Barry, Climate change, in *Mountains of the world: a global priority*, edited by B. Messerli and J.D. Ives, pp. 409-445, The Parthenon Publishing Group, London, 1997.

Pristachová, G., Quantitative geomorphology, stream networks, and instantaneous unit hydrograph, in *Hydrology of mountainous areas*, edited by L. Molnar, pp. 369-375, IAHS Publ. no. 190, Wallingford, UK, 1990.

Pruess, J., E.E. Wohl, and R.D. Jarrett, Methodology and implications of maximum paleodischarge estimates for mountain channels, upper Animas River basin, Colorado, USA, *Arctic and Alpine Research*, 30, 40-50, 1998.

Pyrce, R.S., *A field investigation of planimetric knickpoint morphology from rock-bed sections of Niagara Escarpment fluvial systems*, MA thesis, Wilfrid Laurier University, Canada, 119 pp., 1995.

Raffaelli, D.G., A.G. Hildrew, and P.S. Giller, Scale, pattern and process in aquatic systems: concluding remarks, in *Aquatic ecology: scale, pattern and process*, edited by P.S. Giller, A.G. Hildrew, and D.G. Raffaelli, pp. 601-606, Blackwell Scientific Publications, Oxford, 1994.

Ralph, S.C., G.C. Poole, L.L. Conquest, and R.J. Naiman, Stream channel morphology and woody debris in logged and unlogged basins of western Washington, *Canadian Journal of Fisheries and Aquatic Sciences*, 51, 37-51, 1994.

Ralston, D.R. and A.G. Morilla, Ground-water movement through an abandoned tailings pile, in *Water resources problems related to mining*, edited by R.F. Hadley and D.T. Snow, pp. 174-183, American Water Resources Association, Minneapolis, Minnesota, 1974.

Rapp, A., Recent development of mountain slopes in Karkevagge and surroundings, northern Sweden, *Geografiska Annaler*, 41, 65-200, 1960.

Rapp, A. and R. Nyberg, Alpine debris flows in northern Scandinavia, *Geografiska Annaler*, 63A, 183-196, 1981.

Rapp, A. and L. Strömquist, Slope erosion due to extreme rainfall in the Scandinavian Mountains, *Geografiska Annaler*, 58A, 193-200, 1976.

Rawat, J.S. and M.S. Rawat, Accelerated erosion and denudation in the Nana Kosi watershed, Central Himalaya, India. Part I: Sediment load, *Mountain Research and Development*, 14, 25-38, 1994.

Rees, D.E., *Indirect effects of heavy metals observed in macroinvertebrate availability, brown trout (Salmo trutta) diet composition, and bioaccumulation in the Arkansas River, Colorado*, Unpublished MS thesis, Colorado State University, Ft. Collins, Colorado, 47 pp., 1994.

Reeves, G.H., L.E. Benda, K.M. Burnett, P.A. Bisson and J.R. Sedell, A disturbance-based ecosystem approach to maintaining and restoring freshwater habitats of evolutionarily significant units of anadromous salmonids in the Pacific Northwest, *American Fisheries Society Symposium*, 17, 334-349, 1995.

Reid, I. and L.E. Frostick, Dynamics of bedload transport in Turkey Brook, a coarse-grained alluvial channel, *Earth Surface Processes and Landforms*, 11, 143-155, 1986.

Reid, I., L.E. Frostick, and A.C. Brayshaw, Microform roughness elements and the selective entrainment and entrapment of particles in gravel-bed rivers, in *Dynamics of gravel-bed rivers*, edited by P. Billi, R.D. Hey, C.R. Thorne and P. Tacconi, pp. 253-275, John Wiley and Sons, Chichester, 1992.

Reid, I., L.E. Frostick and J.L. Layman, The incidence and nature of bedload transport during flood flows in coarse-grained alluvial channels, *Earth Surface Processes and Landforms*, 10, 33-44, 1985.

Reid, L.M. and T. Dunne, Sediment production from forest road surfaces, *Water Resources Research*, 20, 1753-1761, 1984.

Reiser, D.W. and T.C. Bjornn, Influence of forest and rangeland management on anadromous fish habitat in the western U.S. and Canada. Part I: Habitat requirements of anadromous salmonids, *USDA Forest Service General Technical Report PNW-96*, 54 pp., 1979.

Renard, K.G., G.R. Foster, G.A. Weesies, and J.P. Porter, RUSLE- revised universal soil loss equation, *Journal of Soil and Water Conservation*, 46, 30-33, 1991.

Reneau, S.L. and D.P. Dethier, Late Pleistocene landslide dammed-lakes along the Rio Grande, White Rock Canyon, New Mexico, *Geological Society of America Bulletin*, 108, 1492-1507, 1996.

Reneau, S.L. and W.E. Dietrich, The implications of hollows in debris flow studies; examples from Marin County, California, in *Debris flows/avalanches: process, recognition, and mitigation*, edited by J.E. Costa and G.F. Wieczorek, pp. 165-180, Geological Society of America, Reviews in Engineering Geology, v. 7, Boulder, Colorado, 1987.

Renwick, W.H., Erosion caused by intense rainfall in a small catchment in New York State, *Geology*, 5, 361-364, 1977.

Resh, V.H., A.V. Brown, A.P. Covich, M.E. Gurtz, H.W. Li, G.W. Minshall, S.R. Reice, A.L. Sheldon, J.B. Wallace, and R. Wissmar, The role of disturbance in stream ecology, *Journal of the North American Benthological Society*, 7, 433-455, 1988.

Reynolds, B., P.J. Chapman, M.C. French, A. Jenkins and H.S. Wheater, Major, minor, and trace element chemistry of surface waters in the Everest region of Nepal, in Biogeochemistry of seasonally snow-covered catchments, edited by K.A. Tonnessen, M.W. Williams and M. Tranter, pp. 405-412, IAHS Publ. no. 228, 1995a.

Reynolds, B., W.H. Robertson, M. Hornung and P.A. Stevens, Forest manipulation and solute production: modelling the nitrogen response to clearcutting, in *Solute modelling in catchment systems*, edited by S.T. Trudgill, pp. 211-233, John Wiley and Sons, Chichester, 1995b.

Rhea, J.O. and L.O. Grant, Topographic influences on snowfall patterns in mountainous terrain, in *Adv. concepts and techniques in study of snow and ice resources*, pp. 182-192, National Academy of Sciences, Washington, D.C., 1974.

Rice, K.C. and O.P. Bricker, Seasonal cycles of dissolved constituents in streamwater in two forested catchments in the mid-Atlantic region of the eastern USA, *Journal of Hydrology*, 170, 137-158, 1995.

Rice, S., Which tributaries disrupt downstream fining along gravel-bed rivers?, *Geomorphology*, 22, 39-56, 1998.

Richards, K., Fluvial geomorphology: initial motion of bed material in gravel-bed rivers, *Progress in Physical Geography*, 395-415, 1990.

Richards, K., Sediment delivery and the drainage network, in *Channel network hydrology*, edited by K. Beven and M.J. Kirkby, pp. 221-254, John Wiley and Sons, Chichester, 1993.

Richards, K.S., The morphology of riffle-pool sequences, *Earth Surface Processes*, 1, 71-88, 1976.

Richards, K.S., Simulation of flow geometry in a riffle-pool stream, *Earth Surface Processes*, 3, 345-354, 1978.

Richards, K.S. and L.M. Milne, Problems in the calibration of an acoustic device for the observation of bedload transport, *Earth Surface Processes*, 4, 335-346, 1979.

Richards, K.S. and R. Wood, Urbanization, water redistribution, and their effect on channel processes, in *River channel changes*, edited by K.J. Gregory, pp. 369-388, John Wiley and Sons, New York, 1977.

Richmond, A.D. and K.D. Fausch, Characteristics and function of large woody debris in subalpine Rocky Mountain streams in northern Colorado, *Canadian Journal of Fisheries and Aquatic Sciences*, 52, 1789-1802, 1995.

Rickenmann, D., Debris flows 1987 in Switzerland: modelling and fluvial sediment transport, in *Hydrology in mountainous regions II. Artificial reservoirs, water and slopes*, edited by R.O. Sinniger and M. Monbaron, pp. 371-378, IAHS Publication no. 194, Wallingford, UK, 1990.

Rickenmann, D., Bed load transport and hyperconcentrated flow at steep slopes, in *Fluvial hydraulics of mountain regions*, edited by A. Armanini and G. DiSilvio, pp. 429-441, Springer-Verlag, Berlin, 1991.

Rickenmann, D., An alternative equation for the mean velocity in gravel-bed rivers and mountain torrents, in *Hydraulic engineering '94*, edited by G.V. Cotroneo and R.R. Rumer, pp. 672-676, Proceed of the 1994 Conf, Hydraul Div, ASCE, New York, 1994a.

Rickenmann, D., Bedload transport and discharge in the Erlenbach stream, in *Dynamics and geomorphology of mountain rivers*, edited by P. Ergenzinger and K.-H. Schmidt, pp. 53-66, Springer-Verlag, Berlin, 1994b.

Rickenmann, D., Sediment transport in Swiss torrents, *Earth Surface Processes and Landforms*, 22, 937-951, 1997.

Rickenmann, D. and T. Koch, Comparison of debris flow modelling approaches, in *Debris-flow hazards mitigation: mechanics, prediction, and assessment*, edited by C.-L. Chen, pp. 576-585, ASCE, 1997.

Ricklefs, R.E., Community diversity: relative roles of local and regional processes, *Science*, 235, 167-171, 1987.

Rijskijk, A. and L.A. Bruijnzeel, Erosion, sediment yield and land-use patterns in the Upper Konto watershed, East Java, Indonesia, Part III, results of the 1989-1990 measuring campaign, *Konto River Project Communication Series No. 18*, DHV Consultants, The Netherlands, 1991.

Rinaldi, M. and A. Simon, Bed-level adjustments in the Arno River, central Italy, *Geomorphology*, 22, 57-71, 1998.

Ritter, D.F., Rates of denudation, *Journal of Geological Education*, 15, 154-159, 1967.

Ritter, D.F., Floodplain erosion and deposition during the December 1982 floods in southeast Missouri, in *Flood geomorphology*, edited by V.R. Baker, R.C. Kochel, and P.C. Patton, pp. 243-259, John Wiley and Sons, New York, 1988.

Ritter, D.F., R.C. Kochel, and J.R. Miller, *Process geomorphology*, 3rd edition, Wm. C. Brown Publishers, Dubuque, Iowa, 546 pp., 1995.

Ritter, D.F., R.C. Kochel, and J.R. Miller, The disruption of Grassy Creek: implications concerning catastrophic events and thresholds, *Geomorphology*, 29, 323-338, 1999.

Roberson, J.A. and C.T. Crowe, *Engineering fluid mechanics*, John Wiley and Sons, New York, 823 pp., 1993.

Robert, A., Characteristics of velocity profiles along riffle-pool sequences and estimates of bed shear stress, *Geomorphology*, 19, 89-98, 1998.

Robert, A., A.G. Roy, and B. De Serres, Space-time correlations of velocity measurements at a roughness transition in a gravel-bed river, in *Turbulence: perspectives on flow and sediment transport*, edited by N.J. Clifford, J.R. French, and J. Hardisty, pp. 165-183, John Wiley and Sons, Chichester, 1993.

Roberts, G., J. Hudson, G. Leeks, and C. Neal, The hydrological effects of clear-felling established coniferous forestry in an upland area of mid-Wales, in *Integrated river basin development*, edited by C. Kirby and W.R. White, pp. 187-199, John Wiley and Sons, Chichester, 1994.

Roberts, M.D., M.P. O'Neill, J.P. Dobrowolski, J.C. Schmidt, and P.G. Wolf, Hydro-geomorphic influences on clonal recruitment of cottonwood in a narrow, steep gradient, mountain valley, *EOS, Transactions, American Geophysical Union*, 79, F346, 1998.

Roberts, R.G. and M. Church, The sediment budget in severely disturbed watersheds, Queen Charlotte Ranges, British Columbia, *Canadian Journal of Forest Research*, 16, 1092-1106, 1986.

Robinson, S.K., Coherent motions in the turbulent boundary layer, *Annual Reviews in Fluid Mechanics*, 104, 387-405, 1990.

Robison, E.G. and R.L. Beschta, Coarse woody debris and channel morphology interactions for undisturbed streams in southeastern Alaska, USA, *Earth Surface Processes and Landforms*, 15, 149-156, 1990.

Rodriguez-Iturbe, I., The geomorphological unit hydrograph, in *Channel network hydrology*, edited by K. Beven and M.J. Kirkby, pp. 43-68, John Wiley and Sons, Chichester, 1993.

Rodriguez-Iturbe, I., E. Ijjasz-Vasquez, R.L. Bras, and D.G. Tarboton, Power law distributions of discharge mass and energy in river basins, *Water Resources Research*, 28, 1089-1093, 1992a.

Rodriguez-Iturbe, I., A. Rinaldo, R. Rigon, R.L. Bras, A. Marani, and E. Ijjasz-Vasquez, Energy dissipation, runoff prediction, and the three-dimensional structure of river basins, *Water Resources Research*, 28, 1095-1103, 1992b.

Roesli, U. and C. Schindler, Debris flows 1987 in Switzerland: geological and hydrogeological aspects, in *Hydrology in mountainous regions II. Artificial reservoirs, water and slopes*, edited by R.O. Sinniger and M. Monbaron, pp. 379-386, IAHS Publication no. 194, Wallingford, UK, 1990.

Roline, R.A. and J.R. Boehmke, Heavy metals pollution of the upper Arkansas River, Colorado, and its effects on the distribution of the aquatic macrofauna, *U.S.D.I. Bureau of Reclamation, REC-ERC-81-15*, 71 pp., 1981.

Rose, J., Alluvial terraces of an equatorial river, Melinau drainage basin, Sarawak, *Zeitschrift für Geomorphologie*, 28, 155-177, 1984.

Rosenbloom, N. and R.S. Anderson, Hillslope and channel evolution in a marine terraced landscape, Santa Cruz, California, *Journal of Geophysical Research*, 99, 14,013-14,029, 1994.

Rosenfeld, C.L. 1998. Storm induced mass wasting in the Oregon Coast Range, USA, in *Geomorphological hazards in high mountain areas*, edited by J. Kalvoda and C.L. Rosenfeld, pp. 167-176, Kluwer Academic Publishers, The Netherlands, 1998.

Rosgen, D.L., A classification of natural rivers, *Catena*, 22, 169-199, 1994.

Röthlisberger, H. and H. Lang, Glacial hydrology, in *Glacio-fluvial sediment transfer*, edited by A.M. Gurnell and M.J. Clark, pp. 207-284, John Wiley and Sons, Chichester, 1987.

Rowbotham, D.N. and D. Dudycha, GIS modelling of slope stability in Phewa Tal watershed, Nepal, *Geomorphology*, 26, 151-170, 1998.

Roy, A.G. and A.D. Abrahams, Rhythmic spacing and origin of pools and riffles: Discussion, *Geological Society of America Bulletin*, 91, 248-250, 1980.

Roy, A.G., T. Buffin-Bélanger and S. Deland, Scales of turbulent coherent flow structures in a gravel-bed river, in *Coherent flow structures in open channels*, edited by P.J. Ashworth, S.J. Bennett, J.L. Best and S.J. McLelland, pp. 147-164, John Wiley and Sons, Chichester, 1996.

Ruhe, R.V., Topographic discontinuities of the Des Moines lobe, *American Journal of Science*, 250, 46-56, 1952.

Ruslan, I.W., Impact of urbanisation and uphill land clearances on the sediment yield of an urbanising catchment of Pulau Pinang, Malaysia, in *Postgraduate research in geomorphology; selected papers from the 17th BGRG Postgraduate Symposium*, edited by S.J. McLelland, A.R. Skellern, and P.R. Porter, pp. 28-33, British Geomorphological Research Group, School of Geography, University of Leeds, 1995.

Russell, A.J., F.G.M. Van Tatenhove, and R.S.W. Van de Wal, Effects of ice-front collapse and flood generation on a proglacial river channel near Kangerlussuaq (Sondre Stromfjord), West Greenland, *Hydrological Processes*, 9, 213-226, 1995.

Russell, S.O., Behavior of steep creeks in a large flood, in *Mountain geomorphology: Geomorphic processes in the Canadian Cordillera*, edited by H.O. Slaymaker and H.J. McPherson, pp. 223-227, Tantalus Research, Vancouver, Canada, 1972.

Rutherfurd, I.D., P. Bishop, and T. Loffler, Debris flows in northeastern Victoria, Australia: occurrence and effects on the fluvial system, in *Variability in stream erosion and sediment transport*, edited by L.J. Olive, R.J. Loughran and J.A. Kesby, pp. 359-369, IAHS Publication no. 224, Wallingford, UK, 1994.

Ryan, S.E., Bedload transport patterns in pool-riffle and step-pool stream systems, in *Effects of human-induced changes on hydrologic systems*, pp. 669-678, Am. Water Resources Assoc., 1994a.

Ryan, S.E., *Effects of transbasin diversion on flow regime, bedload transport, and channel morphology in Colorado mountain streams*, Unpublished PhD dissertation, University of Colorado, Boulder, 236 pp., 1994b.

Ryan, S.E., Morphologic response of subalpine streams to transbasin flow diversion, *Journal Am. Water Resources Association*, 33, 839-854, 1997.

Ryan, S.E. and G.E. Grant, Downstream effects of timber harvesting on channel morphology in Elk River basin, Oregon, *Journal of Environmental Quality*, 20, 60-72, 1991.

Ryan, S.E. and C.A. Troendle, Measuring bedload in coarse-grained mountain channels: procedures, problems, and recommendations, in *Water Resources Education, Training, and Practice: Opportunities for the Next Century*, pp. 949-958, American Water Resources Association, 1997.

Ryder, J.M., The stratigraphy and morphology of paraglacial alluvial fans in south-central British Columbia, *Canadian Journal of Earth Sciences*, 8, 279-298, 1971a.

Ryder, J.M., Some aspects of the morphometry of paraglacial alluvial fans in south-central British Columbia, *Canadian Journal of Earth Sciences*, 8, 1252-1264, 1971b.

Ryder, J.M. and M. Church, The Lillooet terraces of Fraser River: a palaeoenvironmental enquiry, *Canadian Journal of Earth Sciences*, 23, 869-884, 1986.

Sah, M.P. and R.K. Mazari, Anthropogenically accelerated mass movement, Kulu Valley, Himachal Pradesh, India, *Geomorphology*, 26, 123-138, 1998.

Salas, J.D., E.E. Wohl, and R.D. Jarrett, Determination of flood characteristics using systematic, historical and paleoflood data, in *Coping with floods*, edited by G. Rossi, N. Harmancioglu, and V. Yevjevich, pp. 111-134, Kluwer, Dordrecht, 1994.

Salo, E.O. and T.W. Cundy, (Eds.), *Streamside management: forestry and fishery implications*, University of Washington, Institute of Forest Resources, Contribution No. 57., 1987.

Salo, J., R. Kalliola, I. Häkkinen, Y. Mäkinen, P. Niemelä, M. Puhakka, and P.D. Coley, River dynamics and the diversity of Amazon lowland forest, *Nature*, 322, 254-258, 1986.

Sandoz, M., *The beaver men: spearheads of empire*, University of Nebraska Press, Lincoln, 335 pp., 1964.

Sato, T., Y. Kurashige, and K. Hirakawa, Slow mass movement in the Taisetsu Mountains, Hokkaido, Japan, *Permafrost and Periglacial Processes*, 8, 347-357, 1997.

Sauer, V.B., R.E. Curtis, L. Santiago-Rivera, and R. Gonzalez, R. 1985. Quantifying flood discharges in mountainous tropical streams, in *International Symposium on Tropical Hydrology and Second Caribbean Islands Water Resources Congress*, edited by F. Quinones, and A.V. Sanchez, pp. 104-108, American Water Resources Association, Bethesda, Maryland, 1985.

Saunders, I. and A. Young, Rates of surface processes on slopes, slope retreat and denudation, *Earth Surface Processes and Landforms*, 8, 473-501, 1983.

Sawada, T., K. Ashida, and T. Takahashi, Relationship between channel pattern and sediment transport in a steep gravel bed river, *Zeitschrift für Geomorphologie*, 46, 55-66, 1983.

Sawada, T. and T. Takahashi, Sediment yield on bare slopes, in *Proceedings of the International Symposium on Forest Hydrology*, pp. 471-478, Tokyo, Japan, Oct. 1994, 1994.

Saxena, P.B. and S. Prakash, A study of the morphometric determinants of the stage of cycle of erosion in the Nayar Basin (Garhwal Himalayas), in *Perspectives in geomorphology - vol. IV, Essays on Indian geomorphology*, edited by H.S. Sharma, pp. 77-92, Concept Publishing Co., New Delhi, 1982.

Saynor, M.J., R.J. Loughran, W.D. Erskine, and P.F. Scott, Sediment movement on hillslopes measured by caesium-137 and erosion pins, in *Variability in stream erosion and sediment transport*, edited by L.J. Olive, R.J. Loughran, and J.A. Kesby, pp. 87-93, IAHS Publication on. 224, Wallingford, UK, 1994.

Scatena, F.N., An introduction to the physiography and history of the Bisley Experimental Watersheds in the Luquillo Mountains of Puerto Rico, *USDA Forest Service General Technical Report SO-72*, 22 pp., 1989.

Scatena, F.N. and M.C. Larsen, Physical aspects of Hurricane Hugo in Puerto Rico, *Biotropica*, 23, 317-323, 1991.

Scheidegger, A.E. 1995. Geojoints and geostresses, in *Mechanics of jointed and faulted rock*, edited by H.-P. Rossmanith, pp. 3-35, AA Balkema, Rotterdam, 1995.

Scheidegger, A.E. and R. Hantke, On the genesis of river gorges, *Transactions, Japanese Geomorphological Union*, 15, 91-110, 1994.

Schick, A.P., Desert floods: interim results of observations in the Nahal Yael Research Watershed, southern Israel, 1965-1970, in *Symposium on the results of research on representative and experimental basins*, pp. 478-493, IASH-UNESCO, Wellington, New Zealand, Dec. 1970, 1970.

Schick, A.P., Formation and obliteration of desert stream terraces - a conceptual analysis, *Zeitschrift für Geomorphologie*, 21, 88-105, 1974.

Schick, A.P., M.A. Hassan, and J. Lekach, A vertical exchange model for coarse bedload movement: numerical considerations, in *Geomorphological models: theoretical and empirical aspects*, edited by F. Ahnert, pp. 73-83, Catena Supplement, 10, 1987a.

Schick, A.P. and J. Lekach, A high magnitude flood in the Sinai Desert, in *Catastrophic flooding*, edited by L. Mayer and D. Nash, pp. 381-410, Allen and Unwin, Boston, 1987.

Schick, A.P. and J. Lekach, An evaluation of two 10-year sediment budgets, Nahal Yael, Israel, *Physical Geography*, 14, 225-238, 1993.

Schick, A.P., J. Lekach, and M.A. Hassan, Bed load transport in desert floods: observations in the Negev, in *Sediment transport in gravel-bed rivers*, edited by C.R. Thorne, J.C. Bathurst, and R.D. Hey, pp. 617-642, John Wiley and Sons, Chichester, 1982.

Schick, A.P., J. Lekach, and M.A. Hassan, Vertical exchange of coarse bedload in desert streams, in *Desert sediments: ancient and modern*, edited by L. Frostick and I. Reid, pp. 7-16, Geological Society (London) Special Publ. no. 35, 1987b.

Schick, A.P. and D. Magid, Terraces in arid stream valleys: a probability model, *Catena*, 5, 237-250, 1978.

Schlichting, H., *Boundary-layer theory*, McGraw-Hill, New York, 747 pp., 1968.

Schleusener, R.A., G.L. Smith, and M.C. Chen, Effect of flow diversion for irrigation on peak rates of runoff from watersheds in and near the Rocky Mountain foothills of Colorado, *International Association of Hydrologists Bulletin*, 7, 53-61, 1962.

Schmal, R. and T. Wesche, Historical implications of the railroad crosstie industry on current riparian and stream habitat management in the central Rocky Mountains, in *Practical approaches to riparian resource management*, edited by R.E. Gresswell, B.A. Barton and J.L. Kershner, p. 189, U.S. Bureau of Land Management, Billings, Montana, 1989.

Schmidt, J.C., Recirculating flow and sedimentation in the Colorado River in Grand Canyon, Arizona, *Journal of Geology*, 98, 709-724, 1990.

Schmidt, K.-H., River channel adjustment and sediment budget in response to a catastrophic flood event (Lainbach catchment, southern Bavaria), in *Dynamics and geomorphology of mountain rivers*, edited by P. Ergenzinger and K.-H. Schmidt, pp. 109-127, Springer-Verlag, Berlin, 1994.

Schmidt, K.-H. and P. Ergenzinger, Bedload entrainment, travel lengths, step lengths, rest periods - studied with passive (iron, magnetic) and active (radio) tracer techniques, *Earth Surface Processes and Landforms*, 17, 147-165, 1992.

Schmidt, K.-H. and D. Gintz, Results of bedload tracer experiments in a mountain river, in *River geomorphology*, edited by E.J. Hickin, pp. 37-54, John Wiley and Sons, Chichester, 1995.

Schöberl, F., Continuous simulation of sediment transport in the case of glacierized watershed, in *Fluvial hydraulics of mountain regions*, edited by A. Armanini and G. DiSilvio, pp. 71-81, Springer-Verlag, Berlin, 1991.

Schoklitsch, A., *Handbuch des Wasserbaus*, 3rd ed., Springer-Verlag, Vienna, 1962.

Schulze, O., R. Roth, and O. Pieper, Probable maximum precipitation in the Upper Harz Mountains, in *FRIEND: Flow regimes from international experimental and network data*, edited by P. Senna, A. Gustard, N.W. Arnell, and G.A. Cole, pp. 315-321, IAHS Publication no. 221, Wallingford, UK, 1994.

Schumm, S.A., The role of creep and rainwash on the retreat of badland slopes, *American Journal of Science*, 254, 693-706, 1956.

Schumm, S.A., The shape of alluvial channels in relation to sediment type, *U.S. Geological Survey Professional Paper 352B*, p. 17-30, 1960.

Schumm, S.A., A tentative classification of alluvial river channels, *U.S. Geological Survey Circular 477*, 10 pp., 1963a.

Schumm, S.A., The disparity between present rates of denudation and orogeny, *U.S. Geological Survey Professional Paper 454-H*, 13 pp., 1963b.

Schumm, S.A., Seasonal variations of erosion rates and processes on hillslopes in western Colorado, *Zeitschrift für Geomorphologie Supplementband*, 5, 215-238, 1964.

Schumm, S.A., The development and evolution of hillslopes, *Journal of Geological Education*, 14, 98-104, 1966.

Schumm, S.A., Geomorphic thresholds and the complex response of drainage systems, in *Fluvial geomorphology*, edited by M. Morisawa, pp. 299-310, Publications in Geomorphology, State University of New York, Binghamton, 1973.

Schumm, S.A., *The fluvial system*, John Wiley and Sons, New York, 338 pp., 1977.

Schumm, S.A., Evolution and response of the fluvial system, sedimentologic implications, *Soc. Econ. Paleontol. Mineralogists Special Publication*, 31, 19-29, 1981.

Schumm, S.A., Alluvial river response to active tectonics, in *Active tectonics*, pp. 80-94, National Academy Press, Washington, D.C., 1986.

Schumm, S.A., Drainage density: problems of prediction and application, in *Process and form in geomorphology*, D.R. Stoddart, pp. 15-45, Routledge, London, 1997.

Schumm, S.A. and R.F. Hadley, Progress in the application of landform analysis in studies of semi-arid erosion, *U.S. Geological Survey Circular 437*, 14 pp., 1961.

Schumm, S.A. and H.R. Khan, Experimental study of channel patterns, *Geological Society of America Bulletin*, 83, 1755-1770, 1972.

Schumm, S.A. and R.W. Lichty, Time, space and causality in geomorphology, *American Journal of Science*, 263, 110-119, 1965.

Schumm, S.A. and G.C. Lusby, Seasonal variation of infiltration capacity and runoff on hillslopes in western Colorado, *Journal of Geophysical Research*, 68, 3655-3666, 1963.

Schumm, S.A., M.P. Mosley, and W.E. Weaver, *Experimental fluvial geomorphology*, John Wiley and Sons, New York, 413 pp., 1987.

Schumm, S.A. and R.S. Parker, Implications of complex response of drainage systems for Quaternary alluvial stratigraphy, *Nature*, 243, 99-100, 1973.

Schumm, S.A. and M.A. Stevens, Abrasion in place: a mechanism for rounding and size reduction of coarse sediments in rivers, *Geology*, 1, 37-40, 1973.

Scott, G.R., Cenozoic surfaces and deposits in the southern Rocky Mountains, in *Cenozoic history of the southern Rocky Mountains*, edited by B.F. Curtis, pp. 227-248, Geological Society of America Memoir 144, 1975.

Scott, K.M., Origin and sedimentology of 1969 debris flows near Glendora, California, *U.S. Geological Survey Professional Paper 750-C*, C242-C247, 1971.

Scott, K.M. and G.C. Gravlee, Jr., Flood surge on the Rubicon River, California - hydrology, hydraulics, and boulder transport, *U.S. Geological Survey Professional Paper 422-M*, M1-M38, 1968.

Scott, M.L., G.T. Auble, and J.M. Friedman, Flood dependency of cottonwood establishment along the Missouri River, Montana, USA, *Ecological Applications*, 7, 677-690, 1997.

Scott, M.L., J.M. Friedman, and G.T. Auble, Fluvial process and the establishment of bottomland trees, *Geomorphology*, 14, 327-339, 1996.

Scott, P.F. and W.D. Erskine, Geomorphic effects of a large flood on fluvial fans, *Earth Surface Processes and Landforms*, 19, 95-108, 1994.

Sear, D.A., Sediment transport processes in pool-riffle sequences, *Earth Surface Processes and Landforms*, 21, 241-262, 1996.

Sedell, J.R., F.H. Everest, and F.J. Swanson, Fish habitat and streamside management: past and present, in *Proceedings of the Society of American Foresters*, pp. 244-255, Annual Meeting, 1982.

Sedell, J.R. and J.L. Froggatt, Importance of streamside forests to large rivers: the isolation of the Willamette River, Oregon, USA, from its floodplain by snagging and streamside forest removal, *Verhandlungen International Verein. Limnol.*, 22, 1828-1834, 1984.

Sedell, J.R., J.E. Richey, and F.J. Swanson, The river continuum concept: a basis for expected ecosystem behavior of very large rivers?, *Canadian Special Publication Fisheries and Aquatic Sciences*, 106, 110-127, 1989.

Seidl, M.A. and W.E. Dietrich, The problem of channel erosion into bedrock, in *Functional geomorphology*, edited by K.-H. Schmidt and J. de Ploey, pp. 101-124, Catena Supplement 23, 1992.

Seidl, M.A., W.E. Dietrich, and J.W. Kirchner, Longitudinal profile development into bedrock: an analysis of Hawaiian channels, *Journal of Geology*, 102, 457-474, 1994.

Seidl, M.A., R.C. Finkel, M.W. Caffee, G.B. Hudson, and W.E. Dietrich, Cosmogenic isotope analyses applied to river longitudinal profile evolution: problems and interpretations, *Earth Surface Processes and Landforms*, 22, 195-209, 1997.

Selby, M.J., A rock mass strength classification for geomorphic purposes: with tests from Antarctica and New Zealand, *Zeitschrift für Geomorphologie*, 24, 31-51, 1980.

Selby, M.J., *Hillslope materials and processes*, Oxford University Press, Oxford, England, 264 pp., 1982.

Shanley, J.B., C. Kendall, M.R. Albert and J.P. Hardy, Chemical and isotopic evolution of a layered eastern U.S. snowpack and its relation to stream-water composition, in *Biogeochemistry of seasonally snow-covered catchments*, edited by K.A. Tonnessen, M.W. Williams and M. Tranter, pp. 329-338, IAHS Publ. no. 228, 1995.

Sharp, R.P., Mudflow levees, *Journal of Geomorphology*, 5, 222-227, 1942.

Shelford, V.E., Ecological succession. I. Stream fishes and the method of physiographic analysis, *Biological Bulletin of the Marine Biology Lab, Woods Hole*, 21, 9-35, 1911.

Shields, F.D. and C.J. Gippel, Prediction of effects of woody debris removal on flow resistance, *Journal of Hydraulic Engineering*, 121, 341-354, 1995.

Shih, S.-M. and P.D. Komar, Differential bedload transport rates in a gravel-bed stream: a grain-size distribution approach, *Earth Surface Processes and Landforms*, 15, 539-552, 1990a.

Shih, S.-M. and P.D. Komar, Hydraulic controls of grain-size distributions of bedload gravels in Oak Creek, Oregon, USA, *Sedimentology*, 37, 367-376, 1990b.

Shimazu, H., Segmentation of Japanese mountain rivers and its causes based on gravel transport processes, *Transactions, Japanese Geomorphological Union*, 15, 111-128, 1994.

Shimazu, H. and T. Oguchi, River processes after rapid valley-filling due to large landslides, *GeoJournal*, 38, 339-344, 1996.

Shlemon, R.J., R.H. Wright, and D.R. Montgomery, Anatomy of a debris flow, Pacifica, California, in *Debris flows/avalanches: process, recognition, and mitigation*, edited by J.E. Costa and G.F. Wieczorek, pp. 181-199, Geological Society of America, Reviews in Engineering Geology, v. 7, Boulder, Colorado, 1987.

Shroba, R. R., P.W. Schmidt, E.J. Crosby, W.R. Hansen, and J.M. Soule, Geologic and geomorphic effects in the Big Thompson Canyon area, Larimer County, *U.S. Geological Survey Prof Paper 1115B*, pp. 87-152, 1979.

Shroder, J.F., Jr., M.P. Bishop, and R. Scheppy, Catastrophic flood flushing of sediment, western Himalaya, Pakistan, in *Geomorphological hazards in high mountain areas*, edited by J. Kalvoda and C.L. Rosenfeld, pp. 27-48, Kluwer Academic Publishers, The Netherlands, 1998.

Sidle, R.C., Bed load transport regime of a small forest stream, *Water Resources Research*, 24, 201-218, 1988.

Sieben, J., *Modelling of hydraulics and morphology in mountain rivers*, PhD dissertation, Technical University of Delft, The Netherlands, 223 pp., 1997.

Sigafoos, R.S., Vegetation in relation to flood frequency near Washington, D.C., *U.S. Geological Survey Prof Paper 424-C*, pp. C-248 to C-250, 1961.

Sigafoos, R.S., Botanical evidence of floods and flood-plain deposition, *U.S. Geological Survey Professional Paper 485-A*, 35 pp., 1964.

Simon, A., M.C. Larsen, and C.R. Hupp, The role of soil processes in determining mechanisms of slope failure and hillslope development in a humid-tropical forest, eastern Puerto Rico, *Geomorphology*, 3, 263-286, 1990.

Simons, D.B. and R.M. Li, *Procedure for estimating model parameters of a mathematical model*, USDA Forest Service, Rocky Mountain Forest and Range Experiment Station, 1976.

Simons, D.B., R.M. Li, and M.A. Stevens, *Developments of models for predicting water and yield from storms on small watersheds*, USDA Forest Service, Rocky Mountain Forest and Range Experiment Station, 1975.

Simons, D.B. and E.V. Richardson, Resistance to flow in alluvial channels, *U.S. Geological Survey Professional Paper 422J*, 61 pp., 1966.

Simons, Li and Associates, Inc., *Debris and flood control plan for Portland and Cascade Creeks at Ouray, Colorado*, Final report to City of Ouray, Colorado, Colorado Water Board, Denver, 1982.

Singh, T. and J. Kaur, (eds.), *Integrated mountain research*, Himalayan Books, New Delhi, 1985.

Sinniger, R.O. and M. Monbaron, (eds.), *Hydrology in mountainous regions II. Artificial reservoirs, water and slopes*, IAHS Publication no. 194, Wallingford, UK, 446 pp., 1990.

Sklar, L. and W.E. Dietrich, River longitudinal profiles and bedrock incision models: stream power and the influence of sediment supply, in *Rivers over rock: fluvial processes in bedrock channels*, edited by K.J. Tinkler and E.E. Wohl, pp. 237-260, Am. Geophys. Union Geophysical Monograph 107, 1998.

Slaney, P.A., T.G. Halsey, and H.A. Smith, Some effects of forest harvesting on salmonid rearing habitat in two streams in the central interior of British Columbia, *Fisheries Management Report 71, B.C. Ministry of Recreation and Conservation*, 26 pp., 1977.

Slaymaker, H.O., Sediment yield and sediment control in the Canadian Cordillera, in *Mountain geomorphology: geomorphological processes in the Canadian Cordillera*, edited by H.O. Slaymaker and H.J. McPherson, pp. 235-245, Tantalus Research Limited, Vancouver, 1972.

Slaymaker, H.O., Alpine hydrology, in *Arctic and alpine environments*, edited by J.D. Ives and R.G. Barry, pp. 134-155, Methuen, London, 1974.

Slaymaker, H.O. and H.J. McPherson, (eds.), *Mountain geomorphology*, Tantalus Research Ltd., 1972.

Smart, C.C., A deductive model of karst evolution based on hydrological probability, *Earth Surface Processes and Landforms*, 13, 271-288, 1988.

Smart, G.M., Sediment transport formula for steep channels, *Journal of Hydraulic Engineering*, 110, 267-276, 1984.

Smart, G.M., Turbulent velocities in a mountain river, in *Hydraulic engineering '94*, edited by G.V. Cotroneo and R.R. Rumer, pp. 844-848, Proceed of the 1994 Conf, Hydraul Div, ASCE, New York, 1994.

Smart, G.M. and M.N.R. Jaeggi, *Sediment transport on steep slopes*, Versuchsanstalt für Wasserbau, Hydrologie und Glaziologie, Mitteilungen 64, Eidgenössische Technische Hochschule Zürich, Switzerland, 1983.

Smith, A.M. and P.K. Zawada, The role of the geologist in flood contingency planning, *South African Geological Survey, Paper 7.3*, 9 pp., 1988.

Smith, N., *A history of dams*, Peter Davies, London, 1971.

Smith, R.D. and R.L. Beschta, A mechanism of pool formation and maintenance in forest streams, in *Hydraulic engineering '94*, edited by G.V. Cotroneo and R.R. Rumer, pp. 824-828, Proceed of the 1994 Conference, Hydraulics Division, ASCE, New York, 1994.

Smith, R.D., R.C. Sidle, P.E. Porter, and J.R. Noel, Effects of experimental removal of woody debris on the channel morphology of a forest, gravel-bed stream, *Journal of Hydrology*, 52, 153-178, 1993.

Snow, D.T., Landslide of Cerro Condor-Sencca, Department of Ayacucho, Peru, in *Engineering geology case histories*, edited by G.A. Kiersch, pp. 1-6, Geological Society of America, Boulder, Colorado, 1964.

Solbrig, O.T. (Ed.), *From genes to ecosystems: a research agenda for biodiversity*, Report of a

IUBS-SCOPE-UNESCO Workshop, 123 pp., International Union for Biological Sciences (IUBS), 1992.

Sommerfeld, R.A., R.C. Musselman and G.L. Wooldridge, Comparison of estimates of snow input with a small alpine catchment, *Journal of Hydrology*, 120, 295-307, 1990.

Sorriso-Valvo, M., L. Antronico, and E. Le Pera, Controls on modern fan morphology in Calabria, southern Italy, *Geomorphology*, 24, 169-187, 1998.

Spreafico, M. and C. Lehmann, Sediment transport observations in Switzerland, in *Variability in stream erosion and sediment transport*, edited by L.J. Olive, R.J. Loughran and J.A. Kesby, pp. 259-268, IAHS Publication no. 224, Wallingford, UK, 1994.

Springer, G.S. and J.S. Kite, River-derived slackwater sediments in caves along Cheat River, West Virginia, *Geomorphology*, 18, 91-100, 1997.

Stallard, R.F. and J.M. Edmond, Geochemistry of the Amazon 2: The influence of the geologic and weathering environment on the dissolved load, *Journal of Geophysical Research*, 88, 9671-9688, 1983.

Stam, A.C., M.J. Mitchell, H.R. Krouse and J.S. Kahl, Stable sulfur isotopes of sulfate in precipitation and stream solutions in a northern hardwood watershed, *Water Resources Research*, 28, 231-236, 1992.

Stanford, J.A. and F.R. Hauer, Mitigating the impacts of stream and lake regulation in the Flathead River catchment, Montana, USA: an ecosystem perspective, *Aquatic Conservation: Marine and Freshwater Ecosystems*, 2, 35-63, 1992.

Stanford, J.A. and J.V. Ward, The hyporheic habitat of river ecosystems, *Nature*, 335, 64-66, 1988.

Stanford, J.A. and J.V. Ward, An ecosystem perspective of alluvial rivers: connectivity and the hyporheic corridor, *Journal North American Benthological Society*, 12, 48-60, 1993.

Stanford, J.A., J.V. Ward, W.J. Liss, C.A. Frissell, R.N. Williams, J.A. Lichatowich, and C.C. Coutant, A general protocol for restoration of regulated rivers, *Regulated Rivers: Research and Management*, 12, 391-413, 1996.

Stanley, E.H. and A.J. Boulton, Hyporheic processes during flooding and drying in a Sonoran Desert stream. I. Hydrologic and chemical dynamics, *Arch. Hydrobiol.*, 134, 1-26, 1995.

Starkel, L., The role of catastrophic rainfall in the shaping of the relief of the Lower Himalaya (Darjeeling Hills), *Geografiska Pol.*, 21, 103-147, 1972.

Starkel, L., Tectonic, anthropogenic and climatic factors in the history of the Vistula River valley downstream of Cracow, in *Lake, mire and river environments during the last 15,000 years*, edited by G. Lang and C. Schluchter, pp. 161-170, A.A. Balkema, Rotterdam, 1988.

Statzner, B. and D. Borchardt, Longitudinal patterns and processes along streams: modelling ecological responses to physical gradients, in *Aquatic ecology: scale, pattern and process*, edited by P.S. Giller, A.G. Hildrew and D.G. Raffaelli, pp.113-140, Blackwell Scientific Publications, Oxford, 1994.

Statzner, B., U. Fuchs, and L.W.G. Higler, Sand erosion by mobile predaceous stream insects: implications for ecology and hydrology, *Water Resources Research*, 32, 2279-2287, 1996.

Stedinger, J.R. and V.R. Baker, Surface water hydrology: historical and paleoflood information, *Reviews of Geophysics*, 25, 119-124, 1987.

Stedinger, J.R. and T.A. Cohn, Flood frequency analysis with historical and paleoflood information, *Water Resources Research*, 22, 785-793, 1986.

Stein, O.R. and P.Y. Julien, Criterion delineating the mode of headcut migration, *ASCE, Journal of Hydraulic Engineering*, 119, 37-50, 1993.

Stewart, J.H. and V.C. LaMarche, Jr., Erosion and deposition produced by the flood of December 1964 on Coffee Creek, Trinity County, California, *U.S. Geological Survey Professional Paper 422-K*, K1-K22, 1968.

Stock, J.D. and D.R. Montgomery, Geologic constraints on bedrock river incision using the stream power law, *Journal of Geophysical Research*, 14 (B3), 4983-4993, 1999.

Strahler, A.N., Equilibrium theory of erosional slopes approached by frequency distribution analysis, Part II, *American Journal of Science*, 248, 673-696, 1950.

Strahler, A.N., Dynamic basis of geomorphology, *Geological Society of America Bulletin*, 63, 923-938, 1952.

Strahler, A.N., Quantitative analysis of watershed geomorphology, *Transactions, American Geophysical Union*, 38, 913-920, 1957.

Strahler, A.N., *Physical geography*, John Wiley and Sons, New York, 1960.

Strahler, A.N., Quantitative geomorphology of drainage basins and channel networks, in *Handbook of applied hydrology*, edited by V.T. Chow, pp. 4-40 to 4-74, McGraw Hill, New York, 1964.

Strand, R.I., Bureau of Reclamation procedures for predicting sediment yield, *Agricultural Research Service, ARS-S-40*, p. 10-15, 1975.

Stromberg, J.C., D.T. Patten and B.D. Richter, Flood flows and dynamics of Sonoran riparian forests, *Rivers*, 2, 221-235, 1991.

Stromberg, J.C., B.D. Richter, D.T. Patten and L.G. Wolden, Response of a Sonoran riparian forest to a 10-year return flood, *Great Basin Naturalist*, 53, 118-130, 1993.

Strunk, H., Reconstructing debris flow frequency in the southern Alps back to AD 1500 using dendrogeomorphical analysis, in *Erosion, debris flows and environment in mountain regions*, edited by D.E. Walling, T.R. Davies, and B. Hasholt, pp. 299-306, IAHS Publ. no. 209, Wallingford, United Kingdom, 1992.

Stüve, P.E., Spatial and temporal variation of flow resistance in an Alpine river, in *Hydrology in mountainous regions I. Hydrological measurements; the water cycle*, edited by H. Lang and A. Musy, pp. 307-314, IAHS Publication no. 193, Wallingford, UK, 1990.

Sueker, J.K., Chemical hydrograph separation during snowmelt for three headwater basins in Rocky Mountain National Park, Colorado, in *Biogeochemistry of seasonally snow-covered catchments*, edited by K.A. Tonnessen, M.W. Williams and M. Tranter, pp. 271-281, IAHS Publ. no. 228, 1995.

Sullivan, K., T.E. Lisle, C.A. Dolloff, G.E. Grant, and L.M. Reid, Stream channels: the link between forests and fishes, in *Streamside management: forestry and fishery implications*, edited by E.O. Salo and T.W. Cundy, pp. 39-97, University of Washington, Institute of Forest Resources, Contrib. No. 57, 1987.

Summerfield, M.A. and N.J. Hulton, Natural controls of fluvial denudation rates in major world drainage basins, *Journal of Geophysical Research*, 99, B7, 13,871-13,883, 1994.

Suszka, L., Modification of the transport rate formula for steep channels, in *Fluvial hydraulics of mountain regions*, edited by A. Armanini and G. DiSilvio, pp. 59-70, Springer-Verlag, Berlin, 1991.

Sutherland, A.J., Static armour layers by selective erosion, in *Sediment transport in gravel-bed rivers*, edited by C.R. Thorne, J.C. Bathurst, and R.D. Hey, pp. 243-268, John Wiley and Sons, Chichester, 1987.

Sutherland, R.A., Caesium-137 and sediment budgeting within a partially closed drainage basin, *Zeitschrift für Geomorphologie*, 35, 47-63, 1991.

Suzuki, K. and K. Kato, Mobile armouring of bed surface in steep slope river with gravel and sand mixture, in *Fluvial hydraulics of mountain regions*, edited by A. Armanini and G. DiSilvio, pp. 393-404, Springer-Verlag, Berlin, 1991.

Swank, W.T., Biological control of solute losses from forest ecosystems, in *Solute processes*, edited by S.T. Trudgill, pp. 85-139, John Wiley and Sons, Chichester, 1986.

Swank, W.T. and C.E. Johnson, Small catchment research in the evaluation and development of forest management practices, in *Biogeochemistry of small catchments: a tool for environmental research*, edited by B. Moldan and J. Cerny, pp. 383-408, John Wiley and Sons, Chichester, 1994.

Swanson, F.J., L.E. Benda, S.H. Duncan, G.E. Grant, W.F. Megahan, L.M. Reid, and R.R. Ziemer, Mass failures and other processes of sediment production in Pacific Northwest forest landscapes, in *Streamside management: forestry and fishery implications*, edited by E.O. Salo and T.W. Cundy, pp. 9-38, University of Washington, Institute of Forest Resources, Contrib. No. 57, 1987.

Swanson, F.J., S.L. Johnson, S.V. Gregory and S.A. Acker, Flood disturbance in a forested mountain landscape, *BioScience*, 48, 681-689, 1998.

Swanson, F.J., T.K. Kratz, N. Caine, and R.G. Woodmansee, Landform effects on ecosystem patterns and processes, *BioScience*, 38, 92-98, 1988.

Swanson, F.J., G.W. Lienkaemper, and J.R. Sedell, History, physical effects, and management implications of large organic debris in western Oregon streams, *USDA Forest Service General Technical Report PNW-56*, 1976.

Swanson, F.J., S.M. Wondzell, and G.E. Grant, Landforms, disturbance, and ecotones, in *Landscape boundaries: consequences for biotic diversity and ecological flows*, edited by A.J. Hansen and F. di Castri, pp. 304-323, Springer-Verlag, New York, 1992.

Swanston, D.N. and F.J. Swanson, Timber harvesting, mass erosion, and steepland forest geomorphology in the Pacific Northwest, in *Geomorphology and engineering*, edited by D.R. Coates, pp. 199-221, Dowden, Hutchinson, and Ross, 1976.

Tabacchi, E., A.M. Planty-Tabacchi, M.J. Salinas, and H. Decamps, Landscape structure and diversity in riparian plant communities: a longitudinal comparative study, *Regulated Rivers: Research and Management*, 12, 367-390, 1996.

Takahashi, G., A study on the riffle-pool concept, *Transactions, Japanese Geomorphological Union*, 11, 319-336, 1990.

Takahashi, T., *Debris flows*, A.A. Balkema, Rotterdam, 1991a.

Takahashi, T., Mechanics and the existence criteria of various types of flows during massive sediment transport, in *Fluvial hydraulics of mountain regions*, edited by A. Armanini and G. DiSilvio, pp. 267-278, Springer-Verlag, Berlin, 1991b.

Takahashi, T., H. Nakagawa, and S. Kuang, Estimation of debris flow hydrograph on varied slope bed, in *Erosion and sedimentation in the Pacific Rim*, edited by R.L. Beschta, T. Blinn, G.E. Grant, G.G. Ice and F.J. Swanson, pp. 167-177, IAHS Publ. no. 165, 1987.

Tanaka, Y., Y. Onda, and Y. Agata, Effect of rock properties on the longitudinal profiles of river beds: comparison of the mountain rivers in granite and Paleozoic sedimentary rock basins, *Geographical Review Japan*, 66A, 203-216, 1993.

Teleki, P.G., Areal sorting of bed-load material: the hypothesis of velocity reversal: discussion, *Geological Society of America Bulletin*, 83, 911-914, 1972.

Tennekes, H. and J.L. Lumley, *A first course in turbulence*, MIT Press, Cambridge, Massachusetts, 300 pp., 1994.

Thompson, A., Secondary flows and the pool-riffle unit: a case study of the processes of meander development, *Earth Surface Processes and Landforms*, 11, 631-642, 1986.

Thompson, A., Channel response to flood events in a divided upland stream, in *International geomorphology 1986*, edited by V. Gardiner, Part I, pp. 691-709, John Wiley and Sons, Chichester, 1987.

Thompson, D.M., *Hydraulics and sediment transport processes in a pool-riffle Rocky Mountain stream*, Unpublished MS thesis, Colorado State University, Ft. Collins, Colorado, 288 pp., 1994.

Thompson, D.M., The effects of large organic debris on sediment processes and stream morphology in Vermont, *Geomorphology*, 11, 235-244, 1995.

Thompson, D.M., *Hydraulics and pool geometry*, Unpublished PhD dissertation, Colorado State University, Ft. Collins, Colorado, 260 pp., 1997.

Thompson, D.M. and K.S. Hoffman, Pool dimensions in coarse-grained, New England channels, *Geological Society of America, 1999 Annual Meeting, Abstracts with Programs*, 31, A-49, 1999.

Thompson, D.M., J.M. Nelson, and E.E. Wohl, Interactions between pool geometry and hydraulics, *Water Resources Research*, 34, 3673-3681, 1998.

Thompson, D.M., E.E. Wohl, and R.D. Jarrett, A revised velocity-reversal and sediment-sorting model for a high-gradient, pool-riffle stream, *Physical Geography*, 17, 142-156, 1996.

Thompson, D.M., E.E. Wohl, and R.D. Jarrett, Velocity reversals and sediment sorting in pools and riffles controlled by channel constrictions, *Geomorphology*, 27, 229-241, 1999.

Thompson, S.M. and J.E. Adams, Suspended load in some major rivers of New Zealand, in *Physical hydrology: New Zealand experience*, edited by D.L. Murray and P. Ackroyd, pp. 213-229, New Zealand Hydrological Society Inc., Wellington North, 1979.

Thorne, C.R., J.C. Bathurst, and R.D. Hey, (eds.), *Sediment transport in gravel-bed rivers*, John Wiley and Sons, Chichester, 1987.

Thorne, S.D., *Stable bed features and their influence on flow structure, sediment transport and channel evolution in high mountain streams*, Unpublished PhD dissertation, Florida State University, Tallahassee, Florida, 301 pp., 1997.

Thornes, J.B. and I. Alcantara-Ayala, Modelling mass failure in a Mediterranean mountain environment: climatic, geological, topographical and erosional controls, *Geomorphology*, 24, 87-100, 1998.

Thurman, E.M., *Organic geochemistry of natural waters*, Martinus Nijhoff/Dr. W. Junk, Dordrecht, 497 pp., 1985.

Tianche, L., R.L. Schuster and J. Wu, Landslide dams in south-central China, in *Landslide dams: processes, risk, and mitigation*, pp. 146-162, American Society of Civil Engineers, New York, 1986.

Tinkler, K.J., Fluvially sculpted rock bedforms in Twenty Mile Creek, Niagara Peninsula, Ontario, *Canadian Journal of Earth Sciences*, 30, 945-953, 1993.

Tinkler, K.J., Critical flow in rockbed streams with estimated values for Manning's n, *Geomorphology*, 20, 147-164, 1997a.

Tinkler, K.J., Indirect velocity measurement from standing waves in rockbed rivers, *ASCE, Journal of Hydraulic Engineering*, 123, 918-921, 1997b.

Tinkler, K.J., J.W. Pengelly, W.G. Parkins, and G. Asselin, Postglacial recession of Niagara Falls in relation to the Great Lakes, *Quaternary Research*, 42, 20-29, 1994.

Tinkler, K.J. and E.E. Wohl, A primer on bedrock channels, in *Rivers over rock: fluvial processes in bedrock channels*, edited by K.J. Tinkler and E.E. Wohl, pp. 1-18, Am. Geophys. Union Geophysical Monograph 107, 1998.

Tranter, M., P. Brimblecombe, T.D. Davies, C.E. Vincent, P.W. Abrahams and I. Blackwood, The composition of snowfall, snowpack and meltwater in the Scottish Highlands - evidence for preferential elution, *Atmospheric Environment*, 20, 517-525, 1986.

Trayler, C.R., *Spatial and temporal variability in sediment movement, and the role of woody debris in a sub-alpine stream, Colorado*, Unpublished MS thesis, Colorado State University, Ft. Collins, Colorado, 155 pp., 1997.

Trayler, C.R. and E. E. Wohl, Seasonal changes in a step-pool channel, Rocky Mountains, Colorado, U.S.A., *Arctic, Antarctic, and Alpine Research*, 32, 95-103, 2000.

Tribe, S. and M. Church, Simulations of cobble structure on a gravel streambed, Water Resources Research, 35, 311-318, 1999.

Trieste, D.J., Supercritical flows versus subcritical flows in natural channels, in *Hydraulic engineering '94*, edited by G.V. Cotroneo and R.R. Rumer, pp. 732-736, Proceed of the 1994 Conf, ASCE, New York, 1994.

Trieste, D.J. and R.D. Jarrett, Roughness coefficients of large floods, in *Proceed., Conf. On Irrig. Systems for the 21st Century*, edited by L.G. James and M.J. English, pp. 32-40, Am. Soc Civ Engineer., Portland, Oregon, 1987.

Trimble, S.W., Erosional effects of cattle on streambanks in Tennessee, USA, *Earth Surface Processes and Landforms*, 19, 451-464, 1994.

Trimble, S.W. and A.C. Mendel, The cow as a geomorphic agent - a critical review, *Geomorphology*, 13, 233-253, 1995.

Tritton, D.J., *Physical fluid dynamics*, Clarendon Press, Oxford, 519 pp., 1988.

Troendle, C.A., Sediment transport for instream flow/channel maintenance, *Proceed of the Technical Workshop on Sediments*, pp. 1-4, EPA/Forest Service, 3-7 Feb 1992, Corvallis, Oregon, 1992.

Troendle, C.A., J.M. Nankervis, and S.E. Ryan, Sediment transport from small, steep-gradient watersheds in Colorado and Wyoming, in *Sedimentation technologies for management of natural resources in the 21st century*, pp. IX-39 to IX-45, Sixth Federal Interagency Sedimentation Conference, March 1996, Las Vegas, Nevada, 1996.

Troll, C., Über das Wesen der Hochgebirgsnatur, *Jahrbuch Deutsch. Alpenvereins*, 80, 142-157, 1954.

Tsujimoto, T., Bed-load transport in steep channels, in *Fluvial hydraulics of mountain regions*, edited by A. Armanini and G. DiSilvio, pp. 89-102, Springer-Verlag, Berlin, 1991.

Ugarte, A. and M. Madrid, Roughness coefficient in mountain rivers, in *Hydraulic engineering '94*, edited by G.V. Cotroneo and R.R. Rumer, pp. 652-656, Proceed of the 1994 Conf, Hydraul Div, ASCE, New York, 1994.

Urbonas, B. and B. Benik, Stream stability under a changing environment, in *Stormwater runoff and receiving systems: impact, monitoring, and assessment*, edited by E.E. Herricks, pp. 77-101, Lewis Publishers, Boca Raton, Florida, USA, 1995.

US Department of Transportation, *Restoration of fish habitat in relocated streams*, Federal Highway Administration, Washington, D.C., 63 pp., 1979.

USDI (US Department of the Interior, Bureau of Reclamation), *Riparian area management: process for assessing proper functioning condition*, Technical Reference 1737-9, 51 pp., 1993.

USFS (U.S. Forest Service), *R1-WATSED-PC handbook*, USDA Forest Service Region 1, Missoula, Montana, 1992.

U.S. National Academy of Sciences, *Changing climate*, National Academy of Sciences, National Academy Press, Washington, D.C., 1983.

Valdiya, K.S., *Environmental geology: Indian context*, Tata-McGraw Hill, New Delhi, 1987.

Valero-Garcés, B.L., A. Navas, J. Machín, and D. Walling, Sediment sources and siltation in mountain reservoirs: a case study from the Central Spanish Pyrenees, *Geomorphology*, 28, 23-41, 1999.

Valett, H.M., Surface-hyporheic interactions in a Sonoran Desert stream: hydrologic exchange and diel periodicity, *Hydrobiologia*, 259, 133-144, 1993.

Valett, H.M., S.F. Fisher, N.B. Grimm, and P. Camill, Vertical hydrologic exchange and ecological stability of a desert stream ecosystem, *Ecology*, 75, 548-560, 1994.

Valett, H.M., S.F. Fisher, N.B. Grimm, E.H. Stanley and A.J. Boulton, Hyporheic-surface water exchange: implications for the structure and functioning of desert stream ecosystems, in *Proceedings, First International Conference on Groundwater Ecology*, edited by J.A. Stanford and J.J. Simon, pp. 395-405, Am. Water Resources Association, Bethesda, Maryland, 1992.

Valett, H.M., S.G. Fisher and E.H. Stanley, Physical and chemical characteristics of the hyporheic zone of a Sonoran Desert stream, *Journal of North American Benthological Society*, 9, 201-215, 1990.

Van Cleve, K., C.T. Dyrness, G.M. Marion and R. Erickson, Control of soil development on the Tanana River floodplain, interior Alaska, *Canadian Journal of Forest Research*, 23, 941-955, 1993.

Van Haveren, B.P., Placer mining and sediment problems in interior Alaska, in *Proceedings of the 5th Federal Interagency Sedimentation Conference*, edited by S.-S. Fan and Y.-H. Kuo, v. 2, pp. 10-69—10-74, 1991.

Van Nieuwenhuyse, E.E. and J.D. LaPerriere, Effects of placer gold mining on primary production in subarctic streams of Alaska, *Water Resources Bulletin*, 22, 91-99, 1986.

Van Steijn, H., J. De Ruig, and F. Hoozemans, Morphological and mechanical aspects of debris flows in parts of the French Alps, *Zeitschrift für Geomorphologie*, 32, 143-161, 1988.

Vannote, R.L., G.W. Minshall, K.W. Cummins, J.R. Sedell, and C.E. Cushing, The river continuum concept, *Canadian Journal of Fisheries and Aquatic Sciences*, 37, 130-137, 1980.

Varnes, D.J., Landslide types and processes, in *Landslides and engineering practice*, edited by E. Eckel, pp. 20-47, Highway Research Board Special Report 29, 1958.

Veatch, A.C., Geology and underground water resources of northern Louisiana and southern

Arkansas, *U.S. Geological Survey Professional Paper 46*, 422 pp., 1906.

Velbel, M.A., Geochemical mass balances and weathering rates in forested watersheds of the southern Blue Ridge. III. Cation budgets and the weathering rate of amphibole, *Am. Journal Science*, 292, 58-78, 1992.

Velbel, M.A., Weathering and pedogenesis at the watershed scale: some recent lessons from studies of acid-deposition effects, *Chemical Geology*, 107, 337-339, 1993.

Velbel, M.A., Interaction of ecosystem processes and weathering processes, in *Solute modelling in catchment systems*, edited by S.T. Trudgill, pp. 193-209, John Wiley and Sons, Chichester, 1995.

Vincent, K.R. and J.G. Elliott, Effect of ore milling on the Animas River channels and flood plain near Eureka, Colorado, *Geological Society of America, 1999 Annual Meeting, Abstracts with Programs*, 31, A-253, 1999.

Vischer, D., Impact of 18th and 19th century river training works: three case studies from Switzerland, in *Historical change of large alluvial rivers: western Europe*, edited by G.E. Petts, H. Moller and A.L. Roux, pp. 19-40, John Wiley and Sons, Chichester, 1989.

Vitek, J.D. and D.F. Ritter, Geomorphology in the USA, in *The evolution of geomorphology*, edited by H.J. Walker and W.E. Grabau, pp. 469-481, John Wiley and Sons, New York, 1993.

Vogt, K.A., D.J. Vogt, P. Boon, A. Covich, F.N. Scatena, H. Asbjornsen, J.L. O'Hara, J. Pérez, T.G. Siccama, J. Bloomfield, and J.F. Ranciato, Litter dynamics along stream, riparian and upslope areas following Hurricane Hugo, Luquillo Experimental Forest, Puerto Rico, *Biotropica*, 28, 458-470, 1996.

Von Humboldt, A., *Cosmos: a sketch of a physical description of the universe* (translated by E.C. Otté), Harper and Brothers, New York, 1852.

Von Storch, H., E. Zorita, and U. Cubasch, Downscaling of climate changes to regional scales: an application to winter rainfall in the Iberian Peninsula, *Journal of Climate*, 6, 1161-1171, 1993.

Vuichard, D. and M. Zimmermann, The 1985 catastrophic drainage of a moraine-dammed lake, Khumbu Himal, Nepal: cause and consequences, *Mountain Research and Development*, 7, 91-110, 1987.

Wagener, S.M. and J.D. LaPerriere, Effects of placer mining on the invertebrate communities of an interior Alaska stream, *Freshwater Invertebrate Biology*, 4, 208-214, 1985.

Wahl, K.L., Bias in regression estimates of Manning's n, in *Hydraulic engineering '94*, edited by G.V. Cotroneo and R.R. Rumer, pp. 727-731, Proceed of the 1994 Conf, Hydraul Div, ASCE, New York, 1994.

Waide, J.B., W.H. Caskey, R.L. Todd, and L.R. Boring, Changes in soil nitrogen pools and transformations following forest clearcutting, in *Forest hydrology and ecology at Coweeta*, edited by W.T. Swank and D.A. Crossley, Jr., pp. 221-232, Ecological Studies, 66, Springer-Verlag, New York, 1998.

Walder, J.S. and J.E. Costa, Outburst floods from glacier-dammed lakes: the effect of mode of lake drainage on flood magnitude, *Earth Surface Processes and Landforms*, 21, 701-723, 1996.

Walder, J.S. and J.E. O'Connor, Methods for predicting peak discharge of floods caused by failure of natural and constructed earthen dams, *Water Resources Research*, 33, 2237-2348, 1997.

Walford, G.M. and W.L. Baker, Classification of the riparian vegetation along a 6-km reach of the Animas River, southwestern Colorado, *The Great Basin Naturalist*, 55, 287-303, 1995.

Walker, L.R. and F.S. Chapin, Physiological controls over seedling growth in primary succession on an Alaskan floodplain, *Ecology*, 67, 1508-1523, 1986.

Walker, L.R., J.C. Zasada, and F.S. Chapin, The role of life history processes in primary succession on an Alaskan floodplain, *Ecology*, 67, 1243-1253, 1986.

Wallace, J.B. and J.R. Webster, The role of macroinvertebrates in stream ecosystem function, *Annual Review of Entomology*, 41, 115-139, 1996.

Wallace, J.B., S.L. Eggerton, J.L. Meyer, and J.R. Webster, Multiple trophic levels of a forest stream linked to terrestrial litter inputs, *Science*, 277, 102-104, 1997.

Wallbrink, P.J., J.M. Olley, and A.S. Murray, Measuring soil movement using ^{137}Cs: implications of reference site variability, in *Variability in stream erosion and sediment transport*, edited by L.J. Olive, R.J. Loughran and J.A. Kesby, pp. 95-102, IAHS Publication no. 224, Wallingford, UK, 1994.

Walling, D.E. and A.H.A. Kleo, Sediment yield of rivers in areas of low precipitation: a global view, in *The Hydrology of mountainous areas*, pp. 479-493, IAHS Publication no. 128, 1979.

Walling, D.E. and B.W. Webb, Suspended load in gravel-bed rivers; UK experience, in *Sediment transport in gravel-bed rivers*, edited by C.R. Thorne, J.C. Bathurst, and R.D. Hey, pp. 691-732, John Wiley and Sons, Chichester, 1987.

Walton, I., *The compleat angler*, Clarendon Press, Oxford, 435 pp., 1653 (1983).

Wang, N.L. and M.K. Han, Geomorphology in China (The People's Republic of), in *The evolution of geomorphology*, edited by H.J. Walker and W.E. Grabau, pp. 93-105, John Wiley and Sons, New York, 1993.

Warburton, J., Comparison of bed load yield estimates for a glacial meltwater stream, in *Hydrology in mountainous regions I. Hydrological measurements; the water cycle*, edited by H. Lang and A. Musy, pp. 315-323, IAHS Publication no. 193, Wallingford, UK, 1990.

Warburton, J., Channel change in relation to meltwater flooding, Bas Glacier d'Arolla, Switzerland, *Geomorphology*, 11, 141-149, 1994.

Warburton, J. and T. Davies, Variability of bedload transport and channel morphology in a braided river hydraulic model, *Earth Surface Processes and Landforms*, 19, 403-421, 1994.

Ward, J.V., The four-dimensional nature of lotic ecosystems, *Journal of North American Benthological Society*, 8, 2-8, 1989.

Ward, J.V., A mountain river, in *The rivers handbook*, edited by P. Calow and G.E. Petts, pp. 493-510, Blackwell Scientific Publications, Oxford, UK, 1992.

Ward, J.V. and B.C. Kondratieff, *An illustrated guide to the mountain stream insects of Colorado*, University Press of Colorado, Niwot, 191 pp., 1992.

Ward, J.V. and J.A. Stanford, The serial discontinuity concept of lotic ecosystems, in *Dynamics of lotic ecosystems*, edited by T.D. Fontaine and S.M. Bartell, pp. 29-42, Ann Arbor Science, Ann Arbor, MI, 1983.

Wasson, R.J., A debris flow at Reshun, Pakistan, Hindu Kush, *Geografiska Annaler*, 60A, 151-159, 1978.

Wathen, S.J. and T.B. Hoey, Morphologic controls on the downstream passage of a sediment wave in a gravel-bed stream, *Earth Surface Processes and Landforms*, 23, 715-730, 1998.

Wathen, S.J., T.B. Hoey, and A. Werritty, Quantitative determination of the activity of within-reach sediment storage in a small gravel-bed river using transit time and response time, *Geomorphology*, 20, 113-134, 1997.

Wathen, S.J., R.I. Ferguson, T.B. Hoey, and A. Werritty, Unequal mobility of gravel and sand in weakly bimodal river sediments, *Water Resources Research*, 31, 2087-2096, 1995.

Wathne, B.M., A. Henriksen, and S. Norton, Buffering capacity of river substrates during acid episodes, in *Acidic deposition; its nature and impacts*, edited by G.D. Holmes and F.T. Last, p. 405, Royal Society of Edinburgh, Edinburgh, United Kingdom, 1990.

Waylen, M.J., Chemical weathering in a drainage basin underlain by Old Red Sandstone, *Earth Surface Processes*, 4, 167-178, 1979.

Waythomas, C.F. and R.D. Jarrett, Flood geomorphology of Arthurs Rock Gulch, Colorado: paleoflood history, *Geomorphology*, 11, 15-40, 1994.

Waythomas, C.F., J.S. Walder, R.G. McGimsey, and C.A. Neal, A catastrophic flood caused by drainage of a caldera lake at Aniakchak Volcano, Alaska, and its implications for volcanic hazards assessment, *Geological Society of America Bulletin*, 108, 861-871, 1996.

Webb, R.H., Debris flows from tributaries of the Colorado River, Grand Canyon National Park, Arizona: Executive summary, *U.S. Geological Survey Open-File Report 87-117*, 7 pp., 1987.

Webb, R.H. and J.L. Betancourt, Climatic variability and flood frequency of the Santa Cruz River, Pima County, Arizona, *U.S. Geological Survey Open-File Report 90-553*, 69 pp., 1990.

Webb, R.H, P.T. Pringle, S.L. Reneau, and G.R. Rink, Monument Creek debris flow, 1984:

Implications for formation of rapids on the Colorado River in Grand Canyon National Park, *Geology*, 16, 50-54, 1988.

Webb, R.H., P.T. Pringle, and G.R. Rink, Debris flows from tributaries of the Colorado River, Grand Canyon National Park, Arizona, *U.S. Geological Survey Open-File Report, 87-118*, 64 pp., 1987.

Webb, R.H. and S.L. Rathburn, Paleoflood hydrology research in the southwestern United States, *Transporation Research Record*, 1201, 9-21, 1988.

Weber, W.A., Plant geography in the southern Rocky Mountains, in *The Quaternary in the United States*, edited by H.E. Wright and D.G. Frey, pp. 453-468, Princeton University Press, Princeton, New Jersey, 1965.

Webster, J.R. and B.C. Patten, Effects of watershed perturbation on stream potassium and calcium dynamics, *Ecological Monographs*, 49, 51-72, 1979.

Weirich, F.H., Sediment transport and deposition by fire-related debris flows in southern California, in *Erosion and sedimentation in the Pacific Rim*, edited by R.L. Beschta, T. Blinn, G.E. Grant, G.G. Ice, and F.J. Swanson, pp. 283-283, IAHS Publ. no. 165, 1987.

Weiss, F.H. 1994. Luminophor experiments in the Saalach and Salzach rivers, in *Dynamics and geomorphology of mountain rivers*, edited by P. Ergenzinger and K.-H. Schmidt, pp. 83-91, Springer-Verlag, Berlin, 1994.

Weissel, J.K. and M.A. Seidl, Inland propagation of erosional escarpments and river profile evolution across the southeast Australian passive continental margin, in *Rivers over rock: fluvial processes in bedrock channels*, edited by K.J. Tinkler and E.E. Wohl, pp. 189-206, Am. Union Geophys. Union Geophysical Monograph 107, 1998.

Welcomme, R.L., R.A. Ryder, and J.R. Sedell, Dynamics of fish assemblages in river systems - a synthesis, *Canadian Special Publication Fisheries and Aquatic Sciences*, 106, 569-577, 1989.

Wells, W.G., II, The effects of fire generation on the generation of debris flows in southern California, in *Debris flows/avalanches: process, recognition, and mitigation*, edited by J.E. Costa and G.F. Wieczorek, pp. 105-114, Geological Society of America, Reviews in Engineering Geology, v. 7, Boulder, Colorado, 1987.

Wells, W.G., P.M. Wohlgemuth, A.G. Campbell, and F.H. Weirich, Postfire sediment movement by debris flows in the Santa Ynez Mountains, California, in *Erosion and sedimentation in the Pacific Rim*, edited by R.L. Beschta, T. Blinn, G.E. Grant, G.G. Ice, and F.J. Swanson, pp. 275-276, IAHS Publ. no. 165, 1987.

Werritty, A., Downstream fining in a gravel-bed river in southern Poland: lithologic controls and the role of abrasion, in *Dynamics of gravel-bed rivers*, edited by P. Billi, R.D. Hey, C.R. Thorne and P. Tacconi, pp. 333-350, John Wiley and Sons, Chichester, 1992.

Wetzel, K., The significance of fluvial erosion, channel storage and gravitational processes in sediment production in a small mountainous catchment area, in *Dynamics and geomorphology of mountain rivers*, edited by P. Ergenzinger and K.-H. Schmidt, pp. 141-160, Springer-Verlag, Berlin, 1994.

Whetton, P.H., M.R. Haylock, and R. Galloway, Climate change and snow cover duration in the Australian Alps, *Climatic Change*, 32, 447-449, 1996.

Whipple, K.X., Predicting debris-flow runout and deposition on fans: the importance of the flow hydrograph, in *Erosion, debris flows and environment in mountain regions*, edited by D.E. Walling, T.R. Davies, and B. Hasholt, pp. 337-345, IAHS Publ. no. 209, 1992.

Whipple, K.X., Interpreting debris-flow hazard from study of fan morphology, in *Hydraulic engineering '93*, edited by H.W. Shen, S.T. Su and F. Wen, v. 2, pp. 1302-1307, ASCE, 1993.

Whipple, K.X. and T. Dunne, The influence of debris-flow rheology on fan morphology, Owens Valley, California, *Geological Society of America Bulletin*, 104, 887-900, 1992.

Whipple, K.X. and C.R. Trayler, Tectonic control of fan size: the importance of spatially variable subsidence rates, *Basin Research*, 8, 351-366, 1996.

White, A.F., A.E. Blum, M.S. Schulz, D.V. Vivit, D.A. Stonestrom, M. Larsen, S.F. Murphy and D. Eberl, Chemical weathering in a tropical watershed, Luquillo Mountains, Puerto Rico: I. Long-term versus short-term weathering fluxes, *Geochimica et Cosmochimica Acta*, 62, 209-226, 1998.

White, P.S., Pattern, process, and natural disturbance in vegetation, *The Botanical Review*, 45, 229-299, 1979.

White, S., Soil erosion and sediment yield in the Philippines, in *Sediment and water quality in river catchments*, edited by I. Foster, A. Gurnell, and B. Webb, pp. 391-406, John Wiley and Sons, Chichester, 1995.

White, W.B., *Geomorphology and hydrology of karst terrains*, Oxford University Press, New York, 464 pp., 1988.

White, W.D. and S.G. Wells, Forest-fire devegetation and drainage basin adjustments in mountainous terrain, in *Adjustments of the fluvial system*, edited by D.D. Rhodes and G.P. Williams, pp. 199-223, George Allen and Unwin, London, 1979.

Whiting, P.J., The effect of stage on flow and components of the local force balance, *Earth Surface Processes and Landforms*, 22, 517-530, 1997.

Whiting, P.J. and J.B. Bradley, A process-based classification system for headwater streams, *Earth Surface Processes and Landforms*, 18, 603-612, 1993.

Whiting, P.J. and W.E. Dietrich, The role of bedload sheets in the transport of heterogeneous sediment (abstract), *EOS*, 66, 910, 1985.

Whiting, P.J. and W.E. Dietrich, Convective accelerations and boundary shear stress over a channel bar, *Water Resources Research*, 27, 783-796, 1991.

Whiting, P.J., W.E. Dietrich, L.B. Leopold, T.G. Drake, and R.L. Shreve, Bedload sheets in heterogeneous sediment, *Geology*, 16, 105-108, 1988.

Whiting, P.J., J.F. Stamm, D.B. Moog, and R.L. Orndorff, Sediment-transporting flows in headwater streams, *Geological Society of America Bulletin*, 111, 450-466, 1999.

Whitley, J.R. and R.S. Campbell, Some aspects of water quality and biology of the Missouri River, *Transactions, Missouri Academy of Science*, 8, 60-72, 1974.

Whittaker, J.G., Modelling bed-load transport in steep mountain streams, in *Erosion and sedimentation in the Pacific Rim*, edited by R.L. Beschta, T. Blinn, G.E. Grant, G.G. Ice, and F.J. Swanson, pp. 319-332, Proceed of the Corvallis Symposium, Aug 1987, IAHS Publ no. 165, 1987a.

Whittaker, J.G., Sediment transport in step-pool systems, in *Sediment transport in gravel-bed rivers*, edited by C.R. Thorne, J.C. Bathurst, and R.D. Hey, pp. 545-579, John Wiley and Sons, 1987b.

Whittaker, J.G. and M.N.R. Jaeggi, Origins of step-pool systems in mountain streams, *ASCE Journal of Hydraulics Division*, 108, 758-773, 1982.

Wiberg, P.L. and J.D. Smith, Calculations of the critical shear stress for motion of uniform and heterogeneous sediments, *Water Resources Research*, 23, 1471-1480, 1987.

Wiberg, P.L. and J.D. Smith, Velocity distribution and bed roughness in high-gradient streams, *Water Resources Research*, 27, 825-838, 1991.

Wickham, M.G., *Physical microhabitat of trout*, Unpublished MS thesis, Colorado State University, Ft. Collins, Colorado, 42 pp., 1967.

Wieczorek, G.F., Effect of rainfall intensity and duration on debris flows in central Santa Cruz Mountains, California, in *Debris flows/avalanches: process, recognition, and mitigation*, edited by J.E. Costa and G.F. Wieczorek, pp. 93-104, Geological Society of America, Reviews in Engineering Geology, v. 7, Boulder, Colorado, 1987.

Wieczorek, G.F., Assessment and prediction of debris-flow hazards, in *Hydraulic engineering '93*, edited by H.W. Shen, S.T. Su and F. Wen, pp. 1272-1283, ASCE, 1993.

Wieczorek, G.F., E.W. Lips, and S.D. Ellen, Debris flows and hyperconcentrated floods along the Wasatch Front, Utah, 1983 and 1984, *Bulletin of the Association of Engineering Geologists*, 26, 191-208, 1989.

Wieczorek, G.F., G. Mandrone, and L. Decola, The influence of hillslope shape on debris-flow initiation, in *Debris-flow hazards mitigation: mechanics, prediction, and assessment*, pp. 21-31, Proceedings of the First International Conference, Water Resources Division Engineering, ASCE, San Francisco, CA, 1997.

Wiesmann, U., Socioeconomic viewpoints on highland-lowland systems: a case study on the north-west side of Mount Kenya, *Mountain Research and Development*, 12, 375-381, 1992.

Wilcock, P.R., Experimental investigation of the effect of mixture properties on transport dynamics, in *Dynamics of gravel-bed rivers*, edited by P. Billi, R.D. Hey, C.R. Thorne and P. Tacconi, pp. 109-139, John Wiley and Sons, Chichester, 1992a.

Wilcock, P.R., Flow competence: a criticism of a classic concept, *Earth Surface Processes and Landforms*, 17, 289-298, 1992b.

Wilcock, P.R. Critical shear stress of natural sediments, *ASCE Journal of Hydraulic Engineering*, 119, 491-505, 1993.

Wilcock, P.R., Estimating local bed shear stress from velocity observations, *Water Resources Research*, 32, 3361-3366, 1996.

Wilcock, P., Friction between science and practice: the case of river restoration, *EOS, Transactions of the Am. Geophysical Union*, 78 (41), 454, 1997.

Wilcock, P.R., A.F. Barta, and C.C.C. Shea, Estimating local bed shear stress in large gravel-bed rivers, in *Hydraulic engineering '94*, edited by G.V. Cotroneo and R.R. Rumer, pp. 834-838, Proceed of the 1994 Conf, Hydraul Div, ASCE, New York, 1994.

Wilcock, P.R., A.F. Barta, C.C. Shea, G.M. Kondolf, W.V.G. Matthews, and J. Pitlick, Observations of flow and sediment entrainment on a large gravel-bed river, *Water Resources Research*, 32, 2897-2909, 1996a.

Wilcock, P.R., G.M. Kondolf, W.V.G. Matthews, and A.F. Barta, Specification of sediment maintenance flows for a large gravel-bed river, *Water Resources Research*, 32, 2911-2921, 1996b.

Wiley, M.J., L.L. Osborne, and R.W. Larimore, Longitudinal structure of an agricultural prairie river system and its relationship to current stream ecosystem theory, *Canadian Journal of Fisheries and Aquatic Sciences*, 47, 373-384, 1990.

Wilhelm, F., Human impact and exploitation of water resources in the Northern Alps (Tyrol and Bavaria), in *Dynamics and geomorphology of mountain rivers*, edited by P. Ergenzinger and K.-H. Schmidt, pp. 15-35, Springer-Verlag, Berlin, 1994.

Willgoose, G., R.L. Bras, and I. Rodriguez-Iturbe, Results from a new model of river basin evolution, *Earth Surface Processes and Landforms*, 16, 237-254, 1991.

Willi, H.P., Review of mountain river training procedures in Switzerland, in *Fluvial hydraulics of mountain regions*, edited by A. Armanini and G. Di Silvio, pp. 317-329, Springer-Verlag, Braunschweig, 1991.

Williams, G.P., Paleohydrological methods and some examples from Swedish fluvial environments. I. Cobble and boulder deposits, *Geografiska Annaler*, 65A, 227-243, 1983.

Williams, G.P. and H.P. Guy, Debris avalanches - a geomorphic hazard, in *Environmental geomorphology*, edited by D.R. Coates, pp. 25-46, Publications in Geomorphology, State University of New York, Binghamton, 1971.

Williams, G.P. and H.P. Guy, Erosional and depositional aspects of Hurricane Camille in Virginia, 1969, *U.S. Geological Survey Professional Paper 804*, 80 pp., 1973.

Williams, G.P. and D.L. Rosgen, Measured total sediment loads (suspended and bedloads) for 93 United States streams, *U.S. Geological Survey Open-File Report 89-67*, 128 pp., 1989.

Williams, G.P. and M.G. Wolman, Effects of dams and reservoirs on surface-water hydrology; changes in rivers downstream from dams, *U.S. Geological Survey Professional Paper 1286*, 83 pp., 1984.

Williams, G.P. and M.G. Wolman, Effects of dams and reservoirs on surface-water hydrology - changes in rivers downstream from dams, *U.S. Geological Survey, National Water Summary 1985*, p. 83-88, 1985.

Williams, M.W. and T. Platts-Mills, Selectivity of chemical weathering in high elevation catchments of the Colorado Front Range, *EOS, Transactions, Am. Geophys. Union*, 79, F337, 1998.

Wilson, R.C., J.D. Torikai, and S.D. Ellen, Development of rainfall warning thresholds for debris flows in the Honolulu district, Oahu, *U.S. Geological Survey Open-File Report 92-521*, 35 pp., 1992.

Winterbourn, M.J. and C.R. Townsend, Streams and rivers: one-way flow systems, in *Fundamentals of aquatic ecology*, edited by R.S.K. Barnes and K.H. Mann, 2nd ed., pp. 230-242, Blackwell Scientific Publications, Oxford, 1991.

Wischmeier, W.H. and D.D. Smith, *Predicting rainfall-erosion losses - a guide to conservation planning*, Agricultural Handbook No. 537, 1978.

Wissmar, R.C. and F.J. Swanson, Landscape disturbances and lotic ecotones, in *Ecology and management of aquatic-terrestrial ecotones*, edited by R.J. Naiman and H. DéCamps, 1990.

Wohl, E.E., Bedrock benches and boulder bars: Floods in the Burdekin Gorge of Australia, *Geological Society America Bulletin*, 104, 770-778, 1992a.

Wohl, E.E., Gradient irregularity in the Herbert Gorge of northeastern Australia, *Earth Surface Processes and Landforms*, 17, 69-84, 1992b.

Wohl, E.E., Bedrock channel incision along Piccaninny Creek, Australia, *Journal of Geology*, 101, 749-761, 1993.

Wohl, E.E., Estimating flood magnitude in ungauged mountain channels, Nepal, *Mountain Research and Development*, 15, 69-76, 1995.

Wohl, E.E., Bedrock channel morphology in relation to erosional processes, in *Rivers over rock: fluvial processes in bedrock channels*, edited by K.J. Tinkler and E.E. Wohl, pp. 133-151, Am. Geophys. Union Geophysical Monograph 107, 1998.

Wohl, E.E., Incised bedrock channels, in *Incised river channels: processes, forms, engineering and management*, edited by S. Darby and A. Simon, pp. 187-218, John Wiley and Sons, Chichester, 1999.

Wohl, E.E., Geomorphic effects of floods, in *Inland flood hazards: human, riparian, and aquatic communities*, pp. 167-193, edited by E.E. Wohl, Cambridge University Press, 2000.

Wohl, E.E., D.J. Anthony, S.W. Madsen, and D.M. Thompson, A comparison of surface sampling methods for coarse fluvial sediments, *Water Resources Research*, 32, 3219-3226, 1996.

Wohl, E.E. and D.A. Cenderelli, Flooding in the Himalaya Mountains, in *Flood Studies in India*, edited by V.S. Kale, pp. 77-99, Geological Society of India Memoir 41, Bangalore, 1998.

Wohl, E.E. and Cenderelli, D.A., Sediment deposition and transport patterns following a reservoir sediment release, *Water Resources Research* 36, 319-333, 2000.

Wohl, E.E., D.A. Cenderelli, and M. Mejia-Navarro, Channel change from extreme floods in canyon rivers, in *The Schumm Volume*, edited by D.J. Anthony and M.D. Harvey, Water Resources Publications, Littleton, Colorado, in press.

Wohl, E.E. and Y. Enzel, Data for palaeohydrology, in *Global continental palaeohydrology*, edited by K.J. Gregory, L. Starkel, and V.R. Baker, pp. 23-59, John Wiley and Sons, Chichester, 1995.

Wohl, E.E., N. Greenbaum, A.P. Schick, and V.R. Baker, Controls on bedrock channel incision along Nahal Paran, Israel, *Earth Surface Processes and Landforms*, 19, 1-13, 1994a.

Wohl, E.E. and T. Grodek, Channel bed-steps along Nahal Yael, Negev desert, Israel, *Geomorphology*, 9, 117-126, 1994.

Wohl, E.E. and H. Ikeda, The effect of roughness configuration on velocity profiles in an artificial channel, *Earth Surface Processes and Landforms*, 23, 159-169, 1998.

Wohl, E.E., S. Madsen, and L. MacDonald, Characteristics of log and clast bed-steps in step-pool streams of northwestern Montana, USA, *Geomorphology*, 20, 1-10, 1997.

Wohl, E.E. and P.A. Pearthree, Debris flows as geomorphic agents in the Huachuca Mountains of southeastern Arizona, *Geomorphology*, 4, 273-292, 1991.

Wohl, E.E. and D.M. Thompson, Velocity characteristics along a small step-pool channel, *Earth Surface Processes and Landforms*, 2000.

Wohl, E.E., K.R. Vincent, and D.J. Merritts, Pool and riffle characteristics in relation to channel gradient, *Geomorphology*, 6, 99-110, 1993.

Wohl, E.E., R.H. Webb, V.R. Baker, and G. Pickup, *Sedimentary flood records in the bedrock canyons of rivers in the monsoonal region of Australia*, Colorado State University Water Resources Papers 107, 102 pp., 1994b.

Wolcott, J. and M. Church, Strategies for sampling spatially heterogeneous phenomena: the example of river gravels, *Journal of Sedimentary Petrology*, 61, 534-543, 1991.

Wolman, M.G., A method of sampling coarse river-bed material, *EOS, Transactions American Geophysical Union*, 35, 951-956, 1954.

Wolman, M.G., The natural channel of Brandywine Creek, Pennsylvania, *U.S. Geological Survey Professional Paper 271*, 1955.

Wolman, M.G., A cycle of sedimentation and erosion in urban river channels, *Geografiska Annaler*, 49A, 385-395, 1967.

Wolman, M.G. and R. Gerson, Relative scales of time and effectiveness of climate in watershed geomorphology, *Earth Surface Processes*, 3, 189-208, 1978.

Wolman, M.G. and J.P. Miller, Magnitude and frequency of forces in geomorphic processes, *Journal of Geology*, 68, 54-74, 1960.

Wolman, M.G. and A.P. Schick, Effects of construction on fluvial sediment, urban and suburban areas of Maryland, *Water Resources Research*, 3, 451-464, 1967.

Womack, W.R. and S.A. Schumm, Terraces of Douglas Creek, northwestern Colorado: an example of episodic erosion, *Geology*, 5, 72-76, 1977.

Wondzell, S.M. and F.J. Swanson, Seasonal and storm dynamics of the hyporheic zone of a fourth-order mountain stream. I. Hydrologic processes, *Journal North American Benthological Society*, 15, 3-19, 1996a.

Wondzell, S.M. and F.J. Swanson, Seasonal and storm dynamics of the hyporheic zone of a fourth-order mountain stream. II: Nitrogen cycling, *Journal North American Benthological Society*, 15, 20-34, 1996b.

Wondzell, S.M. and F.J. Swanson, Floods, channel change, and the hyporheic zone, *Water Resources Research*, 35, 555-567, 1999.

Woodward, J.C., Patterns of erosion and suspended sediment yield in Mediterranean river basins, in *Sediment and water quality in river catchments*, edited by I. Foster, A. Gurnell, and B. Webb, pp. 365-389, John Wiley and Sons, Chichester, 1995.

Wotton, R.S., The use of silk life-lines by larvae of Simulium noelleri (Diptera), *Aquatic Insects*, 8, 255-261, 1986.

Wright, J.P., Effects of an ecosystem engineer, the beaver, on regional patterns of species richness of the streamside herbaceous plant community, *Ecological Society of America, 1999 Annual Meeting Abstracts*, p. 326, 1999.

Wroblicky, G.J., M.E. Campana, H.M. Valett, and C.N. Dahm, Seasonal variation in surface-sub-surface water exchange and lateral hyporheic area of two stream-aquifer systems, *Water Resources Research*, 34, 317-328, 1998.

Wroten, W.H., *The railroad tie industry in the central Rocky Mountain region: 1867-1900*, Unpublished PhD dissertation, Colorado State University, Ft. Collins, Colorado, 287 pp., 1956.

Wyzga, B., Changes in the magnitude and transformation of flood waves subsequent to the channelization of the Raba River, Polish Carpathians, *Earth Surface Processes and Landforms*, 21, 749-763, 1996.

Yair, A. and J. De Ploey, Field observations and laboratory experiments concerning the creep process of rock blocks in an arid environment, *Catena*, 6, 245-258, 1979.

Yair, A. and H. Lavee, Runoff generation in arid and semi-arid zones, in *Hydrological forecasting*, edited by M.G. Anderson and T.P. Burt, pp. 183-220, John Wiley and Sons, New York, 1985.

Yalin, M.S., An expression for bedload transportation, *ASCE Journal of the Hydraulics Division*, 89, 221-250, 1963.

Yamada, S., Mountain ordering: a method for classifying mountains based on their morphometry, *Earth Surface Processes and Landforms*, 24, 653-660, 1999a.

Yamada, S., The role of soil creep and slope failure in the landscape evolution of a head water basin: field measurements in a zero order basin of northern Japan, *Geomorphology*, 28, 329-344, 1999b.

Yang, C.T., Formation of riffles and pools, *Water Resources Research*, 7, 1567-1574, 1971.

Yang, C.T., Minimum unit stream power and fluvial hydraulics, *ASCE, Journal of the Hydraulics Division*, 102, 919-934, 1976.

Yanosky, T.M., Effects of flooding upon woody vegetation along parts of the Potomac River flood plain, *U.S. Geological Survey Professional Paper 1206*, 21 pp., 1982a.

Yanosky, T.M., Hydrologic inferences from ring widths of flood-damaged trees, Potomac River, Maryland, *Environmental Geology*, 4, 43-52, 1982b.

Yanosky, T.M., Evidence of floods on the Potomac River from anatomical abnormalities in the wood of flood-plain trees, *U.S. Geological Survey Professional Paper 1296*, 42 pp., 1983.

Yanosky, T.M., Documentation of high summer flows on the Potomac River from the wood anatomy of ash trees, *Water Resources Bulletin*, 20, 241-250, 1984.

Yatsu, E., On the longitudinal profile of the graded river, *Trans., American Geophysical Union*, 36, 655-663, 1955.

Yesenov, U.Y. and A.S. Degovets, Catastrophic mudflow on the Bol'shaya Almatinka River in 1977, *Soviet Hydrology*, 18, 158-160, 1979.

Young, A., *Slopes*, Oliver and Boyd, Edinburgh, 1972.

Young, D.R., I.C. Burke, and D.H. Knight, Water relations of high-elevation phreatophytes in Wyoming, *The American Midland Naturalist*, 114, 384-392, 1984.

Young, G.J., Monitoring glacier outburst floods, *Nordic Hydrology*, 11, 285-300, 1980.

Young, G.J. and K. Hewitt, Hydrology research in the upper Indus basin, Karakoram Himalaya, Pakistan, in *Hydrology of mountainous areas*, edited by L. Molnar, pp. 139-152, IAHS Publ. no. 190, Wallingford, United Kingdom, 1990.

Young, M.K., Movement and characteristics of stream-borne coarse woody debris in adjacent burned and undisturbed watersheds in Wyoming, *Canadian Journal of Forest Research*, 24, 1933-1938, 1994.

Young, M.K., D. Haire, and M.A. Bozek, The effect and extent of railroad tie drives in streams of southeastern Wyoming, *Western Journal of Applied Forestry*, 9, 125-130, 1994.

Young, M.K., R.N. Schmal, and C.M. Sobczak, Railroad tie drives and stream channel complexity: past impacts, current status, and future prospects, in *Proceedings of the Annual Meeting of Society of American Foresters*, pp. 126-130, Spokane, Washington, Publ. 89-02, SAF, Bethesda, Maryland, 1990.

Young, R. and I. McDougall, Long-term landscape evolution: early Miocene and Modern rivers in southern New South Wales, Australia, *Journal of Geology*, 101, 35-49, 1993.

Young, R.W., Waterfalls: form and process, *Zeitschrift für Geomorphologie*, 55, 81-95, 1985.

Young, R.W., Crustal constraints on the evolution of the continental divide of eastern Australia, *Geology*, 17, 528-530, 1989.

Young, R.W. and C.R. Twidale, Geomorphology in Australia, in *The evolution of geomorphology*, edited by H.J. Walker and W.E. Grabau, pp. 29-43, John Wiley and Sons, New York, 1993.

Young, W.J. and T.R.H. Davies, Bedload transport processes in a braided gravel-bed river model, *Earth Surface Processes and Landforms*, 16, 499-511, 1991.

Yu, B., Contribution of heavy rainfall to rainfall erosivity, runoff, and sediment transport in the wet tropics of Australia, in *Natural and anthropogenic influences in fluvial geomorphology*, edited by J.E. Costa, A.J. Miller, K.W. Potter and P.R. Wilcock, pp. 113-123, Geophysical Monograph 89, American Geophysical Union, Washington, D.C., 1995.

Yu, B. and D. Neil, Temporal and spatial variation of sediment yield in the Snowy Mountains region, Australia, in *Variability in stream erosion and sediment transport*, edited by L.J. Olive, R.J. Loughran and J.A. Kesby, pp. 281-289, IAHS Publication no. 224, Wallingford, UK, 1994.

Zen, E. and K.L. Prestegaard, Possible hydraulic significance of two kinds of potholes: examples from the paleo-Potomac River, *Geology*, 22, 47-50, 1994.

Zgheib, P.W., Large bed element channels in steep mountain streams, in *Hydrology in mountainous regions. II - Artificial reservoirs, water and slopes*, pp. 277-283, IAHS Publ. no. 194, 1990.

Zicheng, K. and L. Jing, Erosion processes and effects of debris flows, in *Erosion and sedimenta-*

tion in the Pacific Rim, edited by R.L. Beschta, T. Blinn, G.E. Grant, G.G. Ice, and F.J. Swanson, pp. 233-242, IAHS Publ. no. 165, 1987.

Ziemer, R.R., Storm flow response to road building and partial cutting in small streams of northern California, *Water Resources Research*, 17, 907-917, 1981.

Ziemer, R.R., Monitoring watersheds and streams, in *Proceedings of the conference on coastal watersheds: the Caspar Creek story*

SUBJECT INDEX

The Water Resources Monograph Series

Volume 1
Synthetic Streamflows
M. B. Flering and B. B. Jackson (1971)
Available in microfiche only
ISBN 0-87590-300-2

Volume 2
Benefit-Cost Analysis for Water System Planning
C. W. Howe (1971), 144 pages
ISBN 0-87590-302-9

Volume 3
Outdoor Recreation and Water Resources Planning
J. L. Knetsch (1974)
Available in microfiche only
ISBN 0-87590-304-5

Volume 4
Multiobjective Water Resource Planning
D. C. Major (1977), 81 pages
ISBN 0-87590-305-3

Volume 5
Groundwater Management: The Use of Numerical Models
Y. Bachmat, J. Bredehoeft, B. Andrews, et al. (1985),
127 pages, 2nd ed.
ISBN 0-87590-314-2
Includes planning, implementation, and adaptive control of policies and programs related to the exploration, inventory, development, and operation of water resources containing groundwater.

Volume 6
Metropolitan Water Management
J. Gordon Milliken and G. Taylor (1981), 180 pages
ISBN 0-87590-307-X
Deals with design and implementation of water supply planning in areas suffering from limited water resources. Social, environmental, and economic costs are considered in this comprehensive evaluation and analysis of new and existing alternative water strategies.

Volume 7
Urban Stormwater Hydrology
D. F. Kibler (1982), 271 pages
ISBN 0-87590-308-8
A practical guide to current methods and models used in analyzing different types of stormwater management problems. Bridges the gap between current practices and new studies. A major reference work for environmental researchers, practicing engineers, and urban planners.

Volume 8
The Scientist and Engineer in Court
M. D. Bradley (1983), 111 pages
ISBN 0-87590-309-6
To be an expert witness the scientist or engineer must have a working knowledge of the judicial process and courtroom procedures. This volume offers a complete introduction to the role of an expert witness in litigation proceedings.

Volume 9
Groundwater Hydraulics
J. S. Rosenshein and G. D. Bennett (1984), 420 pages
ISBN 0-87590-310-X
Provides state-of-the-science insight into groundwater hydraulics and an application of hydraulics toward solving groundwater problems. Principal areas covered are aquifer hydraulics, heat transport, and modeling.

Volume 10
Groundwater Transport: Handbook of Mathematical Models
I. Javandel, C. Doughty, and C. F. Tsang (1984)
228 pages
ISBN 0-87590-313-4
Reviews, selects, and demonstrates the best and most practical mathematical models to predict the extent of groundwater subsurface contamination.

Volume 11
Hillslope Stability and Land Use
R. C. Sidle, A. J. Pierce, and C. L. O'Loughlin (1985),
140 pages
This book emphasizes the natural factors affecting slope stability, including soils and geomorphic, hydrologic, vegetation, and seismic factors. It also provides basic information on landslide classification, global damage, and analytical methods.

Volume 12
River Meandering
S. Ikeda and G. Parker (1989), 485 pages
ISBN 0-87590-316-9
The topics covered include boundary shear stress, sediment transport, sedimentary controls, linear theory, alternate bars, and topographic response of a bar.

Volume 13
Groundwater Modeling by the Finite Element Method
Jonathan Istok (1989), 495 pages
ISBN 0-87590-317-7